Oil and Security

Oil and Security

A SIPRI MONOGRAPH

Stockholm International Peace Research Institute

Humanities Press
New York

Almqvist & Wiksell International
Stockholm

First published by Almqvist & Wiksell International
26 Gamla Brogatan, S-111 20 Stockholm

in collaboration with

Humanities Press
171 First Avenue
Atlantic Highlands, New Jersey 07716

ISBN 91-85114-25-1

(USA) SBN 0-391-00370-4

Printed in Sweden by Tryckindustri AB, Solna, 1974

PREFACE

Oil is a resource of vital importance to national and international economic and military security. In the latter half of 1973, the actual or possible consequences of the uneven distribution of this finite resource were suddenly brought home to all echelons of society.

The immediate "oil crisis" is over, but the seriousness of the energy problem remains. If the crisis accomplished nothing else, it did demonstrate the urgent need for studies of the role of energy, and the risks that shortages of energy will imply.

This study outlines and discusses some of the security problems raised by the prospect of oil shortages. It deals particularly with a number of conflict potentials involved in a situation of oil shortage, and the arms race that these conflicts may stimulate. Such stimuli could originate in, for instance, the increased competition for oil among consumer countries, or from the producers' need to protect their oil fields and installations, or again, from different countries' concern about the security of their sea lanes and tankers.

In addition, the expected transfers of enormous sums of money as payment for oil is likely to give some countries, particularly those in the Arabian/Persian Gulf, the means not only to develop their economies, but also to purchase large amounts of arms. Such a build-up of military potential in these countries may have very destabilizing effects on the region itself, and directly or indirectly on the world balance of power.

The report was written by Bo Heinebäck, a member of the SIPRI staff. The report went to print in early June 1974. Events occurring during June-September 1974 highlighting the contents of the report have been listed in an addendum on page 186.

August 1974

Frank Barnaby
Director

CONTENTS

TABLES AND CHARTS

CONVENTIONS

The following conventions have been used in the tables:

..   Data not available
—   Nil or less than half of final digit shown; negligible; not applicable
( )   Greater degree of uncertainty about estimate
[ ]   Crude estimate

Introduction

Notes, thus[2] *refer to the list of notes on page 146. Square-bracketed references, thus* [1] *refer to the list of references on page 170.*

Energy is a basic requirement for all human activity. A main characteristic of every culture and society throughout history has been the way in which it has used the energy resources at its disposal, and the *per capita* consumption of energy is a common measure of its level of development.[1]

The discovery in 1859 in the United States of a new source of energy, oil, marked the beginning of a new era in the history of mankind. The exploitation of oil soon became a necessary prerequisite for large-scale industrialization and for achieving the way of life seemingly desired by modern cultures. Clearly, however, this new energy source was not limited to peaceful uses; its military importance was also quickly recognized. The use of oil, in fact, substantially contributed to changing the processes of war, opening up hitherto unknown dimensions of strategy both on the ground, in the air and on and under the surface of the seas.

Since oil is one of the resources considered to be of vital importance to the economic and military security of nations, it seems natural that a shortage of oil would pose a great potential threat to national and international security. The primary effort of a country faced with insufficient oil for its requirements is therefore likely to be directed towards eliminating the risk of shortage.

Competition for scarce or unevenly distributed resources is not a new phenomenon; throughout history such competition has often been the cause of conflict or war. But never before the current scramble for oil resources has such competition been so widespread that it encompassed the whole globe and entailed such drastic implications for national and international security.

Oil is indeed very unevenly distributed throughout the world. This geological fact gives the oil-producing countries an economic, political and strategic importance hitherto surprisingly little appreciated in world affairs. In the last months of 1973, however, the actual or possible consequences of the uneven distribution of finite oil resources and of changes in the established systems of their redistribution were suddenly recognized by and brought home to all echelons of society. The immediate "oil crisis" passed over within a few months, but the seriousness of the energy problem remains. If the "crisis" accomplished nothing else, it did demonstrate the urgent need for thorough studies of the role of energy in a complex world and the implications of oil for the economies, trade and diplomacy of all countries. Thus, since the vast majority of nations are dependent on imports of this vital resource to sustain their economic, social and military security, matters relating to oil will, from now on, have a much higher priority in every nation's foreign policy and defence strategy. In other words, decisions regarding national and strategic security will be heavily and increasingly influenced by a host of considerations related not only to potential indigenous energy supplies, but also to the geographic location and expected availability of foreign sources of supply.

The bilateral relations between those countries which primarily produce and export oil (*PE-countries*) on the one hand, and those which primarily import and consume oil (*IC-countries*) on the other,[2] are becoming increasingly important, especially as the current trend is for the PE-countries to take over some of the so far dominant role of the multinational oil companies by trading directly with their oil-consuming customers. This bilateral aspect also derives a special security significance from the fact that arms often make up a considerable part of the payment for supplies of oil.

The fact that large oil reserves are found in only a few areas of the world, notably the Arabian/Persian Gulf region,* makes these areas very important to the whole system of international relations. The oil-rich producing countries will therefore be the focus of intense interest from a number of cooperating or competing parties in the foreseeable future. Changes in the political, military or economic structure of these countries may have repercussions not only for the countries themselves and their neighbours, but also for a wide range of IC-countries as well. Moreover, there is the possibility that the IC-countries themselves might directly or indirectly initiate or prevent such changes in the PE-countries. The use of military force in such processes cannot be excluded.

Future developments will be decided by the nature of the policies adopted by the different interest groups involved — the PE-countries, the IC-countries and the multinational oil companies. As these policies are pursued, a complex pattern of cooperation and competition among these three groups will emerge. The competitive forces engendered could well predominate over the cooperative to a very dangerous extent, since national security interests usually supersede those of global responsibility.

Intensified competition for the natural resources of the Earth seems likely further to spur the arms race in the world in general and in the oil-possessing areas in particular. On the other hand, in a situation of world shortage of energy, the use of substantial quantities of oil for military purposes is likely to come increasingly under discussion. Nevertheless, although a slowing down of the arms race may have some appeal, particularly in a period of peace and détente, an opposite trend is more likely, not only because of the seeds of conflict inherent in the competition for oil but also because of its crucial importance for military maintenance and operations.

To sum up, the facts behind the exploitation, distribution and use of oil give rise to numerous problems, in which a variety of security aspects are involved. These facts may be outlined as follows:

1. Oil is essential for the economic and military security of nations; to secure sufficient supplies of this resource by imports is of primary importance to all those countries not possessing oil.

2. Efforts to achieve this goal, by the IC-countries and the adoption of adverse oil supply policies by the PE-countries, will entail risks for international stability and security. These risks are heightened when the oil supplies are located in disputed territories.

---

* In Western literature the Gulf is usually referred to as the Persian Gulf. Since the nomenclature of the Arab countries is the Arabian Gulf, a combination of these two names will be used in this report. The "Gulf countries" are those bordering on the Arabian/Persian Gulf.

3. The transfer of substantial amounts of money from IC- to PE-countries as payment for oil will engender economic security problems in the IC-countries and problems related to security of investments in the PE-countries.

4. Despite the prospect that a worldwide shortage of oil might under favourable circumstances encourage moves towards disarmament, the transfer of money in payment for oil will encourage the build-up of arms in the PE-countries with implications for the national, regional and international security of nations and for the world arms race.

5. The transport of oil in increasingly larger tankers involves risks of hostile attack, sabotage or accident. The same applies to oil rigs and oil installations in general. The protection of such installations and means of transportation will also be a contributing factor in the arms race.

6. The environmental consequences of increasing trade in and use of fossil fuels give rise to problems related to the ecological security of nations and the well-being of their populations.

The following chapters will deal with some of the security aspects involved.

Finally, it might be noted that countries possessing other raw materials, such as bauxite, tin, copper and so on, may, to a certain extent, be influenced by the success of the PE-countries in forming similarly coordinated export policies.[3] This will give rise to security problems of a similar type, albeit less far-reaching and serious in their separate effects.

Chapter 1. Dependence on oil supplies

A great many considerations influence an individual country's judgement of its oil requirements and its attitude to securing supplies to fill those requirements. The oil dependence of a country can be assessed in different ways: (*a*) in relation to the level of its total domestic energy consumption; (*b*) in relation to the level of indigenous production and availability of reserves on its territory; or (*c*) in relation to the levels of its imports, or, more specifically, to the levels of its imports from a certain country or a certain region| – in practice usually the Middle Eastern PE-countries. (See table 1.)

Another factor influencing oil dependence is the refining capacity of the country. In a country with a shortage of refined products, even a sufficient supply of crude oil will be of little benefit if that country has only a low refining capacity; on the other hand, heavy investment in a refining industry is not a guarantee for obtaining sufficient supplies of crude oil. In deciding its optimal refining capacity, therefore, each IC-country must seek a delicate balance between different economic

Table 1. The dependence on oil of three major importing regions[a]

Per cent

	Japan	Western Europe	United States
Requirement for oil as percentage of total domestic energy consumption	*80*	*64*	*47*
Requirement for oil imports as percentage of total oil consumption	*100*[b]	*98*	*38*
Requirement for oil from the Middle East[c] as percentage of total oil imports	*76*	*84*	*19*
Refining capacity as percentage of total domestic oil consumption	*91*	*100*[b]	*87*

[a] Imports comprise crude oil and products.

[b] The actual figures for Japan and Western Europe were, in fact, above 100 per cent. Japan's figure of 106 per cent indicates the possibility of some storage during 1973. Western Europe's figure of 124 per cent is an indication of its refining over-capacity, which enables it to export 405 thousand barrels daily (b/d) or 19.6 million tons a year (t/y).

[c] Including North Africa.

Source: The table is based on statistics in appendices 1 and 2.

and supply-security interests, taking into consideration also the fact that the PE-countries themselves seem to be determined to transform as large a part of their crude oil as possible into refined products before exportation.

When assessing a country's security of supplies, the different options the country has of reducing its *dependence on oil in general* must also be considered. One way of doing so is to use energy more efficiently; another is to decrease the level of consumption; and a third to replace oil with other forms of energy in the total energy budget. Developing and exploiting alternative conventional energy sources (such as other fossil fuels, hydroelectric power and nuclear fission energy) is one measure which may be taken. New methods for enabling more efficient use of well-appreciated resources, such as secondary or tertiary recovery of oil, is another. Exploiting more novel resources (such as oil shale, tar sand, coal gasification and liquefaction, nuclear fusion energy, geothermal power, solar energy, wind and tidal energy and so on) is a third possibility. A more detailed description of these alternative energy sources and technologies is given in appendix 3. The conclusion which seems to emerge from this appendix is that the problems of technical feasibility and social acceptability (costs, safety, dependability, environmental effects and so on) are so intractable as often to seem insoluble, at least in the short-term (the next 10 years) or medium-term (the next 10 to 30 years) perspective.

Consideration must also be given to the possibilites of diminishing *dependence on oil imports in general* or with regard to specific suppliers, for example by reducing dependence on oil in the overall economy, as outlined above, by emergency stockpiling, by sharing-agreements between various countries, or by diversifying sources of supply. Emergency stockpiling may tide a country over a short-term crisis, but it is a very expensive way of maintaining a steadier supply situation and it gives no productive return. Sharing-agreements have not yet been tested in practice. An alternative worth considering in more detail is that of diversifying imports.

Diversification of imports is fairly easy to achieve when there are plentiful supplies, when multinational oil companies act as politically neutral middlemen, and when each PE-country acts in its own separate interest. It is considerably more difficult now that there is a sellers' market, with some of the role of the multinational oil companies being gradually taken over by the PE-countries, and the majority of these countries choosing to act as a united front. Furthermore, the actual number of countries outside the traditional suppliers' group that would be potentially able to take over their role is limited. Few of the newer oil regions seem to hold potential oil reserves of such magnitude that they might for a prolonged period facilitate diversification and thus improve the bargaining power of the heavily dependent IC-countries. Even if such reserves are eventually found, they are likely to be comparatively difficult and very costly to exploit, since for the most part they will either be offshore reserves or require much deeper and more complicated drilling. Recent oil price increases have nevertheless substantially augmented the economic attractions of such regions.

Finally, when discussing security of supplies, it is pertinent to examine the reasons for actual or possible shortages, reasons which will largely determine the countermeasures taken by the IC-countries to secure their supplies. Some of the reasons for shortages may be summarized as follows.

1. Most countries foresee an increasing demand for oil in the growth of national economies, implying growing reliance on imports from PE-countries. The brunt of this demand will fall on the Middle East because of the limited possibilities of finding adequate reserves elsewhere and the technological difficulties and costliness of developing them.[4]

2. Oil prices might increase even further as a consequence of increased demand. This market factor will adversely affect development in a number of countries, particularly those which are both oil-poor and less developed, just as a real physical shortage would. But these effects may also become a serious domestic issue in the developed countries, since a slowdown of economic growth would diminish the possibilities for increasing economic and social benefits to the broad layers of the population, thus stimulating political unrest. However, in the short term, high prices for this vital commodity are likely to be preferred by these countries to constant worry about adequate and steady supplies.

3. The PE-countries have a variety of incentives for restricting their oil production, one of these being to raise oil prices. Their interest in conserving a non-renewable natural resource favours the policy of limiting the rate at which they make it available on the market.

4. Lower production and higher prices are not the only causes of oil shortages. Some IC-countries and regions may experience a shortage because traditional patterns of distribution have been altered. The possible entrance of the United States into the centre of the world market, with a resulting disadvantage to other importers, is an obvious example of such a development.

5. A change in the traditional distribution pattern may also be a result of a deliberate policy by one or several PE-countries aimed at excluding some country or countries from oil supplies to the benefit of others — for political or other reasons.

The following general remarks might be added to these points. The restrictions recently imposed by some PE-countries were indeed responsible for a belated and painful awakening in several of the IC-countries to the fact that existing plans for economic expansion, based on the assumption of correspondingly expanding energy consumption, are so unrealistic as to require substantial revision. Earlier supply estimates have been derived from an optimistic focus on the still considerable physical world reserves of oil with no sharp delineation of the more important question of who owns and controls them. Too much planning has rested on assumptions about political, economic and military continuity in the PE-countries which no longer necessarily apply. Furthermore, these supply estimates have taken little account of the fact that a slowdown of the consumption of fossil fuels, with the exception of coal, would probably have had to take place before very long, with or without a political crisis, because of the extreme difficulties in developing any satisfactory alternatives. Moreover, whatever value these potentially expensive alternatives might have to industrialized countries, it remains very questionable whether they have much relevance to the future needs of the underdeveloped countries of the world with their rapid population expansion.

Chapter 2. The oil security of various countries and regions

This chapter describes briefly the dependence on oil and oil imports (crude oil and products) of various countries and regions and their possibilities of reducing the dependence. A more detailed analysis of their "oil security"* situation is made in appendices 1 and 2. This "oil security" is of course only part of a country's total "energy security", although usually the most important component.

The *United States* is the dominant oil-consuming country; it consumes more than 29 per cent of world production, and there are indications that it will continue to increase its consumption heavily. At the same time it is the world's largest oil producer, and although its oil reserves are dwindling, they are still extensive. Nevertheless, although imports make up a comparatively small part (38 per cent) of US consumption, the quantity in absolute terms is of great significance. Moreover, its advanced technology and extensive reserves of capital provide it with unequalled opportunities to develop alternative energy sources and methods. As the host country of most of the multinational oil companies it can turn their great experience, expertise and investment capacity to its advantage.

In view of its favourable position, the United States may achieve or come close to its goal of virtual independence from foreign energy supplies by 1980 (Project Independence) — a likelihood doubted, however, by many experts. Great expense will be entailed, but if this endeavour succeeds, the economic and military security of that nation will undoubtedly be enhanced in so far as it can be through the elimination of dependence on imports for energy purposes.

Canada shares many of these advantages with the United States. For economic reasons, it has so far exploited only a relatively small part of its own oil reserves, importing instead cheaper oil from Venezuela and the Middle East. Nevertheless, since production costs are even higher in some areas of the United States, a large proportion of Canadian production has been exported there. Furthermore, Canada's possession of what are probably the world's largest reserves of tar sand enhances its energy security.

Western Europe, as a region compared to the United States, lacks most of the features which favour the latter in dealing with the problems of oil security. It must be borne in mind, however, that the individual countries vary considerably with regard to their energy resources, their relations with PE-countries, their technological competence, and so on.

Only in the United States itself is more oil consumed than in Western Europe (27 per cent of world consumption), yet this region neither produces nor could produce more than a fraction of what it consumes.

Although North Sea oil reserves are quite extensive they cannot significantly affect the overall situation (being at present only 2 per cent of world total reserves),

---

* The term "oil security" will be used throughout to refer to the degree of security of access to oil possessed by a country or region.

although some countries bordering on the North Sea — primarily the UK and Norway — will certainly profit considerably. There are similar limitations on Europe's other, more traditionally available sources of energy, while the institutional forms for the coordination of the region's advanced technology in the development of new sources or methods are weak. Dependence on imported oil is heavy (98 per cent of total consumption), the bulk of supplies coming from one region only (the Middle East, including North Africa). Refining capacity, although very high, is concentrated in the few countries where there are large markets.

Thus West European security, in as much as it depends on oil, is comparatively precarious. Its resilience depends on continued substantial imports from the Middle East region, including North Africa. If these should fail, the United States may share its supplies with Western Europe, as it did during the 1956 and 1967 Middle East Wars but its own increasing reliance on imports makes this doubtful. The Soviet Union may be in a position to increase its supplies to Western Europe if other sources were threatened; however, not only would the effect be marginal but any long-term transaction would require a stable relationship of *détente* between them. Finally, Western Europe's capacity significantly to augment its total energy supplies from indigenous sources must not be overlooked, but to achieve this will take time.

Japan is in a seemingly even worse situation than Western Europe. Its recent burgeoning economic growth has had to depend almost entirely on oil, practically all of which is imported, mainly from the Middle East and, to a far lesser extent, from Indonesia. On the other hand, Japan has certain advantages: a strong, tightly-knit technical base for the development of alternative methods and resources and a solid technological and commercial base for developing strong interdependent relationships with the PE-countries, including trade in competitively priced manufactured goods.

Japan's security, in terms of an adequate supply of energy to sustain its future economic development, depends to a high degree on its cooperation with other nations (the United States in particular) in the search for replacement of oil by satisfactory alternatives. The Soviet Union may also become a major oil supplier should Japan take part in the exploitation of Siberian resources on a barter basis. There is also a possibility of some similar arrangement with China. However, because of political difficulties and security commitments, Japan is not likely to have access to cooperation on a large scale with all three of the great powers. Finally, Japan's offshore reserves may prove more substantial than surveys have so far indicated.

The Soviet Union has apparently little to fear for its security so far as its supplies of oil in the foreseeable future are concerned. Its large, indigenous sources supply more than enough for its domestic consumption (the third highest consumption in the world or 12 per cent of the world total), so that limited export is possible. Despite this advantage, the Soviet Union still imports a relatively small quantity from the Middle East, apparently for politico-economic reasons. In fact, the Soviet Union's proximity to Middle East reserves gives it a particular geographical advantage denied most other major industrialized states.

Estimates of oil and, particularly, gas reserves in the Soviet Union are impressive. The untapped bulk is in Siberia (with the potential of its eastern parts still not fully known) and on the continental shelf in the Arctic Ocean. Enormous capital and the most advanced technology will be needed, however, and, for the present, exploitation may largely depend on agreements on technical cooperation from the United States, Western Europe and Japan. Nevertheless, the Soviet Union has a highly developed technological basis of its own with which to augment its energy supplies currently derived from oil and gas by alternative sources and methods of production. Thus, the dwindling of its more accessible oil reserves, predicted for the 1980s, is unlikely to have a deleterious effect on Soviet security.

China is among the more favourably placed countries in terms of secured energy supplies. It should, however, be regarded as a special case because of its present very low *per capita* consumption. Although China's oil security situation is obscured by the lack of official data, it is clear that its indigenous oil production covers its present domestic consumption. It has also begun to export oil on a small scale and it is believed that the country has substantial reserves, some of the more promising of these being offshore. China's main alternative energy source is coal and it is the third most coal-rich country in the world. It is also well-endowed with oil-shale, However, China's present level of technological sophistication is not sufficient for the large-scale modern harnessing of such alternative resources, nor is it sufficient for a major effort to exploit less accessible oil resources offshore.

To some extent, therefore, China's future oil potential depends on its preparedness and ability to attract expertise and capital from abroad. But it will depend even more on the kind of policy China intends to follow in terms of energy consumption. If China were to emulate the life style of countries in the fully industrialized part of the world, its need for outside supplies, and also technological assistance, would be inestimably greater. There is no evidence, however, that China has such ambitions, quantitatively speaking. It will most probably continue to secure its energy needs from indigenous resources, linked with the enormous energy contributions of its huge, manually labouring population, which furthermore exercises strict and highly developed discipline in matters of energy-recycling. This combination of factors obviously makes China less vulnerable to the possible imposition of restrictions by possible future suppliers of oil.

The third world can hardly be considered as one region with respect to oil and security, as the situation of one country can vary markedly from that of another. India, with a population of 560 million and with limited oil resources, is in a particularly precarious position. Bangladesh, Pakistan and several of the other Asian countries, as well as most Sub-Saharan African countries, Brazil and most of the other Latin American countries, are also at a grave disadvantage.

Prospects of oil security for these countries are poor. The extra burden on most of them of the recent rocketing oil prices will be disruptive to their already problem-beset programmes of economic advancement. It is not only oil that will cost considerably more than before, but, perhaps even more important, essential products made from oil, such as fertilizers and other vital imported goods from advanced countries which are passing on part of the increased costs of their own imported oil. The advanced countries will also be less inclined to pursue beneficial aid programmes. In the face of growing economic and military weakness and consequent changes of balance in economic and military power, third world countries may realign themselves; those oil-poor countries which are situated in regions together with countries that do not face the same energy problems are especially likely to establish or further their relations with the oil-rich countries.

But there are also some fortunate third world countries which possess valuable oil resources. These can be utilized to great effect within the next few years, especially where large populations provide opportunity for large-scale investment in their domestic economies — such as in Algeria, Indonesia, Iran, Iraq, Nigeria and Venezuela and also Argentina, Ecuador and Mexico, although these latter are less important as producers.

In oil-producing countries with relatively small populations (Abu Dhabi, Kuwait, Qatar, Saudi Arabia and the United Arab Emirates), a special problem arises. Supplies are assured for domestic consumption, leaving a wide range of economic, political and military options open for the disposal both of the bulk of the oil and afterwards of the surpluses earned from its export. Since investment can only be small inside the sparsely populated countries themselves, it is bound to spill over into others, with international economic repercussions.

The oil-producing countries have one thing in common, however; international interest will focus upon them competitively, an interest which may even turn to aggression in the face of oil shortage. The currently accelerating development of arms acquisitions by most of these PE-countries is a clear indication of their awareness of the danger to their security.

Chapter 3. The three main groups of interest

The international oil business has often been described as a play with three actors: the PE-countries, the IC-countries, and the multinational oil companies, the third group acting as a kind of buffer or intermediary between the first two.

At different periods of time, the relative power of these three interest groups has shifted and the affiliations and relations between them have changed in character. The relations between the various factions within the three groups have also been influenced by a mixture of sometimes contradictory motives, some of which have promoted cooperation and others competition.

The recent overall trend has been towards increased power and involvement of the PE-countries, accompanied by a rather sudden change from a buyers' to a sellers' market, and, lately, a trend towards direct trade contacts between the PE- and IC-countries, thus bypassing the multinational oil companies.

A brief outline will be given below of the development of the relations within and among the three groups of interest.

Regarding the relations within the first group, *the PE-countries*, the question of cooperation or competition among them was not pertinent during the period when oil companies were the dominant actors and little room remained for individual manoeuvring by the governments involved. Until recently, the PE-countries still generally controlled only a minor part of the total production on their territory and the main producers and exporters were still the major oil companies. But the first group's gradually increasing share in activities surrounding the extraction of their oil has stimulated the incentive to cooperate mutually. This trend has been particularly strong since 1960, when the PE-countries formed the Organization of the Petroleum Exporting Countries (OPEC)[5] to unify and coordinate their petroleum policies and to safeguard their interests generally.

The initial incentive for the PE-countries to unite and defend their interests came with unilateral decisions in 1959—60 by the multinational oil companies to reduce oil prices without prior consultations with the producing countries.[6] In recent years, OPEC has gradually become an increasingly strong power factor in the international oil business, thus radically transforming traditional patterns of relationship. After a cautious beginning, OPEC began to pressure the oil companies to make increasingly large concessions at an accelerated rate, thus forcing up oil prices and extending its control over the supply position.[7] OPEC has no unifying political objectives, however. Among its members there is a certain common denominator in the aim to uphold United Nations principles concerning permanent sovereignty over natural resources,[8] but it is obvious that each member has its own attitudes to particular political questions.

This became evident during the Arab-Israeli conflict of 1967, when the Arab countries decided to suspend petroleum supplies to countries "sympathetic" to Israel. This measure could not *ipso facto* bind the non-Arab OPEC members, nor could OPEC provide the right forum for the discussion and resolution of problems of pure politics as distinct from questions of petroleum policy. Because a need was felt for such a forum, the Arab PE-countries established a special organization, the Organization of Arab Petroleum Exporting Countries (OAPEC)[9], in 1968 to promote a wide range of cooperative endeavours. In the economic field, for instance, the OAPEC members have agreed to cooperate in the establishment of an Arab Maritime Petroleum Transport Company and to build a dry dock for large crude oil carriers. [12] In the political field, OAPEC became the forum for coordinated Arab policy in restricting oil supplies during the autumn of 1973. (For further discussion of these events, see page 27.)

With regard to the relations among the *IC-countries,* some of those in the socialist world have established forms of mutual economic cooperation under the jurisdiction of various state agencies. In the non-socialist world, however, the oil business has been left to national or multinational companies. As long as these companies could guarantee a sufficient and continuous supply of oil, far-reaching governmental interference seemed unwarranted. Furthermore, the very different oil needs of the IC-countries, their widely differing supply and demand situations, economic and technological aspirations, and security and strategic ambitions have meant that incentives for organized forms of cooperation in the energy field have been minimal except in certain areas and among certain countries — for example, within the Oil Committee of the Organization for Economic Cooperation and Development (OECD), and the European Economic Community (EEC).

Nevertheless, the oil supply shortage in the autumn of 1973 stimulated the exchange of cooperative ideas and proposals.

As the foremost proponent of such cooperation between IC-countries, the United States convened an energy conference in Washington in February 1974 in which some of the major IC-countries participated. However, France has taken a disapproving stand on the matter of exclusive IC-country cooperation, favouring instead bilateral and direct cooperation with the PE-countries. Despite France's withdrawal from further discussions within this forum, the other countries participating in the Washington Conference continued discussions during the spring of 1974 in the coordinating group established during the February meeting.

Whatever is finally achieved by the Washington Conference, it now seems clear that governments of the IC-countries will certainly tend to involve themselves more eagerly in matters related to the security of their energy supplies, and also to cooperate more with each other, particularly in the search for and development of new energy sources and methods. (For further discussion of the cooperation among the IC-countries, see page 30.)

A detailed description of relations within the third group, the *multinational oil companies*, is beyond the scope of this book. Suffice it here to say that the multinational oil companies form an enterprise-complex operating internationally, with a network of business affiliations connecting most countries of the world. The greater part of this enterprise-complex is in the hands of a small group of companies known, in oil-industry terminology, as the "international majors" or "the seven sisters". The ownership and direction of these companies is essentially limited to three countries, of which the USA plays by far the dominant role; five of the seven "international majors" have their headquarters and the majority of their shareholders in the USA (Exxon, Mobil, Standard Oil of California, Gulf Oil and Texaco). The two remaining companies are centred in the United Kingdom and the

22

Netherlands. One of them, the Royal Dutch/Shell group, is an Anglo-Dutch enterprise with headquarters in London and the Hague; the other, British Petroleum, is a wholly British-owned enterprise in which the state has a 49 per cent holding.[10] An eighth company — Compagnie Française des Petroles (CFP) — is often added to the group, not because it ranks with the others in size, but rather because it participates in joint operations with the other companies in parts of the Middle East. Until recently, as far as the world outside the socialist countries and North America is concerned, these companies were responsible for about 80 per cent of all oil production, owning or controlling about 70 per cent of the total refining capacity and operating over 50 per cent of the tonnage of internationally operating tankers.[11] [14]

Before World War II, the seven companies collectively constituted a near-cartel, having agreed on market shares. World War II and US anti-trust legislation eliminated formal agreements among them, but until the past two decades they were still very much able to control the way the industry as a whole worked by a mutual understanding regarding such matters as pricing policy.

During recent years their ability to dominate the industry has declined considerably for several reasons, one of them being the emergence of independent and competitive oil companies, both state- and privately-owned, while another is the emergent nationalism and desire of the host countries to free themselves from a foreign economic power structure. In spite of current developments, however, it is still true to say that these large companies continue to dominate the oil business as producers and, particularly, as participants in the downstream operations (transporting, refining and marketing). Moreover, their leading role is no longer centred entirely around oil, since they have been investing heavily in other energy sources, such as coal and nuclear energy, thus becoming general energy companies.

Despite uncertainties, strong factors are still operating in favour of the oil companies; only they have the technical know-how, the financial resources and the managerial skill both to exploit and distribute existing oil, and above all, to recover the remaining untapped reserves, particularly in the deep sea-bed. Nevertheless, more direct arrangements between PE- and IC-countries and less *laissez-faire* domestic policies will certainly be a considerable challenge to the hegemony of the oil companies.

Very briefly, relations between the *PE-countries* and the *multinational oil companies* are under the formative influence of developments in the following areas: territorial coverage of concessions; participation in or nationalization of the operations of the oil companies; the financial terms under which the oil companies operate, which are closely associated with the price of oil; and PE-governments' oil policies, particularly their curbs on production.[12] The view expressed in many PE-countries is that the multinational oil companies have played out their role as intermediaries in the oil trade but that they are still useful in the technical field to facilitate downstream operations.[13] It is probably true that in this field they will remain useful and even essential for many years to come.

In considering the relations between the *multinational oil companies* and the *IC-countries*, a distinction must be made between the IC-countries which are host countries of the major oil companies (the United States, the United Kingdom, the Netherlands, and, to a lesser extent, France and Italy) and those which are not.

The relations between the latter category of countries and the oil companies have usually been strictly limited to the business level. As long as the oil companies have been able to deliver the quantities of oil needed, the IC-countries have seen no reason to change the prevailing state of affairs — leaving aside the fact that an international discussion has been under way for some time regarding the problems associated with the multinational companies in general, among which the international oil companies form a very important group. However, the problematic oil situation which began at the end of 1973 greatly quickened the interest taken by IC-governments in the activities of the oil companies in their respective countries. Symptomatic of this new trend was the agreement of the IC-countries taking part in the 1974 Washington energy conference to examine in detail the role of the international oil companies.[14]

Relations between the international oil companies and their host governments are dependent on politico-economic factors as well as purely commercial ones. A good illustration is the anti-trust legislation in the United States, one aim of which has been to prevent the establishment of an oil cartel among the major US oil companies. Another illustration is the United States government's political and diplomatic support to the oil companies whose property and operations have been nationalized but not accompanied by provisions for prompt, adequate and effective compensation.[15]

The relations which have not yet been outlined are those between the *PE-countries* and the *IC-countries*. These consist of complex political, economic and military affiliations, the pattern of which is largely determined by in-group developments on each side. Thus, the PE-countries' cooperation within OPEC, and even more the cooperation of the Arab PE-countries within OAPEC, have spurred increased cooperation among the IC-countries, particularly with the view to developing new energy sources and methods. On the other hand, the united front of the PE-countries has tended to encourage competition among the IC-countries, a trend clearly demonstrated during the shortage of oil supplies in late 1973 and early 1974, when there was a rush to set up bilateral agreements with the PE-countries. Finally, the prospects of a long-term and global shortage of oil supplies have initiated discussions for a global supply arrangement, including both PE- and IC-countries.

From this entangled web of forces and relationships, a basic question for all parties has emerged: is it in the best interests of one's own nation to choose a policy of cooperation, or is competition with other PE- and IC-countries likely to be more advantageous in the long run? And if the latter course is taken, what are the conflict potentials involved?

The current trend of bilateral relations between PE- and IC-countries makes prediction of the oil companies' role difficult. As middlemen, the oil companies have absorbed most of the friction that inevitably occurs in the negotiations over various oil arrangements. In direct dealings among governments, such friction might have more far-reaching political consequences for the countries concerned than has hitherto been the case.

In chapter 4 some of the actual or probable consequences of the new situation will be examined, with emphasis on the competitive aspects of policy choices and realignments and the conflict potentials raised by them.

Chapter 4. Potentials for cooperation and conflict

World affairs underwent a dramatic change in the autumn of 1973 when the importance of oil to national economic and military security suddenly became emphasized. This change was reflected in the conduct of governments, both within their own countries and towards other governments. The crisis faded by March 1974, but the impression it has left on the political leadership is undoubtedly deep and lasting.

The PE-countries had found that their oil resources could be used not only as an invaluable source of income but also as a means of exercising vast economic and political influence, if used in a coordinated and decisive way. But they also realized that the effects of an extensive use of a restrictive oil policy or excessive prices could disadvantage themselves even to the extent of endangering their own long-term military and economic security. This could be as a result of the development of new energy sources, the breakdown of national economies, the increased focusing of military attention on the areas where oil is found, subsequent changes in regional balances, and so on.

Most IC-countries belatedly realized the risks involved in having to rely on imports of oil from countries which could at any time restrict these supplies. It was seen that, politics apart, these suppliers would in any case sooner or later have to reduce their supplies when the resources started to dwindle, which would result in steep price increases, particularly crippling to the poorer countries. It became apparent to the IC-countries that their national interests might no longer be best served by traditional alliances and loyalties to other IC-countries with which they now would have to compete more vigorously for the limited resources of the Earth. Such reasoning was balanced by the contrary view, however, that their interests as a group lay in the unity of a strong bargaining front against the PE-countries, in the mutual exchange of information and in joint research on and development of new energy sources.

Certainly in this new situation, fraught with possibilities of violent confrontation, a new sense of global responsibility seems called for. This difficult process of adjustment will not be accomplished overnight, but will require a long period of transition and re-analysis of the realities underlying the concepts of cooperation and competition.

The search for cooperative solutions will most likely predominate. This can be foreseen in various fields; trade and other interdependent economic activities; security arrangements of various kinds; political cooperation; and scientific endeavour. Such cooperation will be between different parties (various combinations of PE- and IC-countries), for various periods of time (short-, medium- or long-term arrangements) and in various institutional forms (for instance, in specially established international energy organizations). However, since equitable worldwide arrangements are very rare phenomena, it can also be foreseen that cooperation between certain countries or categories of countries is likely to entail competition and confrontation with others.

With this cooperative/competitive duality as the pervading background, the following sections will concentrate on some of the factors and elements which will stimulate the conflict potentials inherent in the fluid situation now prevailing internationally with regard to oil. The description of these potentials does not necessarily amount to any organic or conceptual scheme, but rather constitutes a generalized framework for defining various actual or hypothetical problematic situations.

At the basis of conflict potentials concerning oil is the naturally limited supply of this non-renewable resource and the overall and ever increasing demand for it. If supplies are artificially restricted to conserve, redirect or upvalue them, these conflict potentials increase in magnitude, as was illustrated when oil restrictions were imposed by the Arab PE-countries in 1973-74.

As a consequence of such restrictions, one or several IC-countries may heighten conflict potentials by taking strong countermeasures against certain PE-countries. Such measures encompass a host of possibilities, ranging from consumer cooperation in one form or another to more retaliatory measures, with possible resort to military force.

In addition, the expected heavy flow of capital from some of the IC-countries into the PE-countries will heavily influence the balance of payments, and hence the total economies, of the countries involved. The conflict potentials in this process will depend on the IC-countries' perception of the overall effects of such transactions on their economic security and on how the PE-countries choose to use their accumulated currency stocks.

A considerable part of this currency is used for the purchase of arms; the close connection between oil and weapons has recently been demonstrated in a number of bilateral economic deals, or negotiations for such deals, between certain IC- and Middle Eastern PE-countries. Although these deals have not been exclusively oil-for-arms, this type of linkage has nevertheless played an important role in several instances. (See further appendices 4 and 5.)

The build-up of arsenals of arms in parts of the Arabian/Persian Gulf region because of its enormous reserves of oil cannot be expected to continue as an isolated phenomenon. A "spill-over" effect is bound to take place in the neighbouring states and the Middle East region as a whole. It is significant, too, that the Indian Ocean, which has largely been spared the arms race activities that have spread to almost all other ocean waters, now seems likely to become yet another militarized area.

The Indian Ocean is understandably becoming a crucial area from the IC-countries' point of view. The two major sea lanes used to transport oil pass through its waters: one around the Cape of Good Hope to Western Europe and the United States, and the other eastwards through the Malacca Strait to Japan. The risks involved in the seaborne transport of oil, not to mention its pipeline transport, and the desire to protect such means and routes of transportation are undoubtedly a deep security concern for many nations, involving grave conflict potentials.

Competition for limited oil resources will focus special attention on international disputes over territories possessing or suspected of holding oil. The sea is a potential area of innumerable territorial contentions, and the possibility of oil being found under the sea-bed will be an additional complicating factor in the judicial efforts to solve such territorial conflicts.

I. *Restrictions on supplies*

The use of oil as a means to exert political pressure on another country has so far mainly been discussed within the context of the most recent Arab-Israeli conflict, but the idea is not a new one. During the period from 1948 to 1973 it had on several occasions been suggested by radical Arab politicians, but was tried on only a couple of occasions, both times during Middle East wars and then for short periods and with very limited results. During the Suez crisis of 1956, the canal was blocked and the pipelines from Iraq were cut off but most of the states actually producing oil in the Middle East were ready to continue supplies to Western Europe. During the 1967 June War, the canal was once again closed and this time greater political pressure was generated. Not only did the pipelines from Iraq cease to operate, but also the Trans-Arabian pipeline (TAP-line), built to carry crude oil from Saudi Arabia to Mediterranean terminals. In addition, Arab PE-countries joined in a selective embargo on exports to the United States, the United Kingdom, and to a lesser extent, the Federal Republic of Germany. (Again in July 1967 during the Nigerian Civil War, supplies were cut off from Nigeria. Although the emergency situation which resulted lasted only about two months, its effects upon the pattern of oil trade were felt for a longer period, because it took time to shift to alternative oil sources and to reroute tankers around the Cape of Good Hope.)

By 1973, the Arab countries were better prepared for using oil as a coordinated means of pressure. The change in the whole structure of oil exploitation and trade had considerably strengthened and unified the Arab countries. This became apparent on several occasions during the OPEC-members' negotiations with the oil companies.[16] The increased vulnerability of IC-countries was reflected in their growing apprehension about the prospects of a forthcoming energy crisis, particularly their fears about the prospect of the United States becoming a massive importer of Middle East oil instead of being able, as before, to substitute as a supplier to help tide Western Europe and Japan over supply cut-offs from the Middle East. In addition, politically restrictive action by OAPEC members coincided with the realization by OPEC members of the benefits obtainable from imposing such restrictions for other reasons, such as the desire to raise oil prices or to conserve some of the oil resources for future generations.[17]

The Arab countries issued several warnings before they imposed restrictions in the autumn of 1973. Their capacity to back up these warnings with effective action might have been predicted from the measures already taken on participation and nationalization and the new agreements on prices. During the spring and summer of 1973, and even earlier, countries such as Libya and Saudi Arabia privately and publicly intimated that oil might be used as a weapon to force the United States to adopt a less pro-Israeli policy. Of particular interest was the development of the oil policy of Saudia Arabia, both because of its extreme importance as a PE-country and because of its traditionally pro-US policy. At the beginning of September Saudi Arabian warnings were stepped up in severity, and when the Arab-Israeli War started in October, Saudi Arabia joined the other OAPEC members in curbing oil exports to countries regarded as taking a pro-Israeli stance in the war. [25–35]

On 17 October after a meeting in Kuwait, the Arab states took the first concrete step in restricting production:[18] 11 members of OAPEC announced that they would reduce oil production by 5 per cent each month (calculated on the basis of the September 1974 production) until the international community compelled Israel to withdraw from occupied Arab territories; it was also stated that another goal was the recovery of the legitimate rights of the Palestinian people in accordance with the UN resolutions. The cut in the oil output was aimed at countries that the OAPEC members regarded as supporters of Israel. The main target was the United States, which had by then started to airlift weapons to Israel.

In the succeeding weeks most of the PE-countries announced further cutbacks and stoppages of exports to specific countries (particularly the United States and the Netherlands, but also Canada, South Africa, Denmark, Rhodesia and Portugal).

At a second meeting in Kuwait on 4 November, the OAPEC states decided to cut production by 25 per cent (based on the September production figures) as a means of increasing pressure to achieve an Israeli withdrawal from Arab lands. Such a cut would not, however, affect the share of those "friendly countries" that imported oil from Arab PE-countries. Their share would be based on average imports for the first nine months of 1973.[18] No particular countries were named in the category of "friendly", but it was speculated that France, the UK, Spain and Pakistan could be regarded as included, and that for a country to move to the most-favoured list it must break relations with Israel, apply economic sanctions against Israel and grant military assistance to the Arab states.

On 8 December, after a third meeting in Kuwait, the OAPEC states re-affirmed a 5 per cent cut in oil production and exports for January 1974 and again linked the resumption of supplies to Israel's progressive withdrawal from occupied Arab territories, including the city of Jerusalem.[18] However, two weeks later, on 25 December, the Arab PE-countries announced that they had decided instead to increase production in January 1974 by 10 per cent. They would nevertheless continue their boycott of the United States and the Netherlands, but would on the other hand add Japan and Belgium to the list of countries not subject to delivery cuts.[18]

No PE-countries other than the Arab states restricted their production or their shipments of oil. They limited their actions to adjusting their prices, taking advantage of the actual market situation. Thus Iran, a particularly important producer of oil, stuck to its prior pledge not to use oil as a weapon. For reasons of their own, two Arab countries, Iraq and Libya, did not abide by the decisions on restrictions made by the other Arab countries.

By January 1974, it was beginning to become apparent that the oil embargo would soon be lifted. After the Egyptian-Israeli military disengagement agreement had been signed on 18 January, US pressure for lifting the embargo increased, since it had been understood that removing the embargo was conditional on the agreement being achieved.[19] Thus, on the Arab side, Egypt was reported to have urged the other Arab countries concerned to moderate their embargo against the United States. However, other Arab countries, notably Syria, Libya and Algeria, considered that the disengagement agreement did not represent enough progress towards peace to warrant a lifting of the embargo. It was argued that, according to the original decision taken on 17 October 1973, the embargo was intended to remain until such time as total evacuation of Israeli forces from all Arab territory occupied during the 1967 June War was completed, and the legitimate rights of the Palestinian people were restored.

The stand of OAPEC members became less firm as doubts increased about the effectiveness of the embargo. Most decisive, however, was the fact that Saudi Arabia, previously one of the embargo's chief advocates, increasingly came to regard it as a political protest which had now served its purpose.

After intensive discussions among the Arab countries in various capitals, seven of them (Abu Dhabi, Algeria, Bahrein, Egypt, Kuwait, Qatar and Saudi Arabia) finally announced at a meeting in Vienna on 18 March[18] that the oil embargo against the United States had been lifted because of a change in US Middle East policy.[20] The lifting of the five-month embargo was provisional, however, and the oil ministers were to meet in Cairo on 1 June 1974 to review the decision. Syria and Libya refused to accept the decision and Iraq did not attend the Vienna meeting at all.

With the modification of the embargo, two West European countries, the Federal Republic of Germany and Italy, were explicitly listed as "friendly nations", but the Netherlands and Denmark remained on the embargo list, probably because they had not made clear their position on Israeli withdrawal from occupied territories. (Both the Netherlands and Denmark are members of the EEC, however, and share that group's official stand on Israeli withdrawal.) Nor did the lifting of the embargo apply to Portugal, Rhodesia or South Africa because of the understanding that exists between Arab countries and the black African countries.[21]

Finally, a number of short observations on the overall effects of the embargo are pertinent here.

1. The OAPEC members initially demonstrated a high degree of coordination and cooperation, which for various reasons showed signs of disintegrating after about three months.

2. Partial Egyptian success in the disengagement talks held with Israel under the auspices of the United States weakened the Arab resolution to maintain a punitive attitude towards that country. Although it could hardly be said that the United States changed its policy *vis-à-vis* the Arab-Israeli conflict because of the oil embargo, it definitely seems to have spurred US efforts to achieve a constructive solution to the problem.

3. The success of the embargo was rendered only partial by the flexibility of the international oil market. The international oil companies served as a buffer and evidently evened out the differences in supply and demand fairly successfully by a complicated pattern of redistribution.[22]

4. Furthermore, some non-Arab countries stepped up production during this period and, as already mentioned, Libya and Iraq did not curb theirs. Several press reports claimed "leakages" of Arab oil, more than half of it from Libya, to the United States. [45] It is also possible that the Arab cutbacks were never quite as severe as they appeared to be on the surface.[23]

5. A number of other factors, such as the sharp oil price increases, a mild

winter, and the success of voluntary and mandatory conservation measures, helped to improve the balance of supply and demand in most IC-countries.

6. According to many politicians and economists, the pattern of economic interrelationship of almost all countries would be gravely disrupted by a prolonged embargo, a consideration which probably dissuaded the Arab countries from taking an even harder line. (See page 39.)

7. Whatever the limitations of the embargo, the overall political achievements of those who imposed it were considerable − an impressive test case for countries producing other, although less important, scarce raw materials.

8. Finally, it is worth noting that questions concerning the legal aspects of the embargo were never officially brought up during the period of its imposition, nor were they discussed in other forums.[24]

II. *Measures to counter restrictions*

When confronted with the problem of restricted oil supplies, whether as a result of attempts to conserve natural resources, a desire to achieve a political goal or to obtain a raise in the price of oil, the IC-countries will feel obliged to take certain measures to counter its effects. A host of considerations and circumstances determine the final choice of such measures, but among the basic options a nation must consider before making such a choice are the following: (*a*) to continue to rely on the multinational oil companies as the more or less exclusive suppliers; (*b*) to seek cooperation with other IC-countries in order to form a united front against the PE-countries; (*c*) to seek direct and bilateral arrangements with one or several PE-countries; and (*d*) to seek some combination of the preceding options, the interesting question then being the composition of such a mixture of affiliations, and the net outcome of various choices. Whatever the choices are, they are bound to contain both cooperative and competitive elements.

The following three sections deal with the actual or projected forms of cooperation among IC-countries that have been considered during the past year and particularly as a consequence of the oil restrictions introduced by the OAPEC members, and also the various efforts by some IC-countries to establish bilateral relations directly with the PE-countries in the wake of the imposition of oil restrictions. The two IC-countries which most clearly represented these two policies were the United States and France, respectively. These two approaches have considerably strained relations both within the EEC and within the Atlantic Community.

In working out appropriate measures to counter the imposed restrictions, "solutions" of a more retaliatory nature have been suggested or hinted at. In the second and third sections, economic and military measures of this kind are further discussed.

Various forms of cooperation

Practical plans for increased cooperation among the IC-countries have been slow to materialize although the industrialized countries have long had a forum to discuss strategies and measures against oil shortages: the Oil Committee of the Organization for Economic Cooperation and Development (OECD). The Oil Committee is a consultative organ which can make recommendations about principles of emergency stockpiling and which also has machinery to allocate scarce resources during crisis conditions, although this functions only in the European context.[25] Efforts to incorporate the non-European members of the OECD into this machinery during the autumn of 1973 failed, owing to disagreement on whether oil should be rationed according to each country's total consumption (the European view) or according to its imports (the US and Canadian views).[26] The principles of oil sharing have never been put to the test even among the European OECD countries, since the members of the Oil Committee never found reason to declare such a state of oil shortage as would have allowed them to allocate supplies.[27]

The EEC has also devoted increasing attention to energy problems in recent years, among them the question of securing supplies for member states. In addition, even before the oil crisis, preparations were made for regular discussions on energy matters between the EEC and the United States, with the possibility of including Japan.[28]

In his "energy speech" of 18 April 1973, President Nixon emphasized energy matters as an area of international cooperation, [65] a theme taken up on 24 April by the President's then National Security Assistant Kissinger, in a speech known as "The Year of Europe". [66] Such cooperation should, in the first instance, involve the United States, Canada and Western Europe, but should ultimately embrace Japan as well.[29]

On the bilateral level, cooperation among IC-countries had mainly focused on efforts to find and develop substitutes for conventional energy sources. For example, the United States and Japan had concluded an agreement to exchange technical information on the development of new energy sources.[30] The United States had also agreed with the Soviet Union to pursue joint research in magnetohydrodynamics (MHD)[31] and to exchange information on fusion, fission, the generation of electricity, and so forth. [65]

After the Arab PE-countries introduced their restrictive oil policy in October 1973, the tendencies both for cooperation and for competition among the IC-countries intensified.[18] The difficulties of harmonizing agreed principles of cooperation with harsh realities were notably demonstrated during the October War of 1973, when the highly sensitive Arab-Israeli problem became a hindrance and almost an impasse, not only to political and economic cooperation between the EEC countries, but also to political and military cooperation between Western Europe and the United States.

In addition to taking compulsory or voluntary measures to save energy, the major IC-countries reacted to the restrictions imposed on production and shipments of oil in different ways, varying with the degree of self-sufficiency the countries had, with their general assessment of the prevailing energy situation, and with the state of developments in their bilateral relations with the Arab countries, including of course, their stance on the 1973 Arab-Israeli war.

The Foreign Ministers of the nine *EEC countries* adopted a resolution on 6 November — later confirmed by the EEC heads of state at their meeting in Copenhagen on 13-15 December — in which no reference was made to the Arab restrictions on oil or the boycott measures taken by Arab countries against the Netherlands; it was nevertheless evident that one of the purposes behind the statement was to placate those Arab countries that wanted to use oil as a political weapon against the EEC countries.* Subsequently the OAPEC members exempted the EEC countries, except the Netherlands, from a 5 per cent oil cut-back for the month of December. The EEC Parliament took a somewhat harsher attitude towards the OAPEC countries, however, in adopting a resolution on 14 November which called on member governments not to rule out the possibility of taking economic countermeasures against third countries. At the meeting of the EEC heads of state in Copenhagen on 13-15 December, most of the attention was devoted to the problem of how best to cope with the energy situation. Besides confirming the declaration on the Arab-Israeli conflict of 6 November, the heads of state committed the EEC to establish an energy committee and put forward a plan to study, with the participation of other IC-countries and keeping within the framework of the OECD, ways of dealing with short- and long-term energy problems. Having completed this, the EEC was to launch a programme to promote diversification of energy supplies from existing sources.

Japan, heavily dependent on the Middle East for its oil supplies, anticipated grave consequences for its total economy if the supply restrictions continued. It modified its previous neutral-aimed position on the Arab-Israeli problem into a more pro-Arab stance, after having been urged by various Arab governments to take such a step. In a statement issued on 22 November, the Japanese government deplored Israel's continued occupation of Arab territories, called on Israel to withdraw, and announced that it would continue to observe the situation in the Middle East with grave concern and, depending on future developments, intimated that Japan might have to reconsider its policy towards Israel. Subsequently, the OAPEC states exempted Japan from a 5 per cent oil cut-back for the month of December.

The United States, only to a limited extent dependent on imports of oil from the Middle East, reacted officially to the possibility of restrictions even before they were actually imposed, since it had been the main target of several warnings about such restrictions from April to September 1973. Commenting on these warnings, on 8 September President Nixon remarked that "no nation, and particularly no industrial nation, must be in a position of being at the mercy of any other nation by having its energy supplies suddenly cut off". [71]

Reacting to the decisions of the second OAPEC meeting in Kuwait on 4-5 November, President Nixon announced on 7 November a series of measures designed to reduce oil consumption, which were speedily enacted by Congress. He also emphasized that the United States must embark upon a major effort to achieve self-sufficiency in energy, an effort called Project Independence. If this project were successful, by 1980 it would take the United States to a point where it was no longer dependent to any significant extent upon "potentially insecure foreign supplies of energy". [72]

On 21 November, Secretary of State Kissinger amplified the US view on the oil

* See appendix 6 for the complete text of the communiqué of 6 November 1973 in addition to pertinent sections of the final communiqué of the meeting of EEC heads of state on 13–15 December 1973.

shortage by saying that the United States could not alter its Middle East policy because of the Arab oil embargo; it was clear, however, that if the Arab shut-down of oil to the United States continued "unreasonably and indefinitely", the United States would have to decide what countermeasures were necessary. He hoped, however, that this would not come about. [73]

Three weeks later, in a speech in London on 12 December, Kissinger proposed that the industrialized nations of the world establish an energy action group, comprising senior and prestigious individuals, to develop within three months an initial action programme to solve various energy problems. The producing countries were to be invited to join the action group from the very beginning, should there be matters of common interest on the agenda. [74]

This initiative was followed up by President Nixon in an invitation to the major IC-countries to attend an Energy Conference in Washington on 11-12 February 1974. At the same time, a letter was also sent to the governments of 13 major PE-countries describing the US move as "consistent with the publicly stated views of a number of oil-producing nations which have called for a consultative relationship between producers and consumers". [75]

The invitation was originally extended to six West European countries (France, FR Germany, Italy, the Netherlands, Norway and the United Kingdom) as well as to Canada and Japan. Later the invitation was extended to all nine members of the EEC (thus including Belgium, Denmark, Ireland and Luxembourg). The Secretary-General of the OECD was also invited to the meeting.

The conference was preceded by an intensive coordination of views between the EEC countries, whose foreign ministers agreed unanimously on their mandate for the conference by 5 February. [76]

France was the last country to accept the invitation and during the conference demonstrated very clearly that its attitude to the conference and the ideas behind its convening were different from those of the other participants. France was the only country to make formal reservations on several of the points in the final communiqué.

The main points agreed by the 12 countries, notwithstanding France's reservations, provided for the following: (a) the establishment of a high-level group to deal with all facets of the world energy situation and to coordinate the work of existing institutions such as the OECD, the World Bank and the International Monetary Fund (IMF); (b) cooperation in restraining demand, allocating oil supplies in emergencies, diversifying energy supplies and accelerating energy research and development; (c) cooperation in dealing with monetary and economic problems arising from the current energy situation; and (d) the development of a cooperative multilateral relationship with the producing countries and other consumers. (For the official texts of the communiqué, see appendix 7, which also puts the views of some of the participants into juxtaposition.)

However, before agreement could be reached on the final communiqué, the statements of the various countries had indicated a less harmonious attitude.

In the overall perspective of the nature and scope of energy problems, most countries agreed that they constituted an unprecedented challenge to the prosperity of most nations and to the entire structure of international cooperation. The exceptionally grave situation raised fundamental questions about hopes for global stability, since security and economic considerations are inevitably linked and energy cannot be isolated from either. If the countries of the world were guided by a spirit of confrontation instead of cooperation, the world would be threatened with a vicious circle of competition, rivalry and worldwide depression.

Opinion was most divided on the question of multilateral and collective arrangements between various kinds of countries *versus* individual and bilateral approaches.

The United States was the leading proponent of the view that concerted international action is imperative and that isolated solutions are impossible. Countries such as the United States and Canada are capable of solving the energy problem by largely national means, but even they would suffer some of the impact of a world economic crisis. Furthermore, the United States took the view that narrowly competitive approaches have traditionally ended in disruptive conflict — economic, military or both. Bilateral dealings should take place in accordance with a "code of conduct".

France, on the other hand, emphasized the importance of developing cooperation between IC- and PE-countries. Cooperation in every aspect between Europe and the PE-countries, especially the Arab countries, was seen to be particularly valuable.

The view of the EEC was to emphasize the worldwide nature of the problem and the inadequacy of isolated replies to it. Directly addressing one of its members, France, the EEC spokesman commented that some countries were more prone than others to adopt a beggar-my-neighbour attitude.

Japan finally sided with those who expressed the need for a cooperative international community which would embrace the PE-countries.

All the participating countries felt the burden of the huge price increases, but their official reactions to such increases varied somewhat. The United States stated that the price levels prevailing in February 1974 were simply not sustainable and that for various reasons the PE-countries would be adversely affected by their own measures in the long run. Japan, whose economy was one of the hardest hit by the oil supply restrictions and price increases, suggested that a study should be undertaken together with the PE-countries on a oil price-setting mechanism. All countries present agreed that the effects of the price increases would be disastrous to the oil-poor underdeveloped countries and that special consideration should be given to their predicament.

The United States was the only country to express a more general view on the imposed oil restrictions. It warned that the oil embargo carried profound worldwide implications, namely, the manipulation of raw material supplies in order to prescribe the foreign policies of IC-countries. Concerning emergency sharing, the United States expressed its willingness to share available energy in times of emergency or prolonged shortages. It stated its preparedness to allocate an agreed portion of the total US petroleum supply, provided other IC-countries with indigenous production did likewise. With regard to international cooperation in advanced energy research and development, the United States declared its willingness to make a major contribution, including the sharing of uranium enrichment technology.

In the financial field the United States underlined the congruent interests of the

PE-countries and the IC-countries and the urgency of finding cooperative solutions, including a new mechanism for the distribution of international capital, measures to ensure confidence in investments and measures to encourage PE-countries and underdeveloped IC-countries to take part in existing international institutions.

The EEC's view of the financial aspects was that dangerously conflicting policies must be avoided: competitive devaluation should not be considered a remedy and must be avoided, as must overbidding and commercial protectionism.

Finally, as regards the institutional framework for further discussions with the aim of extending cooperation, views once again differed widely between the United States and France.

The United States suggested that a coordinating group be established to prepare the ground for two other conferences, one including the underdeveloped IC-countries, and the other including both the latter and the PE-countries as well; all preparations were to be completed by 1 May 1974.

France, for its part, would not support any such institutionalization that would constitute the IC-countries as a group independent of the underdeveloped countries and the PE-countries. In any case, flexible exchanges of information could be envisaged among the IC-countries within, for example, the framework of the OECD.[32]

With France holding aloof, the final outcome of the meeting was the establishment of a coordinating group headed by senior officials to direct and coordinate the tasks which the meeting delegated to it, including the preparations of a conference of IC- and PE-countries. This conference would be held at the earliest possible opportunity. The tasks to be taken in hand by the coordinating group were the following: (a) to monitor and bring into focus the tasks to which existing organizations might effectively address themselves; (b) to establish such ad hoc working groups as may be necessary to undertake tasks for which no suitable bodies exist; and (c) to undertake preparations for a conference of IC- and PE-countries to be held at the earliest possible opportunity which would be preceded by a further meeting of consumer countries if necessary. The participants, with the exception of France, also agreed that the preparations should involve consultations with underdeveloped countries and other consumer and producer countries.

The Energy Coordinating Group (ECG) held its first meeting in Washington on 25 February when procedural matters concerning future work seem to have been mainly discussed. At a second meeting in Brussels on 13-14 March, the Coordinating Group endorsed a US proposal that subcommittees be set up to deal with such topics as the role of the oil companies, research into energy sources, the financial aspects of the oil shortage, and the development of enriched uranium. Other aspects of energy problems, such as energy conservation, the reduction of demand, and oil-sharing arrangements, were expected to be turned over to the existing Oil Committee of the OECD. The Coordinating Group was to decide later how the IC-countries should approach the PE-countries. [80] A third meeting with the Coordinating Group was held on 3-4 April. It was then decided that a conference of IC- and PE-countries should be prepared in bilateral contact during the UN Sixth Special Session on raw materials. A fourth meeting was held on 2 May, and at a fifth meeting on 16-18 June the USA was reported to have proposed that plans to pool emergency oil supplies among the 12 nations of the ECG should be linked to efforts to conserve energy and maintain large oil stocks against crises. [81]

Prior to the second Brussels meeting of the Coordinating Group, the EEC had already separately approached the Arab PE-countries. At an EEC meeting in Brussels on 4 March, France proposed and the nine member countries agreed to seek a foreign ministers' conference of themselves and 20 Arab countries to take place during the autumn of 1974. The discussions with the Arab countries were to cover a wide range of topics connected with economics, trade, science and technology, and other mutual concerns. In spite of subsequent assurances by spokesmen of the EEC countries that the proposed conference had nothing to do with current energy problems, it seemed clear enough that the energy crisis had spurred this initative. [82] On 21 May, members of the Arab League decided to establish an *ad hoc* committee to pursue the dialogue with the EEC. [83]

This direct approach was not the first effort by certain IC-countries to strengthen their bilateral relations with the PE-countries. Practically all of the main importers (Japan, France, the UK, FR Germany, Italy, the Nordic countries, and many others) sent delegations to various countries in the Middle East at the end of 1973 and the beginning of 1974 to investigate the possibilities of increased bilateral cooperation. Some of these contacts resulted in firm or preliminary agreements on substantial deals for economic cooperation which entailed the exchange of manufactured goods and various kinds of technical assistance in return for oil supplies. Some of these agreements had the character of oil-for-arms deals, which will be further discussed in chapter 4, and appendices 4 and 5.

The US plans for a conference of consumers and producers did not materialize during the spring of 1974. It gradually became clear that the oil consumers in the third world were less interested in working with the industrialized IC-countries than in devoting their full attention to the UN Sixth Special Session on raw materials which took place from 9 April to 3 May. Although the session dealt with raw materials in general, it was obvious that the discussions were doomed to be heavily influenced by the oil situation.

In summary, it may be said that conflict potentials are likely to arise not so much out of straight competition for oil as out of the rivalry resulting from different patterns of cooperation. Though it is difficult to predict the exact form of such conflicts, some of the more spectacular potential developments deserve mention.

1. The establishment of a united front among the IC-countries promises great difficulties owing to the diversity of their interests and needs, especially between those of the United States and the majority of other Western countries.33 Two things seem certain, however: no small group of states can suffice to constitute an effective bloc, and such a bloc seems bound, sooner or later, to lead to various forms of confrontation with the PE-countries.

2. Japan will have potentially strong incentives to diversify its imports of energy to countries other than those in the Arabian/Persian Gulf area. Although it will continue to cooperate with Indonesia, Japan will also have to consider importing energy from China or the Soviet Union. However, cooperation with one of them will almost inevitably entail strained relations with the other. Thus, for instance, possible Soviet-Japanese cooperation in the development of the East

Siberian oil fields and the construction of pipelines from this area out to the sea, on Soviet territory but along the sensitive northern Chinese border where both powers have many troops stationed, would probably be considered by China as a considerable strengthening of the Soviet military potential there and consequently an increased threat to its national security. Conversely, the development of successful cooperation between China and Japan in response to the energy question could fundamentally change the regional balance in this part of the world with potentially unstabilizing consequences for Soviet national security.

3. The uneven distribution of oil in the North Sea which will substantially favour some European countries, notably the United Kingdom and Norway, and not others, might complicate relations in Western Europe. This will not make it easier for the EEC to develop plans to promote, for instance, common sharing of oil within the EEC.

4. Bilateral arrangements between IC-countries and PE-countries force others to make similar deals, such as those made in early 1974. This will probably shake up traditional alliances and loyalties, but is unlikely to threaten seriously the traditionally strong ties within the Atlantic Community or the mutual interests served by the US-Japanese connection.

5. The attitude of the OPEC countries, and particularly the OAPEC countries, towards cooperation among the IC-countries is quite clear: they consider it a provocation directed against them, to be countered by following an even tougher line. For instance, in January 1974 Saudi Arabia's oil minister, Sheikh Yamani, warned the IC-countries against forming a bloc that might clash with the PE-countries' interests, the result of which would be a disaster. [89] It should be noted, however, that the spirit of several of the decisions taken at the Washington Conference was the same as that in some of the recommendations previously made by the Secretary-General of OPEC.[34]

Economic retaliation

Although the difficulties of cooperation among IC-countries outlined above clearly stand in the way of effective economic retaliatory measures against restrictive oil policies, the possibility of such measures has been considered in the discussions about the oil crisis.

Thus, grain exported to the Arab countries, particularly by the United States, has been discussed as a commodity which could come under such a retaliatory embargo.[35] According to an official US study, however, an embargo on US grain exports would be futile since the Arab countries can meet their relatively small food import needs from other sources and have the money to outbid other food buyers in the world market. [94] Table 2 is based on information presented in this report.

Other forms of economic retaliatory measures – the suspension of the sales of other commodities (such as military equipment), or services (such as Western technological expertise) or the blocking of Arab bank deposits and other funds in the IC-countries – have been considered both futile and inappropriate. [95] Even in the unlikely event that all key Western states cooperated, the Arab countries

Table 2. Imports of food by selected OAPEC countries, 1972

Country	Estimated total imports of foodstuff *US $ mn*	Imports from USA *per cent*
Algeria	198	*16*
Egypt	358	*1*
Iraq	71	*1*
Kuwait	132	*3*
Libya	164	*1*
Saudi Arabia	250	*12*
Syria	52	*5*

Source: The United States Oil Shortage and the Arab-Israeli Conflict. Report of a Study Mission to the Middle East, 22 October–3 November 1973, Committee on Foreign Affairs Report, 20 December 1973 (Washington, 1973).

could apply to other countries, notably the Soviet Union and its allies, to satisfy most of their basic needs.

Military measures

At the extreme end of the scale of retaliatory measures lies military force. Although the contingency of its use was remote during the recent oil shortage, the risks of further developments bringing it closer cannot be lightly dismissed. There are presently many factors operating strongly to inhibit military intervention, but these could certainly be weakened if the PE-countries endangered the internal order and well-being of IC-countries by insisting upon limiting supplies to levels that leave very basic economic and military needs unfulfilled. It might have been with this in mind that Secretary of State Kissinger expressed veiled warnings on 21 November 1973 and US Secretary of Defense Schlesinger stated on 7 January 1974 that the independent powers of sovereign states should not be used in such a way as to cripple the large mass of the industrialized world.[36]

Such warnings justify certain speculations on the risks of armed conflict. Obviously, a powerful country such as the United States would have little difficulty in conquering most of the countries in the Middle East; successful military control over parts of the Arabian/Persian Gulf area could probably be achieved in hours, or even minutes. The problem would be in sustaining such an operation and managing its repercussions. What would make a potential aggressor hesitant to take such steps would be risks for confrontation with other great powers; the long-term need to secure the occupied areas and oil installations, requiring a significant capability for military presence in areas remote from the national territory; and the risk that the occupant's citizens and property would become the target for acts of sabotage all over the world. Obviously, the leaders of some of the Arab countries (Saudi Arabia, Kuwait and Algeria) reckoned on the possibility of such a turn of events during the recent oil crisis, since on numerous occasions, they threatened to blow up their oil installations if threats of military intervention were carried out.[37] [97–100]

It has been speculated that an outside power might use some of the countries in the oil-producing area to act militarily as its "proxy" — the possibility of the United States using Iran as such a "proxy" has been discussed.[38] It seems doubtful, however, that another country would be willing to face the very same risks that the outside power wants to avoid.

On balance, therefore, the prospects of military intervention and occupation by outside powers seem fairly remote at present because of the risks involved in such operations. In addition, such action would seriously compromise the ongoing efforts between some of the outside powers to reach agreement on various matters related to *détente* and security. Moreover, such military operations against another state would imply a breach of the United Nations Charter, which provides that states shall refrain in their international relations from the threat or use of force against the territorial integrity or political independence of other states.[39]

Nevertheless, the value of the Middle Eastern oil resources is so potent a factor in many countries' economic and military policy-making that it could, in a less stable situation, or in a state of general war, completely overshadow what appeared to be the logic of the situation.

III. *Economic implications*

The economic implications of oil price increases, and of acute and long-term oil shortages, are difficult to reduce to a predictable pattern. One must take into account not only such factors as the actual or estimated rates of production, consumption and trade in oil, including the prospects for developing alternative sources, but also those depending on such imponderables as the economic planning and political will of the governments of various countries. The general trend is quite obvious, however. In view of the basic and vital importance of oil to the economies of all countries, shortages in the supply of this resource present the heavily oil-dependent countries with great problems of adaptation if they are to avoid a severe recession in their national economies, with the possible repercussion of a massive depression in the total world economy. Moreover, because of the enormous volumes involved in the exchange of oil and the sudden and sharp increases in oil prices — 400 per cent in 1973 — the IC-countries now face very dramatic changes in their balance of payments, which will negatively affect their national economies. Conversely, the effects of the massive transfer of money to the PE-countries is another important question to be considered. Table 3 shows the price changes of various types of oil from 1972 to 1974.[40]

Since it is not possible to assess with any certainty the practical economic implications of current and prospective conditions in the international oil market, it is natural that estimates of the future figures involved will vary widely and must be frequently revised.

One often quoted estimate [108] indicates that even after reductions in market prices of oil below the levels of February 1974, the following substantial changes in the capital market could take place in 1974: (*a*) the developed IC-countries could have their combined account deficits worsened by as much as $ 40 billion; (*b*) the underdeveloped IC-countries could have their account deficits increased by as much

Table 3. Posted price changes of various types of oil, 1972—74

US $ per barrel

Type of oil	20 Jan 1972	1 Jan 1973	16 Oct 1973	1 Jan 1974
Arabian/Persian Gulf				
Arabian light (34°)	2.479	2.591	5.119	11.651
Abu Dhabi Murban (39°)	2.540	2.654	6.045	12.630
Mediterranean and Africa				
Arabian light (34°)	3.370	3.451	7.149	13.647
Libyan (40°)	3.673	3.777	8.915[a]	15.768
Nigerian (34°)	3.446[b]	3.561	8.310	14.691
Venezuela				
Oficina (35°)	3.261	3.477	7.802[c]	14.247[d]

[a] 19 October.
[b] 15 February.
[c] 1 November.
[d] Excluding the sulphur premium.

Source: *Petroleum Economist,* February 1974, p. 48.

Table 4. Oil revenues of the major producing countries: selected years, 1965—74

US $ bn

	1965	1970	1972	1973[a]	1974[a]
Arabian/Persian Gulf					
Abu Dhabi	—	0.3	0.5	1.0	4.8
Iran	0.5	1.1	2.4	3.9	14.9
Iraq	0.4	0.5	0.6	1.5	5.9
Kuwait	0.7	0.9	1.6	2.1	7.9
Saudi Arabia	0.6	1.2	3.1	4.9	19.4
Qatar	0.1	0.1	0.3	0.4	1.2
Other[b]					
Algeria	..	0.3	0.7	1.0	3.7
Indonesia	..	0.2	0.6	0.8	2.1
Libya	0.4	1.3	1.6	2.2	8.0
Nigeria	..	0.4	1.2	2.0	7.0
Venezuela	1.1	1.4	1.9	2.8	10.0
Total revenues	**3.8**	**7.9**	**14.7**	**23.1**	**86.6**

[a] Figures for 1973 and 1974 are estimates provided by the World Bank.
[b] Not including North America or socialist countries.

Source: "Financial Problems Loom", *Petroleum Economist,* May 1974, p. 165.

as $ 10 billion; and (c) the PE-countries could add as much as $ 50 billion to their holdings of foreign assets.

The oil revenues of the PE-countries for selected years between 1965 and 1974 (with estimates for 1973 and 1974) are shown in table 4.[41]

When assessing the financial implications, it must be borne in mind, however, that the trade in oil, and particularly the volumes and prices involved in this trade, are not the only factors that decide the economic interdependence between PE-countries and IC-countries, even if they are often the most essential ones. Among other factors influencing this interdependence, often in a compensating way, are those which are related to the oil business, such as the money involved in the transportation of oil and the repatriated earnings by the international oil companies. Another is possible investments by PE-countries in the IC-countries, which can be made in oil-related industries and services or in other sectors of the economy — in financial or real assets. Such recycling of capital through investment, however, will also result in repatriated earnings, which will add to the negative effect on the IC-countries' balance of payments. Another compensating factor is the transfer of capital from the PE- to the IC-countries to pay for the transfer of commodities and services in the opposite direction. Economic aid given by PE-countries to underdeveloped IC-countries will also have such a compensating effect.

The total picture of economic interdependence between PE- and IC-countries, when all such offsetting factors have been taken into account, is far from clear. But what is plainly discernible is that the flow of capital from the IC- to the PE-countries will be far stronger than the flow in the opposite direction.

Some of the considerations which will determine the character of these capital transfers and influence the governments of the PE-countries in their use of excess capital will be described below.

The PE-countries have widely different needs and opportunities for channelling oil income into the development of their own economies. Relatively underdeveloped countries with large populations, such as Iran, Iraq, Algeria, Nigeria, Indonesia and Venezuela, will be able to use most of their capital build-up for increased imports of commodities and services. Confronting all the PE-countries is the overwhelmingly important task of establishing a base of economic activity independent of the oil sector — oil wealth has come suddenly and for some of the PE-countries is a fairly short-term benefit. There is now a strong commitment among the PE-countries to the notion that oil wealth must be used to foster capital formation. The required technology and commodities must be imported from already industrialized countries, either in the Western or the Eastern world. In view of present political and economic realities, the Western industrialized IC-countries will continue in the foreseeable future, in heavy competition with each other, to be the main suppliers of such commodities and services, even though barter trade with East European countries has for a number of years been of considerable importance for some Middle Eastern exporters, especially Iran and Iraq.

As far as the sectorial allocations of revenues within the national economy are concerned, however, it is noteworthy that the distribution of such outlays has differed considerably from country to country. Few governments of Middle Eastern countries have devoted more than 50 per cent of oil revenues to the development sector, while a large proportion of foreign exchange has been given over to defence purposes. [111] This observation is further substantiated by information on some recent arms transfers to these countries in appendix 4.

The revenues of some of the PE-countries, however, are expected to be of such magnitude that, apart from a small portion, they cannot be spent or invested in the PE-countries themselves. Table 5 indicates that, until now, the value of imports by the Arabian/Persian Gulf countries has been very limited. Saudi Arabia, Kuwait, Abu Dhabi and Qatar alone, which have a total population of around ten million, are the most obvious among those countries which will have substantial sums of money to allocate to external alternatives such as the build-up of foreign exchange reserves, foreign aid and investments abroad.

It seems likely that the PE-countries will be influenced by the same motivations as any other capital-owner investing money, that is, a wish to acquire assets that produce a reasonable return, but are also secure and not too sensitive to inflation and currency changes.[42] It is likely that a large proportion of the investments will be made in the main IC-countries, that is, the United States, Western Europe and Japan.[43] The National Iranian Oil Company, for example has made arrangements to this effect with US oil distribution interests.[44]

Some PE-countries may also become very important donors of economic aid to

Table 5. Imports by Arabian/Persian Gulf countries from Japan, Western Europe and the United States, 1973

Importing country	Total imports	Japan		Western Europe[a]		United States	
		US$mn	Per cent	US$mn	Per cent	US$mn	Per cent
Bahrain	231[b]	34	15	69	30	30	13
Iran	2 555	358	14	1 125[c]	44[c]	425	17
Iraq[d]	843	35	4	313[e]	37[e]	26	3
Kuwait	797	128	16	218	27	104	13
Oman	185	8	4	144	78	7	4
Qatar	138	17	12	58	42	14	10
Saudi Arabia	1 397	265	19	445[e]	34[e]	346	25
United Arab Emirates	514	98	19	159[f]	31[f]	70	14

[a] Includes France, FR Germany, Italy and United Kingdom, except as noted.
[b] Imports exclude crude petroleum from Saudi Arabia. These amounted to $147 million in 1972; their inclusion would lower all market shares shown above proportionately, but does not distort the relative market positions shown.
[c] Includes, in addition, Belgium, the Netherlands and Switzerland.
[d] The source is the International Monetary Fund Direction of Trade.
[e] Includes, in addition, Austria, Belgium, Denmark, the Netherlands, Norway, Sweden and Switzerland.
[f] Includes, in addition, Switzerland.

Source: Hearings before the Subcommittee on the Near East and South Asia of the Committee on Foreign Affairs, US House of Representatives, 93rd Congress, 1st Session, 28 November 1973.

the oil-poor, less developed countries. A number of Arab countries seem most likely to benefit from such aid; the already existing Kuwait Fund for Arab Economic Development has been a prototype for other countries (Libya, Abu Dhabi and Saudi Arabia) as an instrument to channel such aid. The Arab PE-countries have traditionally also made substantial financial contributions to the build-up of Arab armed forces for use against Israel.

Other countries likely to benefit from aid from the oil-rich Arab countries are the black African countries which have supported the Arab countries in their conflict with Israel.

Some of the other oil-poor countries, however, will most certainly fall far behind in the competition for oil; unless special arrangements can be made to assure them secured supplies at reasonable prices, they will be under the burden both of staggering oil prices and increased costs of other commodities and technologies from industrialized countries. Indeed, most countries in Asia and Africa will not be able to afford the quantities of oil needed for continued development. Worse still, agricultural output can be expected to stagnate or decline because fewer petroleum-dependent fertilizers will be available. This, of course, raises the risk of widespread famine in some parts of the third world. In addition, there is a clear danger that the industrialized nations might be inclined to cut down on their aid programmes for underdeveloped countries in view of their own economic problems.[45]

The estimates in table 6 for some of the hardest-hit underdeveloped IC-countries, among which India has a particularly heavy burden to bear, clearly indicate the effects the increased oil prices had on them; the table assumes a "landed cost" of $10 a barrel, based on an average tax-paid cost of $7.50 a barrel in the Gulf, or over four times the average paid during the previous year.

Table 6. Estimated value of oil imports for selected third world countries, 1974, and their foreign exchange reserves, 1973[a]

US $ mn

Country	Estimated value of oil imports, 1974[b]	Foreign exchange reserves, 1973[c]
Ethiopia	51	114
India	1 241	629
Pakistan	266	254
Philippines	693	606
Sierra Leone	29	36
Sudan	127	28
Tanzania	62	..
Thailand	657	1 107

a   Assuming a landed cost of US $10 per barrel, based on an average tax-paid cost of $7.50 per barrel in the Persian Gulf.
b   Assuming normal requirements for that year.
c   At the end of the first quarter of 1973.

Source: "Shock for the Third World", Petroleum Economist, February 1974.

Intensive international efforts are in fact under way in the search for solutions to the balance-of-payments problems arising from the sharp increases in petroleum prices.[46] Such efforts are imperative since the combination of shortages and price increases is likely to produce a staggering disequilibrium in the worldwide balance of payments, place tremendous pressure on the monetary system and have a strong inflationary impact. Furthermore it will cause lower economic growth rates in the IC-countries, and above all, have devastating effects on the economies of the oil-poor underdeveloped countries.[47]

IV. *The arms race in the Middle East*

Through a combination of factors, the Middle East has become an area of intensified arms trade. The Arab-Israeli conflict, which clearly has been the most important factor in this situation, has spread its effects from the countries bordering on Israel into both the Arabian/Persian Gulf area and North Africa. In recent years the inflow of major weapons has been rising as fast in the countries bordering on the Arabian/Persian Gulf as among those directly involved in the Arab-Israeli War. But there have been other factors leading to an arms build-up in the Middle East, particularly in the region of the Arabian/Persian Gulf. One has been the interest of outside IC-countries in enhancing "stability" there in view of their growing dependence on oil imports, their heavy investments in the region, their perception of the area's strategic importance in the global or regional context, and also their economic interest in improving their balance of payments by arms sales. Another has been internal pressures within the Middle Eastern countries themselves, often caused by tensions and conflicts among or within them, some of which can also be linked to the existence of oil in the area.

When discussing the interests of countries in supplying arms to the Middle East, it must first be mentioned that the number of such suppliers has, in fact, been very limited. Over 90 per cent of the major weapons supplied to Middle Eastern countries during recent decades have come from four countries: the Soviet Union, the United States, the United Kingdom and France. The pattern of supplies has changed considerably during the post-war period, however. In the first half of the 1950s, the Western powers had a monopoly over arms supplies, with Britain alone supplying over half the total. By the 1960s the Soviet Union had become the most important single supplier, accounting for nearly half the total. The share of the United States also increased, amounting to 30 per cent in the late 1960s. The recent restrictions on oil supplies and the substantial increases in oil prices might effect a further change in the pattern of weapon supplies. The main supplying countries will most probably continue to be those four mentioned above, but it is possible that their relative importance as suppliers will change. France in particular has shown a desire to attempt to secure barter arrangements with the major PE-countries in the Middle East, offering French technology and armaments in exchange for long-term supplies of oil.

As previously indicated, the suppliers of arms to the Middle East have been motivated by a variety of factors. Some of these are common to arms trade policies in general, such as to further relations and to establish interdependence between the countries involved, or to stimulate the supplier's own defence industry. Certain strong motivations, however, relate specifically to the situation in the Middle East.

The presence of oil is the paramount factor underlying most political events in the area. Oil reserves in themselves have not been a direct factor in the Arab-Israeli conflict, but their abundance in an area geographically and politically close to the immediate zone of hostilities has rendered them an indirect factor of crucial, and perhaps still underrated, importance. More directly, Israel's exploitation of the oil reserves in the occupied area of Sinai have introduced oil as an additional factor in that conflict.

If the perspective is widened from the Arab-Israeli zone to the whole Middle Eastern area, oil becomes a powerful generator of rivalry, tension and conflict. The great powers have continually sought to protect and secure their vested interests in respective countries by supplying them with substantial amounts of arms and other forms of military assistance.

Another factor contributing to the arms build-up is the strategic importance of the Middle East to the supplying countries, not only because of its oil reserves but also because of its geographical situation as the nexus of the three continents.

Traditionally, the British presence in the area reflected interest in the Suez Canal as a vital communications route to India and the Far East. Since 1971, when Britain ceased to have a military role in the Gulf, the states in the area, and notably Iran, have themselves undertaken to replace the British presence. Nevertheless the great powers, particularly the United States and the Soviet Union, remain heavily involved in the area.

In the postwar period, the Soviet Union has been anxious to break what it considers to be the Western military encirclement on its southern front. This policy has been backed up with periodic arms sales to certain countries in the Middle East since 1955. In recent years, the Soviet Union has concluded a number of military assistance agreements with them; a 15-year treaty of friendship and cooperation was signed in May 1971 with Egypt, and a similar treaty, though with less comprehensive defence provisions, was concluded with Iraq in April 1972. Second, the Soviet Union has traditionally had an interest in gaining more direct access to the Indian Ocean — the only ice-free route between eastern and western USSR — and has therefore shown interest in being able to use naval facilities along the coasts of southwest Asia, particularly as long as the Suez Canal is closed.

The United States has been concerned, first, with the protection of the southern flank of NATO and, subsequently, with building a military alliance bordering the Soviet Union and China. The Baghdad Pact (later the Central Treaty Organization [CENTO]) was formed in 1955 with Britain, Iran, Iraq, Pakistan and Turkey as members and the United States as an associate.[48] The treaty provides for mutual cooperation on security and defence but has neither a central command structure nor forces allocated to it.[49]

Since the UK terminated its protective treaty relationships in 1971, the United States has supported indigenous regional collective security efforts in the area, particularly stressing the importance of cooperation between Iran and Saudi Arabia and also welcoming the strengthening of the defensive capacities of Kuwait, the United Arab Emirates, and North Yemen — in other words, a policy in line with the Nixon Doctrine.[50]

Other motivations behind the supplying countries' interests in the Middle East have been economic. Since oil imports are becoming an increasingly heavy burden on the balance of payments of the IC-countries, there are great pressures for them to try to increase arms sales in order to counteract this. The nature of the economic interdependence between the IC- and PE-countries, including those in the Middle East, is elaborated on page 39.

Finally, because the heavy involvement of the United States and the substantial assistance of the Soviet Union in the Viet-Nam War has come to an end, the possibility cannot be dismissed that the released capacity of the arms industries in these countries may be used for the production of arms intended for the Middle East and that surplus matériel from Viet-Nam is being transferred to countries in the Middle East.

But the arms build-up in the Middle East has also been stimulated by a variety of pressures or conflicts within or among the countries in the area itself. Some of the internal pressures for the acquisition of arms originate in a struggle for independence; others are stimulated by the desire to include defence systems in the general modernization of a country in order to secure its own stability, prestige or position in the regional or global context; and still others are linked to continued conflicts among factions within countries. As examples of such conflicts in recent years might be mentioned the wars or conflicts in Yemen, Democratic Yemen, the Dhofar region of Oman, and in the Kurdish area of Iraq.

The clashes between the states have usually had the character of border conflicts, some of which have now been settled while others are still ongoing. Among this type of conflict can be mentioned those between Iraq and Iran, between Iraq and Kuwait, between Yemen and Democratic Yemen, and the dispute over the Buraimi oasis between Abu Dhabi and Oman, on the one hand, and Saudi Arabia, on the other. Iran's occupation of three islands (Abu Musa and the two Tunb islands) in the Arabian/Persian Gulf in 1971 also deserves mention in this context. Most examples of such border disputes are directly or indirectly related to the existence of oil in the area.

Finally, it seems inevitable that the arms race in the Middle East will continue in the foreseeable future. Unless a lasting political solution is found to the Arab-Israeli conflict, the arms race between the involved parties, including the supply of increasingly sophisticated weapons, is almost certain to continue just as it did between 1967 and 1973. As a matter of fact, within three months of the 1973 ceasefire, each side possessed force levels substantially equal to those before the war; some of the weapons received were even superior to any operated prior to the war. And the arms build-up in the Arabian/Persian countries is likely to be equally serious, because of the importance of oil to the area and for the other reasons discussed above.

Table 7 and chart 1 show the increases in military expenditure between 1970 and 1973 for some of the most important producing countries in the Arabian/Persian Gulf area.

Iran is the outstanding example of a rapid arms build-up among these countries. One explanation for Iran's large military expenditure and acquisition of armaments in recent years has been its intention to become the stabilizing force of the Arabian/Persian Gulf area after the British withdrawal and its concern over the

Table 7. Military expenditure in four major oil-producing countries, 1969—73

US $ mn, at 1970 prices and exchange rates

Country	1969	1970	1971	1972	1973
Iran	835.9	1 262.6	1 441.6	1 419.7	1 828.7
Iraq	392.6	418.9	407.9	383.8	343.0
Kuwait	68.9	73.1	80.6	86.3	314.6
Saudi Arabia	412.3	430.0	538.8	844.4	1 082.2

Source: World Armaments and Disarmament, SIPRI Yearbook 1974 (Stockholm, Almqvist & Wiksell, 1971, Stockholm International Peace Research Institute).

Chart 1. Military expenditure in four major oil-producing countries, 1969—73

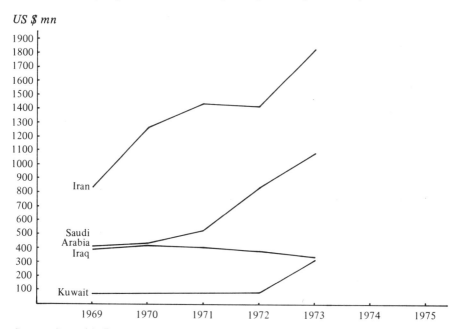

Source: See table 7.

protection of its oil resources.[51] In 1970 Iran began a five-year plan for the modernization of its forces, under which it has received, or will receive, modern aircraft mainly from the United States (F-4 Phantoms, F-14 Tomcats, C-130 Hercules and Bell helicopters), naval units from the United States and the United Kingdom — Iran is now believed to have the largest modern hovercraft fleet in the world — and Chieftain tanks from the United Kingdom. That this trend in Iran is likely to continue is supported by the fact that in 1973 Iran contracted to buy more than $ 2 billion worth of military equipment from the United States over the next five years. At the beginning of 1974 the Federal Republic of Germany and France also entered the Iranian arms market.

Saudi Arabia, too, has vastly expanded and modernized its armed forces during the past five years, particularly through the installation of an extremely sophisticated air defence system. Saudi Arabia's main suppliers of aircraft and air defence systems have been Britain and the United States and in recent years, France. In 1973 the United States and France were competing vehemently for the sale of more modern aircraft to Saudi Arabia (F-4 Phantoms and Mirage 3-Es). During the discussions on these sales, the importance of oil deliveries as a compensation for such arms sales became most obvious.

The build-up of armed forces in *Iraq* has been less remarkable in recent years, despite the fact that its military expenditure has remained at a fairly high level. During the past few years Iraq has bought its matériel mainly from the Soviet Union (aircraft, tanks and missiles).

During the 1960s the forces in *Kuwait* grew rapidly, even if their potential in comparison to some of the other countries in the area is low. The main supplier has been the United Kingdom (supplying in particular Lightning aircraft and missiles). In 1973 Kuwait negotiated for substantial arms deliveries from the United States but there is no confirmation that a deal was ever concluded. At the beginning of 1974 it was reported instead that Kuwait had concluded an agreement with France for the delivery of Mirage fighters, helicopters and other weapons.

The arms build-up in the other Arabian/Persian Gulf countries has been limited. Some recent purchases by *Abu Dhabi* of a total of 32 French Mirage-3s and Mirage-5s deserve to be mentioned, however. Abu Dhabi has a population of about 100 000; its armed forces number 8 000 men led and trained by British, Jordanian and Pakistani officers. Pakistan is reported to be providing training and technical aid for modern aircraft.

Finally, the arms race in the countries around the Arabian/Persian Gulf cannot be isolated from military developments in the *Indian Ocean*, hitherto an area in which the littoral states have had no significant military capability in worldwide terms. Until recently the area was also conspicuously excluded from the naval expansion of the great powers in other oceans and seas, but it now seems increasingly to be attracting their attention. Aside from the more global strategic considerations of the United States and the Soviet Union, the growing importance of the huge oil reserves in the Middle East, the interests in securing undisturbed access to them via sea lanes, the eventual reopening of the Suez Canal, and the consequences of a regional build-up of arms in the nations around the Gulf and their future military presence in the Indian Ocean, are some of the factors which will stimulate a development of the arms race in the Indian Ocean. India's announcement on 18 May 1974 that it had made its first nuclear underground test is likely to stimulate such a race even further in spite of India's assurance that it will use nuclear energy for peaceful purposes only. (For a more detailed description of the arms race in the Middle East, see appendix 4, and references [143–147].)

V. *Disputed territories*

Territorial and boundary disputes have historically been very common and difficult to resolve, especially where the areas involved are considered to be strategically or economically valuable. The expected or known existence of oil in such disputed areas gives them an additional value, and has been the cause of a number of disputes in the past few decades, some of which still remain unresolved.

Before World War II, territorial disputes between coastal states mainly concerned fishing rights, but technological improvements in offshore oil production, enabling exploitation at greater depths, have meant that disputes involving oil are now more and more common.

Offshore oil reserves are estimated to be 18 per cent of the total proved oil reserves of the Earth. In 1972, a similar proportion of the total production of oil came from offshore deposits. Since the future is expected to bring a progressive increase in the ratio of offshore oil to onshore oil as further discoveries are made and already known reserves are brought into production, it is clear that the stakes involved in disputes over such oil-containing sea-bed areas will become higher and more likely to lead to potential conflicts.[52]

Among areas where such disputes have occurred, or possibly might occur, the following deserve special mention. Some of these disputes are further described in appendix 8.

In the Arabian/Persian Gulf region, several territorial disputes have been settled. Most areas containing offshore resources in the Gulf itself have now been shared among the coastal states. For instance, in October 1968 Iran and Saudi Arabia signed an agreement delineating the continental shelf between them. However, some disputes remain unresolved. Iran and Iraq share a long border with a sensitive point at Shatt-al-Arab, an 80-km long estuary formed by the junction of the Euphrates and Tigris rivers in Iraq and the Karum river in Iran. The two nations both claim rights to the waterway as well as to some offshore territory in the Gulf itself. In 1969 Iran abrogated a 1937 treaty governing navigation rights of the Shatt-al-Arab estuary. Clashes between Iraqi and Iranian border troops have occurred on numerous occasions, the most recent being in February and March 1974. Iraq also claims territory along Kuwait's northern border, but is prepared to abstain from these claims if, instead, it is granted sovereignty over the two Kuwaiti islands Bubiyan and Warba. These two islands are of vital importance to Iraq since they are strategically situated in the inlet to Umm Qasr, the important Iraqi harbour built with Soviet assistance. Furthermore, Iraq's internal struggle against the Kurdish liberation movement is significantly linked to the fact that the oil fields of the Kirkuk are situated in the Kurdistan area. (See appendix 8.) Another source of tension in the Gulf area has been the dispute between Abu Dhabi and Oman, on the one hand, and Saudi Arabia, on the other hand, for the rights to the Buraimi oasis, but this conflict now seems to have been settled, or at least is not acute. [148–152] Egyptian demands that Israel withdraw from the occupied territories in Sinai, including the oil wells there, are well known and require no further comment in this context.[53]

In Africa, the most sensitive disputed areas with oil reserves are in Angola, although the discoveries made there so far are still limited and concentrated in the Cabinda enclave. If oil is found off the coasts further south, this will certainly draw worldwide attention to the problem of Namibia and to the question of who has the right to explore its resources. In other parts of southern Africa, no discoveries of oil have been made of such magnitude that they will substantially influence the prevailing tensions and conflicts in the area.

In South Asia, a potential dispute may be under way between India and Sri Lanka over some oil-containing areas on and around the tiny island of Kachchativu in the waters separating the two countries. [154]

In South East Asia, a number of actual or potential conflicts exist related to oil-containing areas. In January 1974 fighting broke out between Chinese and South Viet-Namese forces over the Paracel (Hsisha) islands, which are situated in the South China Sea in what is expected to be an oil-containing area. The fighting ended with the Chinese in possession of the islands. Another group of islands, the Spratly islands, was formally incorporated into the Republic of South Viet-Nam in September 1973. The annexation was denounced by China. South Viet-Nam has also claimed other offshore areas in the South China Sea and the Gulf of Siam, which have been opposed by the Provisional Revolutionary Government in South Viet-Nam, and other countries. (See Appendix 8.)

In East Asia, there are also a number of offshore areas for the possession of which disputes have already taken place or are likely to occur in the future. For instance, there are conflicting claims to an area around Senkaku Island (by Japan, China and Taiwan). Furthermore, Japan and South Korea have previously had conflicting claims to areas in the northern part of the East China Sea, but an agreement signed in January 1974 provided for cooperation between the two nations for the joint development of these oil resources. However, shortly after the agreement was signed, China voiced a protest claiming that the agreement was an "infringement" of its sovereignty over the continental shelf extending from the mainland. (See appendix 8.)

As far as Europe is concerned, the area giving rise to the most territorial problems has been the North Sea. There the area south of the 62nd parallel has been settled in accordance with the principles for the division of the continental shelves laid down in the 1958 Geneva Convention and supplemented by a decision taken by the International Court of Justice (ICJ) in the Hague. Regarding the area north of the 62nd parallel, for which no production licences have been granted, the final boundaries for the Norwegian shelf have not yet been decided. In the north they will also depend upon an agreement being negotiated with the Soviet Union defining the border between the Norwegian and Soviet continental shelves. The prospect of finding oil on or around the Svalbard archipelago gives rise to additional problems. (See appendix 8.)

The recent discoveries of oil on the Swedish island of Gotland have likewise raised the question of the correct delimitation of the continental shelf between Sweden and the Soviet Union in the Baltic Sea. Negotiations between the two countries were opened in April 1974 in Moscow. [155—156]

Among other recently reported events is the discovery of important quantities of oil near the island of Tassos in the Aegean Sea which has caused a dispute between Greece and Turkey concerning the delimitation of the continental shelf between the two countries. (See appendix 8.)

Also in the Mediterranean area, the Maltese Prime Minister, Dom Mintoff announced on 20 February 1974 that there was "a wide divergence of views" between Malta and Libya over the median line for oil exploration rights in the Mediterranean. [157]

In the Western hemisphere there have been fewer territorial disputes related to the existence of oil in disputed areas. Nevertheless, Colombia and Venezuela, for example, claim the same area in the gulf of Venezuela and in the area north of the Paraguana peninsula. [158] Recent reports of prospective oil reserves òn the Falkland Islands, a British Crown Colony in the South Atlantic, will give special significance to the dispute between the United Kingdom and Argentina over which of them has sovereignty in this territory. [159]

VI. *Transport of oil*

The huge growth in worldwide production and consumption of oil must necessarily be matched by an equivalent expansion in facilities to transport the crude oil and refined products. Crude oil is normally transported from the wells via tankers or pipelines or a combination of the two. Whatever the means of transportation, security and strategic considerations are involved, the importance of which is magnified by the increasing quantities of oil to be distributed.

Seaborne oil transportation

Because the main consuming areas of the world are far from the main producing areas, the bulk of oil transportation is by sea. About half the world's seaborne trade in tonnage terms consists of crude oil and oil product shipments. [160] Much of this oil is moved over considerably greater distances than are other types of cargo, partly because of the continued closure of the Suez Canal since 1967.

As of 31 December 1973, the existing world tanker fleet of vessels of 10 000 dead weight tons (dwt) and above amounted to about 215 million dwt. Most of the tankers were registered in Liberia (25 per cent), the United Kingdom (13 per cent), Japan (12 per cent), Norway (10 per cent) and Greece (6 per cent). [161]

The average size of the tankers has undergone a dramatic increase in recent years, particularly after the closure of the Suez Canal. [162] In addition to a large number of, by modern criteria, relatively small ships which are generally old, a group of large modern vessels of 175 000-200 000 dwt − Very Large Crude Carriers (VLCC) − make up the most important part in the system of oil transportation and are bound to play an even greater role in the future since well over two-thirds of all tanker and combined carrier capacity now on order consists of VLCCs. New generations of ever larger tankers are currently being produced, and today 300 000-350 000 dwt ships are common. Under construction at the present time are tankers of as much as 500 000 dwt. Once ports of sufficient capacity are available, ships of up to one million dwt and drawing over 100 feet − already the subject of feasibility studies − are expected to come into service.[54] The closure of the Suez Canal was the immediate cause of this change, but another important factor was the realization that the supertanker had very attractive economic advantages.[55]

Prospects for the reopening of the Suez Canal brightened considerably in the aftermath of the 1973 October War. In January 1974, Egyptian officials announced that Egypt intended to start clearing the canal and that this clearance would possibly be followed by a widening and deepening of the canal to accommodate larger ships. [164–167] The United States and the United Kingdom as well as Arab countries guaranteed the availability of technical aid and the Soviet Union reportedly expressed interest in assisting in the work. [168–169] Technically, it has been estimated that it would take the military authorities about 10 months to locate and remove unexploded mines, to clear the canal of the wreckage of the 1967 and 1973 wars, dredge its silted channels and repair its navigation system. [170] The mine-clearing operations were reported to have been completed in March 1974. [171]

But even if the Suez Canal were opened, it would not have the depth to serve the newer larger tankers. The canal maintains a working-draught of only 36-38 feet and is thus limited to ships in the 60 000 dwt class fully laden, or under. In 1966, 176 million tons of northbound crude oil was distributed through the canal, over 90 per cent of which was bound for Europe, one-third of whose total imports passed through the canal. Thirty-six per cent of the oil loaded in the Arabian/Persian Gulf countries passed through the canal. Today, the passage could be navigated by less than one-third of the world's present tanker tonnage, and these smaller vessels normally do not operate on the Gulf route in any case. For obvious reasons, those countries on or close to the eastern end of the Mediterranean would gain most if the canal were reopened. [172]

Current proposals for the enlargement of the Suez Canal envisage that the draught could be increased to 67-70 feet in six years' time, allowing the canal to take fully loaded tankers of 270 000 tons dwt and partly loaded tankers of 300 000 dwt. This improvement, estimated to cost about $1 280 million, would save the tankers now having to round the Cape of Good Hope 24 days on a round trip. [170]

Whatever the future destiny of the Suez Canal, the sea route around the Cape of Good Hope will continue to be of utmost importance for the movement of oil from the Arabian/Persian Gulf to Western Europe and, increasingly, to the United States.

The continuation of these trading patterns gives rise to certain strategic and military considerations which so far have been given fairly limited attention. The question of the security of the sea lanes has been the subject of official concern, particularly in the United States. It has been pointed out that the interruption of established sea lanes constitutes a growing threat to US national security as the volume of oil imports increases. Moreover, supertankers and large natural gas carriers are extremely high value targets, vulnerable both to different kinds of political coercion — by sabotage, for instance — and to interdiction in times of conflict. This threat has stimulated the US Department of Defense to request additional funds for the development of arms and other facilities to counter such threats.[56]

One possibility is that tanker shipments might be attacked on the open sea. The view of the US Department of Defense is that the only serious threat to the US sea lanes is the Soviet Navy.[57] The US Navy has accordingly been justifying its funding requests to Congress partly on the basis of the need to concentrate its antisubmarine warfare (ASW) efforts on the task of "keeping the sea lanes open". Since Soviet submarines are considered to constitute the only main threat to US convoys or supply ships, it seems worth outlining the conditions under which attacks by Soviet submarines on US merchant ships — or *vice versa* — might take place.

Such attacks by one party would only take place in a situation of war between the two nations and/or their allies. In a protracted conventional war, ASW operations would essentially be the same as those during World War II, that is, US protection of transatlantic supply lines and support of expeditionary and task forces. A conventional war between the two greatest nuclear powers is, however, for several reasons less likely. In a nuclear confrontation, which would drastically shorten any combat, the need to protect sea lanes and expeditionary forces is less obvious. [174]

Some areas of the world pose particular problems, aside from those prevailing in the open ocean. The Arabian/Persian Gulf is perhaps the most sensitive strategic area in the world today. The Gulf is quite shallow and the straits are narrow throughout most of their length. Because of the deep draughts of the supertankers, the manoeuvring room for large tankers is restricted.[58] Moreover, the channels are relatively easy to mine or block. Sinking just a few supertankers in critical passages, notably the Strait of Hormuz, could effectively block shipments from the Gulf for a long time as has been remarked by the US Department of Defense.

This could occur as the accidental or intended consequence of conflict within the gulf region or from the deliberate efforts of an external state to interrupt the flow of oil. In either case, there is little the United States could now do militarily to forestall this possibility.[59]

The Suez Canal, when reopened, will be another such sensitive spot. The problems and risks related to this possible future waterway will largely depend upon the kind of political solution, if any, that Egypt and Israel might eventually agree upon.

Before the oil is shipped into the Red Sea for further transport to the Suez Canal, it must pass the Bab-el-Mandeb Strait (between the Red Sea and the Gulf of Aden, that is, the outlet to the Indian Ocean).[60] The littoral states around the Bab-el-Mandeb Strait are Saudi Arabia, Yemen and Democratic Yemen on the east side, and Ethiopia, French Afar and Issa, and Somalia on the west side. In assessing the prospects for future oil shipments through Bab-el-Mandeb, the development of relations among these states, and between them and the great powers, must be given special significance. Another uncertain factor in assessing the stability of this region is the future internal situation in some of these countries.

Another sensitive spot dependent on free passage through the Bab-El-Mandeb Strait is Sharm-el-Sheikh (between the Gulf of Aqaba and the Red Sea). Sharm-el-Sheikh on the tip of the Sinai peninsula, from which the passage into the strategically vulnerable Eilat port in Israel is controlled, has been under Israeli occupation since the 1967 Arab-Israeli War.

Another area of increasing strategic importance is the sea off the coast of South Africa. As mentioned earlier, the sea route around the Cape of Good Hope will continue to be of great significance for the movement of oil from the Arabian/Persian Gulf to Western Europe and the United States, whatever happens to the Suez Canal. The sea lanes off the Cape are in fact already among the most crowded in the world with a daily passage of over 1.5 million tons of shipping.

About 12 000 ships a year call at the Cape and another 14 000 pass without calling. [176]

South Africa's geographical position is of fundamental strategic interest to the ships sailing round the Cape. In terms of security, availability and the provision of housing, replenishment and repair facilities, as well as sophisticated meteorological and navigational aids, South African support is essential for any adequate future defence of the Cape route.[61] Under the 1967 Simonstown agreement, the South African Navy is primarily responsible for the defence of the area from the northern borders of Namibia round to Madagascar and Mozambique.[62] South Africa can therefore survey, and, should hostilities break out, to a certain extent control the sea traffic round the Cape. It is true that the shipping lanes could be rerouted much further south nearer to the Antarctic, but such detours would prolong the route and pose problems for shipping, since there are few major refuelling ports along the coasts of southern Africa apart from those in South Africa.

The naval base at Simonstown is well-equipped and a berth capable of handling very large ships — including aircraft carriers — is now under construction. Good submarine facilities are also available. Durban is now Africa's largest port, and eleventh in the world ranking.[63]

The *coup d'état* in Portugal on 25 April 1974 and the subsequent discussions between the new Portuguese government and the liberation movements in Portuguese territories in Africa have suddenly brought the strategic situation of southern Africa into sharp focus. Recent revelations in the press about a UN draft report on new NATO contingency plans for aid and naval defence of South Africa and for the defence of the sea routes around this country have caused general concern. It is feared that, through military cooperation with South Africa, NATO countries might compromise their general policy of aversion for the South African apartheid régime in order to gain strategic advantages and increased security for seaborne oil transport around the Cape. [179–184]

A fourth area where problems may arise as a consequence of increased seaborne transport of oil and the extensive use of supertankers is the Straits of Malacca. Together with the adjoining Straits of Singapore, this waterway is of paramount importance to the seaborne trade of oil to Japan, since it provides the shortest sea route between the Indian Ocean and the South China Sea.[64] Among the coastal states, Malaysia and Indonesia, with the support of China, claim jurisdiction over the Straits, whereas Singapore, with the support of Japan, the Soviet Union and other major shipping powers, contends that the Straits are an international waterway.[65]

On 11 November 1971 all these coastal states concluded a tripartite agreement on the Straits of Malacca and Singapore in which they declared their joint management of affairs of the Straits and their decision to set up a cooperative organization to take charge of the safety of navigation there. The most important passage in the agreement, however, was the following.

The governments of Indonesia and Malaysia agreed that the Straits of Malacca and Singapore are not international straits, while fully recognizing their use for international shipping in accordance with the principle of innocent passage.[66] [187]

It is evident, however, that both the coastal states and other states concerned have varying interests to protect when it comes to determining the status of the Straits.

Singapore did not agree with the passage quoted above, but advocated the right of unimpeded passage of all ships of all nations through the Straits. To Singapore it is particularly a matter of its existence as a major trading port and oil refining centre. Malaysia and Indonesia have largely the same economic interests in unimpeded traffic through the Straits but they also have interests relating to military and environmental security. Several accidents with oil tankers have already occurred in the waterway, and they have therefore proposed a ban on oil tankers of over 200 000 dwt (or 61 feet draught) and suggested that such tankers should pass through the Lombok and Makassar Straits between the Indonesian islands. [189]

Japan's economic interest in keeping the traffic through the Straits as unimpeded as possible is quite obvious, particularly in view of its heavy dependence on oil from the Middle East, and it has strongly supported the view of Singapore that the waterway must remain international even to the extent of being controlled internationally. [187]

The Soviet Union and the United States have both economic and military interests in the freedom of passage through this waterway, particularly in view of the growing military presence in the Indian Ocean. China, on the other hand, has expressed strong support for the policies adopted by the Malaysian and Indonesian governments on this issue and has criticized the intentions of the major shipping powers regarding these Straits. [187]

Pipelines

As far as oil pipelines are concerned, those in the Middle East have attracted most attention, both because of their increased importance since the closure of the Suez Canal and because of their location in an area where wars have recently been waged on three different occasions. [190]

The first of these pipelines, opened in 1934, extends from the northern oilfields of Iraq to the Lebanese port of Tripoli. Later, another outlet was built to the Syrian port of Baniyas. The capacity of this pipeline system is 1 million barrels a day (b/d). A second pipeline, the TAP-line, came into operation in 1950. It connected the Saudi Arabian wells to the Mediterranean Zahrani terminal near the port of Saida (ex-Sidon) in southern Lebanon. Its capacity is nearly 500 000 b/d. The pipeline is owned by the Trans-Arabian Pipeline Company, an affiliate of the Arabian-American Company (ARAMCO) operating in Saudi Arabia. Since this pipeline passes through the Golan region, it has been repeatedly exposed to attacks during the the Arab-Israeli wars and on several occasions between the wars it has been the object of sabotage by guerilla groups.[67]

There are also two pipelines of importance on Israeli territory, both of which originate at the port of Eilat in the Gulf of Aqaba. Their outlets are located on the Mediterranean coast: one at Haifa, the other at Askhelon. Nut much is known about the exact capacity or utilization of these pipelines, but it has been estimated that 900 000 b/d passed through these lines shortly before the outbreak of the 1973 October War. Neither is there much accessible information about the origin of the oil being pumped into the pipelines at Eilat. It is generally assumed, however that some of the Iranian oil destined for Eastern Europe under the barter trade agreements has been transported in this way. [190]

Finally, two projected pipelines in the Middle Eastern area should be mentioned. One is planned on Egyptian territory from the Red Sea (Ain Sukhna) to the Mediterranean (Alexandria).[68] The other, the plans for which are at a less advanced stage, has been proposed by Iran and would extend from the oilfields in Iran to the port of Iskenderun in southeastern Turkey.[69]

In the industrialized countries pipelines have been established for many years or are under development. In the United States the system of pipelines is very extensive, whereas the development in Western Europe has been less spectacular. Also in the Soviet Union the problem of the distribution of crude oil and refined products has been solved to a considerable extent by a continuous development of a vast network of pipelines. In recent years, great emphasis has been put on the construction of trunk pipelines which will link the new oilfields in the central or eastern part of the USSR with refineries there or in the western part of the country, where the large population areas are. In addition the so-called "Friendship pipeline", completed in 1963, supplies the Comecon countries of Eastern Europe with crude oil produced in Soviet territory.

Chapter 5. The military use of oil

Oil is a commodity of basic strategic importance. No modern defence system can be maintained and no wars fought without a great supply of oil. A matter of vital importance for those responsible for planning national security, then, is the assurance that the country can count on sufficient supplies of oil to sustain its defence.[70]

World War I provided the first practical demonstration of the revolutionary effect of the military use of oil-powered ships, aircraft and vehicles. In World War II, the strategic importance of oil was even more crucial and oil installations were rated among the top-priority targets of attack. (In appendix 9, a survey is made of the effects of fuel shortage on Germany in World War II.) The strategic importance of oil has not diminished since then, but has increased, with the emphasis on the two main characteristics of modern warfare: extensive mechanization and high mobility. While mechanization entails an increased use of energy in the production and use of arms, high mobility involves ever larger units and worldwide routes of transportation, thus substantially increasing the demand for fuels.

Very little information exists, however, on the magnitude of the *energy* consumption of defence establishments, both with regard to how energy-intensive defence industries are[71] and to the needs for actual maintenance of defence systems under peacetime and wartime conditions. The present interest in making efficient use of energy will most probably result in a more intensive study of the energy requirements of different kinds of industries, materials and products, which will be relevant also in assessing the proportion of energy resources made available to the defence industries.

If the various industrial sectors are examined, it becomes clear that the basic steel industry is a great consumer of energy. In the United States, for example, this industry spends about twice as much as the next largest users, petroleum refineries, to purchase fuels and electrical energy. [201]

As far as the actual maintenance of defence forces in peacetime or wartime is concerned, some light is thrown on the *petroleum* needs of various countries by some openly published information on the United States which might serve as a very rough indicator of the situation in the rest of the world. At Senate hearings in April 1973, some of these aspects were dealt with by representatives of the Department of Defense, who stated that the petroleum requirements during periods of war were of the following magnitude:

The demand for petroleum products by the United States armed forces has been relatively small since World War II. During the Korean War and the Vietnam period, total DoD petroleum usage amounted to only 6 to 8 per cent of total US consumption. In limited wars, DoD requirements do not place a major burden on our nation's domestic oil resources. We have not made a detailed estimate of how much oil DoD would require in a large-scale, prolonged conventional war in the late 1970's or the 1980's. However, it is clear from budget projections that our initial force level will be far below those reached during World War II and even below those maintained during the Vietnam War. Even if the initial requirements in a major conventional war in the 1980's were twice as high as the peak in Vietnam, they would amount to less than 10 per cent of the total US demand and less than a fifth of domestic oil production. Even in a large scale, all-out conventional war, therefore, DoD would use only a small fraction of the oil available in the US. [202]

At previous hearings in April 1972, it was stated that during World War II US military forces consumed 33 per cent of total US consumption. It was therefore considered that meeting defence oil requirements is no longer the overriding factor that it was 30 years ago. "Now it is the national economy which commands our attention. It will avail us little to provide oil to our armed forces if the economic heartbeat of the nation they are protecting is slowed to a half for lack of its energy fuel lifeblood." [173b]

US military petroleum requirements in wartime are probably easily within the capabilities of the domestic petroleum industry, even if foreign imports were denied for military, political or economic reasons. It should nevertheless be added that foreign fuels provided 48 per cent of the total US military bulk in fiscal year 1972. Twenty per cent of the oil bought by the US Department of Defense came from the Middle East. Most of it was used overseas. [202]

Oil consumption during a war is, of course, a function of the type of war being fought. In a limited war the burden imposed on domestic resources may seem bearable. As indicated above, this seems to have been the case in the United States during the Viet-Nam War, although there were press reports in January 1973 that one factor prompting the United States to halt the intensive bombing of North Viet-Nam above the twentieth parallel was the strain the offensive was putting on the already severe shortage of fuel oil in the United States. [203]

In a large-scale, prolonged conventional war, difficulties for oil-poor countries which have been cut off from oil supplies would be very severe, according to their degree of dependence on oil. However, even in such a war the United States would have little difficulty in supplying domestically all the oil which its military could conceivably use, according to the statement quoted above.

In a nuclear war the fuel requirements are likely to be smaller than in a protracted conventional war, primarily because of the assumed brevity of such a war, but possibly also because troop movements would be less necessary. On the other hand, the need to spread out troops as thinly as possible in such a war, could counterbalance such a theory.

The main use of petroleum for military purposes in wartime has been to provide mobility, both for operational demands on the battlefield and for transport of personnel and cargo to and from the battlefield. [204] Excluding nuclear energy, petroleum represents about 72 per cent of total energy requirements for the US Department of Defense which uses most of its petroleum for mobile systems (63.7 per cent for aircraft operations and 14.9 per cent for ship operations in fiscal year 1974). [205]

Concerning the use of oil in peacetime, the US Department of Defense stated that after a wartime peak in 1969, military petroleum requirements in 1972 had levelled off at some 750 000 b/d following the phasedown of operations in South East Asia. This was about 5 per cent of total US consumption demand. [203] On later occasions it has been stated, however, that fuel consumption by the US

58

Department of Defense was 3.7 per cent (or 650 000 b/d) of total US demand in fiscal year 1974, of which the air force took 54.6 per cent, the navy 35.8 per cent and the army 9.6 per cent.[72] [205] (This could be compared to a total yearly consumption by India of 460 000 b/d.)

If a 4 per cent level is accepted as a reasonable average for world military use of oil as a percentage of total world oil consumption — and it must be heavily stressed that this is a very speculative assessment — the actual total quantity for military use in 1973 is 4 per cent of 58 million b/d, which is more than 2.2 million b/d. This equals roughly the total consumption of oil in, for example, the United Kingdom (2.3 million b/d), France (2.5 million b/d) or Italy (2.1 million b/d) and about double the amount consumed in the Scandinavian countries (1.1 million b/d). It is somewhat less than one-third of the total consumption in the third world (7.8 million b/d) excluding China.

Finally, the recent tight oil supply situation as a result of restrictions by some Arab countries had some impact on routine military operations around the world. In November 1973 there were, for instance, reports that the Philippines, Japan and Singapore had restricted their supplies to US forces in the Far East, which forced the US Department of Defense to draw upon its wartime reserves of oil in the Pacific to supply the South Viet-Namese and Cambodian armed forces with a minimum daily military requirement. [207–209] At the beginning of January 1974, the pressure on US military forces eased considerably, however.[73] Another indication of the strained situation were reports that the Danish government had asked its NATO partners to bring their own gasoline and oil to the NATO exercise Absalon Express in November 1973, since Denmark was not able to supply NATO units with engine fuel during the exercise. [215]

It is not surprising, therefore, that efforts to develop supplementary energy sources are particularly vigorous in the defence establishments. During World War II, oil-poor but coal-rich Germany manufactured large quantities of high-grade aircraft fuel from coal (the Fischer-Tropsch process). Recently, the United States used liquefied coal for the first time to power the engines of a destroyer on an experimental trip. It was reported on this occasion that if all went as planned, the coal-derived oil would begin replacing petroleum fuels in US Navy vessels in about three years and within a decade would account for about half of the fleet's total consumption. [216] Nuclear power is of course already a well-appreciated naval fuel source which is now used in about 20 per cent of US Navy ships. [205]

The air force, too, might be considered a candidate user of synthetic fuels. For its needs, hydrogen is clearly the most attractive choice. Overall, the generation of synthetic fuel for army use appears less attractive than for either navy or air force use. [217]

Another possible consequence of a general oil shortage may be that increased importance will be attached to actual or potential weapons which are less oil-dependent in their development, production and use. Nuclear devices can certainly be reckoned among such weapons, particularly since the kind of war in which their use could most easily be envisaged would also be that in which the need for high mobility of masses of conventional forces might be minimal. It has also been speculated that the energy problems associated with the production and use of tanks, aircraft and most naval ships could lead to an unfortunate reappraisal of chemical and biological warfare. [218]

Chapter 6. Summary and conclusions

I. *Conflict patterns*

Oil is a limited and unequally distributed resource. There is no escaping the fact that until other energy sources and technologies are developed to substitute for oil, there will be enormously increased demands on existing reserves of oil by nations aspiring to secure supplies — demands which take on gigantic proportions when the security and well-being of the total world population is taken into account. While these demands may stimulate valuable cooperation between certain categories of nations, they will certainly also harbour the seeds of potential tension and conflict among them. Several patterns of potential conflict are, in fact, already apparent.

One such pattern is a confrontation, possibly even a military one, between the IC- and PE-countries as the two opposing interest groups. The ability of the PE-countries to act cohesively to further their mutual oil interests has now been clearly demonstrated. Indeed, the situation at present seems favourable to them: (*a*) there is a sellers' market; (*b*) prices are high; (*c*) they are gaining increasing control over their oil; (*d*) they are recipients of ever increasing money transfers; and (*e*) they have demonstrated the potency of oil as a political weapon. On the other hand, their advantages have no permanently secure basis. They are the focus of intense interest from the IC-countries, some of vastly superior strength. Although the present situation may certainly bring the PE-countries substantial economic and political benefits, the extreme dangers in it must be obvious to them. Furthermore, in a serious confrontation situation, where other economic, political and strategic interests would be involved, the role of oil as the cohesive force would immediately be diminished or even eliminated. Regarding the IC-countries, their ability to act as a united interest group against the PE-countries is doubtful even during "normal" circumstances because of their very different situations in terms of oil security — not least with regard to their roles as host countries of the multinational oil companies. What seems clear, however, is that should such a united front of the industrialized IC-countries materialize, it would certainly initiate even stronger demands for restrictive policies among the PE-countries, thus fuelling a vicious circle of confrontation.

A development more likely than confrontation between these two blocs, however, is the creation or strengthening of bilateral relations between certain PE- and IC-countries. No doubt such a development will strain existing relations and alliances — the most obvious of which are the relations between the United States, Western Europe and Japan. The combination of the "oil crisis" and the Arab-Israeli War of October 1973 illustrated such strains on well-established alliances and was symptomatic of how the changed climate will probably affect diplomacy in the future. Moreover, such changes occurred at a time when the cohesive forces within the alliances seemed to have weakened for other reasons.

One can assume that the most oil-rich countries (such as Saudi Arabia, Iran and

Kuwait) will be those most coveted by the industrialized countries as partners for such cooperation. The PE-countries, in their turn, will look particularly to the countries which can provide them either with the means for their economic and technical development and their military security, or with profitable and secure investment objects for their surplus oil money. The prospect therefore arises of actual or potentially strong powers — in combination with the multinational oil companies that they control — joining forces in powerful economic and military alignments. Left out of such alignments will be other less fortunate countries, a fact which will contribute to a widening of the existing gaps of economic wealth and prosperity in the world. In addition, such a system would also inevitably lead to undesirable competition between groups of wealthy nations in the rush for the establishment of the best possible bilateral deals, a process in which traditional considerations for trade and arms transfer policies might easily be set aside.[74]

The negative effects of such developments could be reduced if future oil policies gave higher priority to the need for *worldwide* cooperation and *non-competitive* solutions. One form of cooperation that should be encouraged is joint efforts to find and develop substitutes for oil; another is the creation of institutional forms for ensuring that the less fortunate countries are also guaranteed reasonable levels of oil security. It is imperative that both PE- and IC-countries avoid policies which entail economic disruption and subsequent violence. The world is rapidly moving towards an era which will present all governments and peoples with unprecedented problems of adjustment and global responsibility. They must be given time to adjust to a new economic situation; the alternative might very well be economic disaster for everyone. The PE-countries should therefore abstain from unreasonable or legally unacceptable restrictions on their oil for political or economic reasons — whereas their use of restrictive policies for purely conservationist reasons should be strongly encouraged. The IC-countries, in their turn, must avoid worsening the growing incongruity between supply and demand and also abstain from using their present economic and military superiority to secure oil supplies for themselves.

Possible future conflicts related to oil may not only be a result of such new configurations in the total structure of international relations, but may also be caused by more specific circumstances related to this vital resource.

One such potential cause of world insecurity is the increasing vulnerability of pipelines and tankers, both in a situation of full-scale war, and to acts of sabotage in low-level conflicts. Some points along the sea lanes are more sensitive than others, particularly some of the straits through which the major part of the transported oil is shipped. Countries adjacent to these sensitive spots will see their strategic importance increased and their relations with countries depending on oil shipped through their sea lanes will alter accordingly. Of particular interest in this respect is the Cape of Good Hope; the interests of some of the major IC- and PE-countries in securing safe sea lanes around the Cape may very well influence their policies towards South Africa as the controlling power of these waters. Also the need for protection of the sea lanes in the open seas may stimulate naval arms races, particularly that already taking place in the Indian Ocean.

Another potential cause of instability is the fact that every country possessing substantial reserves of oil within or near its territory will feel forced to consider the protection of these reserves and their installations. This consideration will undoubtedly reflect on these countries' defence planning and arms acquisition policies.

Particularly sensitive spots are those areas containing oil reserves that are the subject of territorial disputes between two or more nations. During the spring of 1974, a number of open or latent conflicts of this nature were reported. These disputes become particularly sensitive when the oil-possessing area is situated in a region which, for other reasons as well, is strategically very important. It seems, for instance, justified to assume that the dispute between Greece and Turkey over oil finds in the Aegean sea contributed to the antagonism between the two countries during the Cyprus war of the summer of 1974. The most sensitive region of all, however, is undoubtedly the Arabian/Persian Gulf area.

II. *The Arabian/Persian Gulf area*

As the possessor of the world's most abundant proved oil reserves, the Arabian/Persian Gulf area will no doubt have to bear the brunt of the pressure of oil demand, at least during the next decade and a half. Because of its role as the main supplier of oil, any events occuring in this region will have worldwide repercussions.

The new oil situation will, first and foremost, give the countries in this region an unprecedented chance to rapidly develop their own economies and also to contribute to the development of other less developed and oil-poor countries, particularly those in the same region.

In the political field, some of the countries in the region have in a remarkably short time obtained and demonstrated their power to initiate and influence events of worldwide importance, a power which is certain to remain as a concomitant of their economic strength.

The strengthening of the political and economic power of the Arabian/Persian Gulf nations will go hand-in-hand with a strengthening of their military power, and an intensive arms build-up is presently under way in the region. Its continuation seems unavoidable because of the strong incentives both on the part of the PE-countries to protect their sovereignty and wealth, and of the IC-countries to acquire oil at almost any price. Self-protection and the security of a crucial resource are legitimate interests in themselves, but the destabilizing potential of the regional arms build-up that they are prompting must be heavily emphasized.[75] In assessing the risks involved in this arms build-up, one should take into account such factors as the great differences in political, economic and military strength and ambitions of the states in the region in terms of its impact on those outside it.

Iran and Saudi Arabia are key countries. Non-Arab Iran aspires to be the stabilizing force of the region, and it is strengthening its armed forces accordingly. Whatever Iran's motives, other countries in the area may well interpret this development as a change in the Arabian/Persian Gulf balance of power and seek to counter Iran's growing potential, thus touching off a similar development in, particularly, Saudi Arabia, Iraq and Kuwait. Such an arms race, besides its obvious effects on Israel, may also have repercussions for the Arab world outside the region itself. Once the intensity of the Arab-Israeli conflict lessens or that problem is solved, it is likely that the situation around the Arabian/Persian Gulf will attract the attention of all the Arab countries, presumably with military implications. Countries such as Afghanistan, Pakistan and India are also likely to devote increased attention to their military capacity because of unease over the changing balance in countries immediately to their west. A substantial increase in the military potential of some of the states around the Arabian/Persian Gulf may therefore in the somewhat longer perspective prompt similar arms build-ups in all of southwest and South Asia, in North and East Africa, and in the Indian Ocean.

The changing military situation will be of concern also to the rest of the world, particularly to some of the main IC-countries. Whatever their political configurations, the military capacity of the Arabian/Persian Gulf countries cannot threaten a major power, be it the Soviet Union, China, the United States, Western Europe or Japan. The latters' concern over the military implications of the changed situation is rather with the possibilities of PE-countries' joining forces with one major power against another, particularly in view of the strategic importance of this region. But even such a conjunction could hardly affect the global balance of power. The localized effects could be considerable, however. A growing military potential on its southern border could, for instance, spur the build-up of armed forces in the corresponding region in the Soviet Union. Such an unstabilizing military development around the Arabian/Persian Gulf due to global oil demands could also intensify the arms build-up of major powers in general.

Although the purely military potential of the PE-countries is still limited, their economic-strategic importance to international security is such that all the major powers, and particularly those that heavily import oil (Japan, Western Europe and, at a later date, the United States), would experience a vastly changed situation were the main PE-countries in the region to be dominated by one major power. They would both be an invaluable economic asset to it and a disastrous loss to any competing major power, particularly in a situation of conventional war.

Conflicts may occur among Arabian/Persian Gulf countries, or between them and a neighbour. Such limited wars will be less easy to keep limited because of the enormous vested interests of the great powers in the area. Once these powers are involved in such events they will act for their own economic or military security and in cooperation or conflict with each other, hence threatening the sovereignty of the oil-rich Persian Gulf countries. In that possibility lies one of the present threats to global stability.

Whether it will be realized depends upon the factors discussed, and upon the course of relations between the great powers in other areas. Their demonstrated interest in avoiding confrontation and in furthering *détente* and various forms of interdependence should logically lead to their adopting a similar attitude with regard to the Arabian/Persian Gulf area. Initiatives by them, by other major IC-countries or by the PE-countries in the region themselves to limit the arms build-up there would add a strong impetus to efforts to slow down the arms race in the rest of the world. Unfortunately, the trend points in the opposite direction.

III. *The ethics of energy*

Nations have a legitimate interest in securing natural resources to foster their social and economic well-being and to protect their sovereignty. In a situation of scarcity, however, conflicts may arise over ownership and the distribution of these resources, which may not only be untenable in the present, but which may also render unattainable the corresponding security goals of future generations. Thus, just as no nation should obstruct another's capacity to protect the well-being of its people and to maintain its sovereignty, no generation should consume a vital non-replenishable resource, such as oil, so drastically that it inflicts disaster and hardship on future generations. The present rate of energy exploitation and consumption cannot be allowed to continue so long as no new safe energy sources have been developed to substantially replace oil.

Such resources are not likely to be developed for at least another few decades, and even then, only privileged industrialized countries will be able to muster the immense technical skills and capital investments necessary to utilize the new energy resources — most poor countries will follow only after a considerable time-lag.

The ordering of priorities for the uses of oil is likely to change with the need for energy-efficient and oil-conserving policies and lifestyles. The real need for energy may be seen to relate to the essentials of life and health rather than to exponential demand — a view not incompatible with achieving a high-quality civilization.

It will have to be the industrialized countries that venture first. Underdeveloped countries are no strangers to energy-saving policies and lifestyles. But industrialized countries have so far consumed a disproportionately large part of the world's total reserves. Thus their societies' needs for energy in general and oil in particular clash with the aspirations of the non-industrialized countries to develop similarly. They must therefore reasonably be expected to modify their energy demands.

In future, the huge oil reserves of the major PE-countries should be used primarily for their own economic development, but secondly also to assist the oil-poor, less developed countries, and preferably also for investments in the development of new energy sources. The accumulation of huge oil reserves should not become the incentive for an accumulation of arms in the PE-countries or in their vicinity. The idea that increased security derives from more arms must be proclaimed as illusory and the dangers inherent in such a development fully exposed. Arms limitation efforts by the major PE-countries could even be an incentive for other nations to achieve agreements on arms reduction in other areas.

Finally, in a situation of a world shortage of energy, the use of energy for military purposes will come increasingly under discussion. There is a moral dimension involved here. Oil is not renewable — the saying "beating swords into ploughshares" is not applicable. A limited resource is continually becoming scarcer. Clearly, there are much more urgent and constructive goals it might serve than the fuelling of military conglomerations. A politically more stable and just world would reduce the need of all nations to achieve security through military means, thus releasing for more productive purposes the considerable amount of oil now used for military activities. A concomitant imperative is that a reduced military dependence on oil is not compensated for by the development, production and use of other, less oil-demanding weapons and weapon systems. But although a general shortage might encourage countries proportionally to reduce fuel-consuming armaments, the actual shortage crises are likely to affect the world in patches, emphasizing inequalities. The consequence will be disturbances of military balances, which may subsequently motivate attempts to restore previous balances by increasing the allocation of resources to national defence systems. The outcome of such a vicious circle would be a greater consumption of oil for military purposes.

However, the successful development of practicable alternatives to oil could diminish this likelihood. In this, ironically, the military itself, using its own enormous resources for research and development (R&D) to secure its own energy supplies, might lead the breakthrough, as it did with nuclear energy.

Appendix 1.

World oil resources, 1973

I. *World published proved oil reserves,[a] by oil region,*
as of 31 December 1973

Country/region	Barrels[b] *thousand mn*	Tons *thousand mn*	Share of world total *per cent*
United States	41.8	5.4	*6.6*
Canada	9.3	1.2	*1.5*
Total North America	**51.1**	**6.6**	**8.1**
Venezuela	14.0	1.9	*2.2*
Ecuador	5.7	0.8	*0.9*
Mexico	3.6	0.5	*0.6*
Argentina	2.5	0.3	*0.4*
Trinidad & Tobago	2.2	0.3	*0.3*
Other Latin America	3.6	0.5	*0.6*
Total Latin America	**31.6**	**4.3**	**5.0**
Saudi Arabia	132.0	18.0	*20.8*
Kuwait	64.0	8.8	*10.1*
Iran	60.0	8.2	*9.5*
Iraq	31.5	4.3	*5.0*
Abu Dhabi	21.5	2.9	*3.4*
Neutral Zone	17.5	2.4	*2.8*
Syria	7.1	1.0	*1.1*
Qatar	6.5	0.9	*1.0*
Oman	5.2	0.7	*0.8*
Other Middle East	4.4	0.5	*0.7*
Total Middle East	**349.7**	**47.7**	**55.2**
Libya	25.5	3.4	*4.0*
Nigeria	20.0	2.6	*3.1*
Algeria	7.6	1.0	*1.1*
Egypt	5.1	0.7	*0.8*
Congo (Brazzaville)	4.9	0.6	*0.8*
Other Africa	4.2	0.6	*0.7*
Total Africa	**67.3**	**8.9**	**10.5**
United Kingdom	10.0	1.3	*1.6*
Norway	4.0	0.5	*0.6*
Other Western Europe	2.4	0.4	*0.4*
Total Western Europe	**16.4**	**2.2**	**2.6**
USSR	80.0	10.9	*12.6*
Romania	0.9	0.1	*0.1*
Other Eastern Europe	2.1	0.4	*0.3*
Total Eastern Europe	**83.0**	**11.4**	**13.0**
China	20.0	2.7	*3.1*
Indonesia	10.5	1.4	*1.7*
Other Asia	2.6	0.4	*0.4*
Australasia	2.5	0.4	*0.4*
Total Far East	**35.6**	**4.9**	**5.6**
World total	**634.7**	**86.0**	**100.0**

	FROM			
TO CONVERT	Barrels to Metric Tons	Metric Tons to Barrels	Barrels/Day to Tons/Year	Tons/Year to Barrels/Day
	MULTIPLY BY			
Crude Oil*	0.136	7.33	49.8	0.0201

* Based on world average gravity (excluding natural gas liquids).

Source: BP Statistical Review of the World Oil Industry, 1973 (London, the British Petroleum Co. Ltd., 1973). In a few instances, slight adjustments have been made to the figures in this source, in accordance with information from other sources. The sources of the BP Statistics are: *USA*: American Petroleum Institute; *Canada*: Canadian Petroleum Institute; and *all other areas*: Estimates published by the "Oil & Gas Journal" (worldwide issue, 31 December 1973).

II. *World oil production, by oil region, as of 31 December 1973*

Country/region	Barrels daily *thousand*	Tons yearly *mn*	Share of world total *per cent*
United States	10 925	517.9	*18.3*
Canada	2 105	101.8	*3.6*
Total North America	**13 030**	**619.7**	**21.9**
Venezuela	3.455	178.8	*6.3*
Mexico	550	27.0	*1.0*
Argentina	420	22.0	*0.8*
Colombia	200	10.1	*0.4*
Ecuador	193	9.6	*0.3*
Brazil	165	8.1	*0.3*
Trinidad & Tobago	165	8.5	*0.3*
Other Latin America	155	7.7	*0.3*
Total Latin America	**5 303**	**271.8**	**9.7**
Saudi Arabia	7 345	364.7	*12.9*
Iran	5 895	293.1	*10.2*
Kuwait	2 755	138.4	*4.9*
Iraq	1 980	97.1	*3.4*
Abu Dhabi	1 305	62.6	*2.2*
Qatar	570	27.3	*1.0*
Neutral Zone	515	26.5	*0.9*
Oman	295	14.7	*0.5*
Other Middle East	410	20.8	*0.7*
Total Middle East	**21 070**	**1 045.2**	**36.7**
Libya	2 180	105.1	*3.7*
Nigeria	2 055	100.1	*3.6*
Algeria	1 090	51.0	*1.8*
Egypt	285	14.2	*0.5*
Angola	157	7.8	*0.3*
Gabon	151	7.5	*0.3*
Other Africa	117	5.8	*0.2*
Total Africa	**6 035**	**291.5**	**10.4**
FR Germany	130	6.6	*0.2*
Turkey	70	3.5	*0.1*
Austria	50	2.6	*0.1*
Other Western Europe	195	9.9	*0.3*
Total Western Europe	**445**	**22.6**	**0.7**
USSR	8 455	421.0	*14.7*
Romania	281	14.0	*0.5*
Yugoslavia	60	3.0	*0.1*
Other Eastern Europe	28	1.1	−
Total Eastern Europe	**8 824**	**439.1**	**15.3**
Indonesia	1 300	64.2	*2.3*
China	784	39.0	*1.4*
India	150	7.2	*0.3*
Other Asia	379	17.7	*0.6*
Australasia	390	19.4	*0.7*
Total Far East	**3 003**	**147.5**	**5.3**
World total	**57 710**	**2 837.4**	**100.0**

Source: See table I.

III. *World oil consumption, by oil region, as of 31 December 1973*

Country/region	Barrels daily *thousand*	Tons yearly *mn*	Share of world total *per cent*
United States	16 815	814.7	29.8
Canada	1 755	83.8	3.1
Total North America	**18 570**	**898.5**	**32.9**
Mexico	625	29.6	1.1
Caribbean area	1 335	66.7	2.4
Other Latin America	1 510	73.5	2.7
Total Latin America	**3 470**	**169.8**	**6.2**
Total Middle East	**1 230**	**62.9**	**2.2**
Total Africa	**985**	**48.0**	**1.7**
FR Germany	3 070	149.5	5.4
France	2 555	125.7	4.5
United Kingdom	2 285	112.6	4.0
Italy	2 100	104.5	3.7
Scandinavia	1 120	56.0	2.0
Other Western Europe	4 000	199.4	7.1
Total Western Europe	**15 130**	**747.7**	**26.7**
USSR	6 545	320.9	11.6
Other Eastern Europe	1 456	73.0	2.6
Total Eastern Europe	**8 001**	**393.9**	**14.2**
Japan	5 425	267.2	9.6
China	704	35.0	1.3
Other Asia	2 260	110.0	4.0
Australasia	650	32.9	1.2
Total Far East	**9 039**	**445.1**	**16.1**
World total	**56 425**	**2 765.9**	**100.0**

Source: See table I.

IV. World oil refining capacity, by oil region, as of 31 December 1973

Country/region	Barrels daily thousand	Tons yearly mn	Share of world total per cent
United States	14 250	710	22.1
Canada	1 830	91	2.8
Total North America	**16 080**	**801**	**24.9**
Caribbean area	3 015	150	4.7
Venezuela	1 490	74	2.3
Argentina	630	31	1.0
Mexico	735	37	1.1
Brazil	795	39	1.2
Other Latin America	345	17	0.5
Total Latin America	**7 010**	**348**	**10.8**
Iran	645	32	1.0
Kuwait	525	26	0.8
Saudi Arabia	425	21	0.7
Bahrein	250	12	0.4
Other Middle East	750	38	1.2
Total Middle East	**2 595**	**129**	**4.1**
Total Africa	**1 060**	**53**	**1.7**
Italy	3 830	191	6.0
France	3 160	157	4.9
FR Germany	2 930	146	4.5
United Kingdom	2 835	141	4.4
Netherlands	1 815	90	2.8
Spain	865	43	1.3
Belgium	855	42	1.3
Other Western Europe	2 325	116	3.6
Total Western Europe	**18 615**	**926**	**28.8**
USSR	7 843	390	12.1
Other Eastern Europe	1 708	85	2.7
Total Eastern Europe	**9 542**	**475**	**14.8**
Japan	4 780	242	7.5
China	804	40	1.2
Other Asia	3 190	159	5.0
Australasia	744	37	1.2
Total Far East	**9 608**	**478**	**14.9**
World total	**64 510**	**3 210**	**100.0**

Source: See table I.

v. Total world oil movements, as 31 December 1915, crude oil and products

Exporting countries and regions	Importing countries and regions										Total exports
	USA	Canada	Other W. Hemisphere	W. Europe	Africa	S.E. Asia	Japan	Austral-asia	Other E. Hemisphere	Unknown destination a	
United States	..	1.5	3.0	4.8	0.2	1.3	1.7	..	..	..	12.5
Canada	67.0	..	..	..	..	..	..	..	..	..	67.0
Caribbean area	131.1	25.1	6.2	17.5	0.2	0.3	0.5	..	..	6.6	187.5
Other W. Hemisphere	4.0	..	4.7	..	..	..	..	..	..	1.6	10.3
W. Europe	13.0	..	..	..	3.0	..	..	..	0.5	3.1	19.6
Middle East	40.8	16.0	47.4	513.3	26.0	65.1	215.9	13.9	38.9	11.7	989.0
North Africa	17.8	2.0	8.4	120.8	0.2	1.0	1.0	..	12.6	0.5	163.3
West Africa	25.2	4.4	20.3	50.3	..	..	5.4	..	0.2	..	105.8
S.E. Asia	11.8	..	..	0.5	..	..	54.8	2.0	..	..	69.1
USSR and E. Europe	1.8	..	7.0	48.6	3.6	0.3	2.7	..	1.0	1.8	66.8
Other E. Hemisphere	0.7	..	..	..	..	1.2	1.7	..	0.2	0.3	4.1
Total imports	313.2	49.0	97.0	755.8	33.2	68.2	283.7	15.9	53.4	25.6	1 695.0

Thousand barrels daily

Exporting countries and regions	USA	Canada	Other W. Hemisphere	W. Europe	Africa	S.E. Asia	Japan	Austral-asia	Other E. Hemisphere	Unknown destination a	Total exports
United States	..	30	55	85	5	25	30	..	..	..	230
Canada	1 335	..	..	..	..	..	..	..	..	..	1 335
Caribbean area	2 540	500	130	355	5	5	10	..	..	85	3 630
Other W. Hemisphere	80	..	100	..	..	..	..	..	..	20	200
W. Europe	265	..	..	..	60	..	..	..	10	70	405
Middle East	820	320	1 000	10 350	535	1 315	4 385	290	775	180	19 970
North Africa	360	40	175	2 545	5	..	20	..	265	10	3 420
West Africa	515	90	415	1 030	..	..	110	..	5	..	2 165
S.E. Asia	240	..	..	10	..	..	1 115	40	..	..	1 405
USSR and E. Europe	35	..	145	935	75	5	55	..	20	15	1 285
Other E. Hemisphere	15	..	..	..	..	25	35	..	5	5	85
Total imports	6 205	980	2 020	15 310	685	1 375	5 760	330	1 080	385	34 130

a Includes quantities in transit, transit losses, minor movements not otherwise shown, military uses, and so forth. The table excludes intra-area movements (for instance, as between the USSR and Eastern Europe). Bunkers are not included in exports.
Source: See table I.

71

Appendix 2.

The oil situation in selected countries and regions

The following brief account, based on statistics in appendix 1, gives some basic information on the nature of various countries' and regions' dependence on oil, providing a background to their present and future economic and military potential to the extent that this potential is influenced by the security of oil supplies. It must be emphasized, however, that any estimate of future needs made in the summaries below is very speculative; in most cases these estimates were made before the dramatic changes of 1973. Unless otherwise indicated, the values refer to 1973.

North America

The United States is in several respects a crucial country. It is the chief oil consumer in the world, consuming 16.8 million barrels daily (b/d), or 814.7 million tons a year (t/y). With 6 per cent of the world's population, the United States accounts for about 30 per cent of the total world consumption of oil. Moreover, the major source of US energy is oil, accounting for 47 per cent of the total US energy consumption in 1973.

The United States is fortunate to have very large proved reserves of oil (41.8 billion barrels [5.4 billion tons]) and, as an oil producer, it has always led the world (10.9 million b/d [517.9 t/y]). About two-thirds of the total US production comes from four principal producing states (Texas, Louisiana and, to a lesser extent, California and Oklahoma). More than 1.5 million oil and gas wells have been drilled in the United States and between 25 000 and 30 000 new wells are drilled every year. On current estimates, however, the United States can expect a gradual decline in production within a few years, since the rate of discovery of new deposits is no longer keeping pace with the increasing production rate. New discoveries elsewhere, particularly in 1968 at Prudhoe Bay on the North Slope of Alaska (estimated at 9.6 billion barrels [1.3 billion tons]), have augmentative value, about 25 per cent of US reserves, but too little in relation to expected needs to be more than marginally significant. However, since restrictive economic policies seem to have been a major reason for the decline of the rate of discovery, the substantially increased prices of imported oil are likely to act as an added incentive for US domestic production.

Nevertheless, unless rigorous measures are taken to curb domestic consumption and increase production, the United States will have to import increasingly large quantities of oil to meet its projected needs. US oil imports have in fact tripled since 1960. In 1973, its imports of crude oil and oil products (about half of each) amounted to 6.2 million b/d (313.2 million t/y), but if present trends continue, this may rise to 12.0 million b/d (597.6 million t/y) in 1980, or 50 per cent of the then expected consumption. [65] The main supplies up to now have come from the Western hemisphere, notably the Caribbean area (especially Venezuela) and Canada, but the Middle East — particularly Saudi Arabia — is the only area that can supply the projected needs of the United States.

However, in a study presented in December 1972, the National Petroleum Council's Committee on the US Energy Outlook concluded that the best option available to the United States was to increase the availability of domestic energy supplies, rather than to rely on imports, or to reduce the growth in demand. To rely on increasing imports would be dangerous to US security needs and the national economy, because of the uncertainty of the availability, dependability and price of oil.

As to reducing the growth of demand, it was judged unlikely that growth in consumption would depart significantly from the average 4.2 per cent per year, the rate projected for the 1971—85 period. Restrictions on the growth of energy demand could prove expensive and undesirable, according to this study; among other things, they would alter lifestyles and adversely affect employment, economic growth and consumer choice. Although more efficient use of energy was considered desirable, it was also pointed out that there are a number of inherent limitations in how much the growth in energy demand can be reduced through efficiency improvements during the next 15 years. [219]

In November 1973, President Nixon announced the plan for "Project Independence" by 1980, the aim of which is to achieve self-sufficiency in energy. The strategy of Project Independence is to reduce the rate of growth in demand from 3.6 to 2 per cent a year and to increase the rate of growth in energy production from an average of 3 per cent a year over the past 10 years, to 4.7 per cent, thus bringing supply and demand into balance. [220]

However, some critics — notably the Ford Foundation Energy Policy Project — have described the policy of cutting back imports as nothing but an "impractical and simplistic overreaction"; what is needed instead is greater care and selectivity in planning oil imports for the future. Unless oil imports can be increased at an acceptable economic and political price, which is possible but not very probable, the only way to reduce the gap in the short term will be to restrict consumption, along the lines of the Ford Foundation Energy Policy Project. This would be difficult to achieve in the short term so that no individual or group bears an undue burden. However, in the medium and longer term the picture is brighter. The Ford Foundation Project outlines three descriptive scenarios of the future to show the range of feasible energy consumption patterns from which the nation can choose.

These scenarios differ very markedly in their impacts on availability of energy supply, the environment, foreign policy, lifestyles, and the economy. One scenario is based on the persistence of present growth trends in energy production and consumption and stresses the policies needed to satisfy that growth in a socially acceptable manner; another is a "technical fix" solution, which maintains the same growth in energy services, but stresses policies needed to reduce growth in energy use through improved efficiency; as a third option, we consider a *zero energy growth* scenario which would require changes in both lifestyles and the economy to reach a steady no-growth state in energy consumption by the late 1980's. [199]

The United States is fairly well off in terms of alternative energy resources. Natural gas is inceasingly becoming an exception to this rule, however. Between 1950 and 1970, natural gas provided more than half of the growth in total energy supplies, but by the early 1970s, it had begun to be in short supply. On the other hand, the USA has very large quantities of oil shale, and is in a geographically favourable position to develop and use the rich tar sand fields of Canada. Its coal reserves are among the largest in the world. Because it has been able to build up great economic wealth and a high technological standard, it is among the few countries in the world in a position to develop the costly and complicated processes which facilitate the use of new energy sources. The US federal R&D funding is expected to increase from $999 million in fiscal year 1974 to $1 810 million in fiscal year 1975. The major part of these funds will be spent on nuclear fission development and coal resource development. [199]

While *Canada,* mainly in the provinces of Alberta, Saskatchewan and British Columbia in Western Canada, contains about 18 per cent (or 9.3 billion barrels [1.2 billion tons]) of the total North American proved oil reserves, excluding Alaska, it produces about 16 per cent of the continent's crude oil output (or 2.1 million b/d [102 million t/y]). A considerable proportion of Canada's potential oil production remains unexploited for economic reasons, however, since it has so far been more expensive to produce Canadian crude oils rather than Venezuelan or Middle Eastern ones. For these reasons, only about half of the domestic oil demand is normally supplied from Canadian indigenous sources, while the balance is made up of imported crude oils. Nevertheless, a large proportion of the Canadian annual oil output is exported to the USA, where production costs are even higher in some areas. Discussions have also for some time been under way to obtain a bilateral agreement with the United States for cooperation in the event of emergency situations, but these negotiations are presently at a stalemate. [221]

Canada probably has the world's largest area of tar sand, the Athabasca tar sands in northern Alberta, which are estimated to contain over 600 billion barrels of heavy, high-sulphur crude oil, of which half may be ultimately recoverable. It has also been shown that until 1987, Western Canada has proved gas resources well in excess of the country's projected domestic and export demand. In addition, Canada has reasonable amounts of coal, although coal has a much smaller share of the market than in the United States. Nuclear reactors are projected to provide 26 per cent of the power generated in Canada by 1990. Canada has in fact set a goal similar to that spelled out for the USA by President Nixon — self-sufficiency in energy by 1980.

Exploration for hydrocarbons was largely confined to the western provinces some 10 years ago, but in 1970 the most active exploration areas had become the Canadian Arctic and the eastern offshore region. [222]

It has been remarked that the challenge of the "energy crisis" appears to be serving the cause of the unity of Canada. French-speaking Quebec has been and still is dependent upon oil from abroad which used to be cheap but now costs more than Canada's indigenous oil. The realization that the possession of indigenous oil is a tremendous asset in the world of today has supposedly weakened separatist sentiment in oil-poor Quebec. The increased price of energy may also help to reduce in the long run the regional disparities which have plagued the Canadian economy for a long time, although considerable obstacles will have to be overcome when working out compromises between the producing and consuming provinces and the authorities in Ottawa. [223]

Western Europe

Western Europe, as a region, is the second largest oil consumer in the world. In 1973 its consumption amounted to 15.2 million b/d (747.7 million t/y), which was 27 per cent of the total world consumption. As to expected future consumption, the OECD has estimated that in 1980 Western Europe will require 22.3 million b/d (1 109 million t/y). [222a]

Western Europe has a very limited production of its own (0.4 million b/d [22.6 million t/y]). The Federal Republic of Germany is by far the largest crude oil producer in Western Europe, with an output of 130 000 b/d (6.6 million t/y) which, however, provided only 4.2 per cent of the country's oil requirements. Ninety-five per cent of the proved and probable oil reserves lie in the northwestern areas of FR Germany.

Due to oil reserves in the North Sea (estimated to be between 11.5 and 13 billion barrels of recoverable oil [1.6—1.8 billion tons or more]) [224], those West European countries able to profit from the discovery (particularly Norway and the United Kingdom) will be in a considerably better position. Oil production from the British North Sea should total 2.0—2.8 million b/d (100—140 million t/y) by 1980, enough to make the UK self-sufficient in energy by then; and it will remain at this level at least throughout the decade, according to recent and upwardly revised official figures. [225—226] Norway, for its part, is expected to produce 1 million b/d (50 million t/y) in 1981. [227]

The importance of the North Sea discoveries is not least due to the fact that these huge amounts of oil and gas have been found in the centre of one of the world's largest petroleum-consuming areas. The North Sea is now the world's most important area in offshore activities.

Total North Sea production in 1974 was recently estimated to be 180 000 b/d (9.0 million t/y), which will have risen to 2 million b/d (100 million t/y) by 1978 and in the early 1980s to a possible 4 million b/d (200 million t/y). [224] In view of the projected demand it seems likely, however, that the North Sea oil will have only limited importance to Western Europe as a whole and contribute only marginally to the overall world supply, since no more than 2 per cent of world oil reserves are located in the area. It must be stressed, however, that it is too early to draw meaningful comparisons with the established oil-producing regions. What can be said is that huge investments of capital and technology will be necessary.

Western Europe is therefore heavily dependent upon imports — 15.3 million b/d (755.8 million t/y). It should be noted, however, that part of the imports of crude oil is being re-exported as refined products (0.4 million b/d [19.6 million t/y]). The "net" dependence on imports is therefore 98 per cent of total consumption. The majority of imports in 1973 stemmed from the Middle East (63 per cent) and North Africa (17 per cent).

Unlike the United States, Western Europe has few alternative energy resources to develop. Although some areas are still relatively untouched, most coal reserves have already been much depleted. Coal provided some 60 per cent of total European energy requirements in 1960; by 1973 this contribution had fallen to below 25 per cent. The reserves of oil shale are limited. The consumption of natural gas still represents a share of only about 10 per cent of total consumption, while nuclear energy represents less than 1 per cent. As to the possibilities of developing new methods and sources, the question of whether the capital costs can be met and the required technological ability mustered largely depends upon economic and political cooperation in Western Europe, particularly against the background of the recent oil crisis. Clearly, Western Europe is highly unlikely to find opportunities for investing preliminary capital and technology equal to those of the USA, but it may well benefit directly or indirectly from US successes.

However, during the spring of 1974, the EEC Commission adopted an optimistic attitude toward EEC oil security. In a recent study it was suggested that the EEC may be able to cut its 1985 energy requirements by 10 per cent, and to cover a much larger proportion by using natural gas, nuclear power and coal, all largely from indigenous sources. In this case there would be no significant increase in the overall demand for oil, a growing proportion of which would come from the North Sea in any case. The suggested slow-down in oil consumption and the sharp upturn in indigenous production would result in a decline in the EEC's oil imports from abroad — from over 10 million b/d (500 million t/y) in 1973 to less than 8 million b/d (400 million t/y) in 1985. Experts also suggest that it may be possible to raise supplies of natural gas from all sources so that the share of gas in the EEC's overall energy consumption could rise from about one-eighth in 1973 to as much as one-quarter by 1985. To further its new aims, the EEC Commission advocates a reversal of its former policy under which the long-term decline of the local coal industries was to continue. It is now recommended that the share of coal in the total energy budget be increased. Finally, the EEC Commission advocates a crash programme for the development of nuclear power stations, so that these could supply 17 per cent of Europe's needs. [228]

Eastern Europe, including the Soviet Union

The *Soviet Union* was the world's third largest oil consumer in 1973 (6.4 million b/d [320.9 million t/y]), using over 11 per cent of the world total. No official figures exist as to expected future consumption, but some experts have estimated consumption in 1975 to be somewhat under 7.0 million b/d (350 million t/y), [229] and in 1980, 10.1 million b/d (500 million t/y). [230]

In 1973, the Soviet Union had an output of 8.5 million b/d (421 million t/y), which made it the second largest producer in the world (14.7 per cent of total world production). Under the current five-year plan, crude oil production is scheduled to reach 10 million b/d (496 million t/y) in 1975, an output which the Soviet Union, according to some Western experts, might have difficulties in achieving. The most recently published Western estimates have revised the 1975 production figures to "over 9.6 million b/d (over 480 million t/y)". No official estimates have been published for the ensuing years; the latest available estimated target figures for 1980 are 12.1—12.5 million b/d (600—620 million t/y). [231] Previously published estimates for 1990 amounted to 18.0—19.0 million b/d (900—950 million t/y). [230a] Oil production in recent years has tended to lag behind the plans; output is therefore expected to remain somewhat below the targets set for 1975 and also — in the absence of determined new efforts — below the tentative targets for 1980. [231]

Current Soviet production covers its consumption and allows for some exports. In 1973, exports amounted to over 2 million b/d (100 million t/y), of which more than half went to other East European countries, except Romania, and the rest to countries in Western Europe. In fact, oil has long been the Soviet Union's most important single earner of hard currencies. The Soviet Union also imported about 0.2 million b/d (8–9 million t/y) from certain Arab countries, mainly Iraq.

No recent official figures for crude oil reserves in the Soviet Union are available, but proved reserves are reported to be in the range of 41 billion barrels (5 600 million tons). [230b] Its ultimate potential is considered to be substantially larger than this, particularly since about half of the land area of the country is underlain by sedimentary formations, which have only been partly explored to date. Geologist E.N. Tiratsoo estimates that the "proved" oil reserves were probably 60 billion barrels at the end of 1971, and that total oil reserves amounted to 210 billion barrels on land, with perhaps 39 billion barrels offshore. [232]

Oil production has so far mainly drawn upon the reserves in the Volga Ural region, but the centre of gravity seems likely to move gradually eastward to western Siberia, Kazakhstan and Central Asia, and in the longer term to eastern Siberia; the continuing eastward movement of the focus of operations, which has been a striking trend since the beginning of production, has been the combined result of the depletion of the early discoveries, the desire for wartime security and the development of previously unexplored territories.

The Soviet Union also has an extensive programme for offshore petroleum exploration and development. The Soviet deputy minister of the Ministry of the Petroleum Industry, Mishchevich, has disclosed estimates that 50 per cent of the Soviet Union's subsea oil and gas are concentrated beneath the Barents Sea (north of European USSR) and the Kara Sea (north of western Siberia); it is believed that the Kara Sea has oil and gas reserves several times larger than those in the Barents Sea; but the latter sea is closer to the large Soviet populated centres and to the ice-free port of Murmansk. Until 1990 the main growth of Soviet offshore hydrocarbon production will be provided by the Caspian and Barents Seas and the Sea of Okhotsk. The Far Eastern seas (primarily the Sea of Okhotsk, but also including the Bering and Chukotsk (Chukchi) Seas and the Sea of Japan) have another 10 per cent of potential reserves. The southern seas (the Caspian, Black, Aral and Azov Seas) have 23 per cent of these reserves, while the remaining 17 per cent of potential offshore reserves are located in the Baltic Sea and in the Arctic Sea above central and eastern Siberia. [233]

If the Siberian oil resources are found to be as abundant as some scientists believe and if the enormous technological and capital problems for their development can be solved, with or without assistance from abroad (particularly the United States and Japan), the Soviet Union might have the option of becoming a major world oil exporter in about 15–20 years' time. But if the rate of production increase cannot be considerably boosted beyond the planned 7 per cent a year, the amount of oil that the Soviet Union will have at its disposal will only be sufficient to take care of the rising home consumption, while exports will have to be kept at a fairly steady level. [234] Indeed, a number of statements by Soviet officials in May 1974 raised doubts about the participation by foreign companies in the development of oil and gas resources, and also indicated that there would be no growth in Soviet imports or exports in the foreseeable future. However, Soviet news agencies later made efforts to dispel such interpretations. [235]

As far as alternative resources are concerned, the Soviet Union is in a very favourable position. It has vast resources in natural gas and coal and important reserves of oil shale, primarily in Estonia, where it has been used as a source of oil since World War I. [236] The unexploited hydroelectric power capacity of the eastern parts of the country is significant. The capital investments involved in developing some of these potentials are as enormous, however, as those involved in the exploitation of oil. The Soviet Union is also in the technological forefront in developing other sources and methods, such as fission and fusion nuclear energy and magnetohydrodynamics (MHD). Nuclear power is still in its infancy, however, and cannot be a major factor until the late 1980s at the earliest.

Among *East European* countries outside the Soviet Union, only Romania has an oil production of any importance. East European production in 1973 amounted to 369 000 b/d (18 million t/y). Total East European oil reserves are estimated to be about 3.0 billion barrels (500 million tons).

Eastern Europe is one of the few areas of the world where, until recently, petroleum consumption showed only very slow progress. However, the five-year economic plans announced for the period 1971—75 show that the trend away from the traditional dependence on solid fuels is likely to accelerate. Hydrocarbon fuel production in general is rising slowly in Eastern Europe but it is still insufficient to meet expanding domestic and industrial demands, so that both oil and gas have been imported in increasing quantities from the Soviet Union. However, in recent years the Soviet Union has repeatedly stressed that it will be unable to provide for the bulk of Eastern Europe's growing oil requirements in the late 1970s and the 1980s; the Soviet Union has therefore encouraged the other East European countries to make substantial supplementary supply arrangements from sources in the Middle East and elsewhere, although such an increased dependence on foreign supplies diminishes the security of being self-sufficient within the East European bloc as a whole. [231] Recent figures show that the oil trade within Comecon has declined and that this downward trend has recently been gaining speed. [237] It should be noted that the long-term contracts between the Soviet Union and its allies are negotiated every five years to coincide with the five-year plans of Comecon's members. The next contracts are due to be drawn up in time for the new plans beginning in 1976; an essential point in these discussions will be to what extent the enormous increases in oil prices will reflect on the prices that the Soviet Union and the other Comecon countries will agree upon. [238]

Japan

Japan was the world's fourth largest oil consumer in 1973 (5.4 million b/d [267.2 million t/y] or 9.6 per cent of the world total). The percentage of oil against total energy consumption is very high (80 per cent). The growth in Japan's oil consumption during the past few years has been around 15 per cent a year. If Japan is to continue consuming energy at anything like its present rate, it will inevitably have to depend heavily upon a continued supply of oil. Previous OECD estimates are that Japan's oil requirement in 1980 will be 9.4 million b/d. [222b] Since Japan has practically no oil production of its own and the prospects for finding substantial oil deposits in or around Japan seem fairly small, this 1980 figure is particularly unrealistic unless heavy reliance is placed on import capacity. Japan imported 5.8 million b/d in 1973, in other words, more than it consumed in that year. Japan's main supplier has been the Arabian/Persian Gulf area (76 per cent of total imports) and Indonesia (about 17 per cent). It has been estimated that, on average, every 60 miles of water from the Arabian/Persian Gulf to Japan contains a tanker transporting oil. [239] Such heavy dependence on oil imports is nothing new for Japan. Ninety to 100 per cent of its other vital raw materials, such as iron ore, bauxite, copper ore, nickel, natural gum, wool and cotton, have to be imported as well. Three hundred million tons of natural raw materials are imported every year, of which 200 million tons are oil. In addition, Japan has to import most foodstuffs and feedgrain. [240]

Increased oil prices will place a heavy burden on the Japanese economy both because of its strong reliance on imports and because of the fact that Japan's industry depends on oil for more than 63 per cent of its overall fuel requirements, nearly four times as much as in the United States and considerably more than in Western Europe. This means that a given cut in oil supplies will have a much more significant effect on industrial production in Japan than in most other developed countries. [241] The Economic Planning Agency has estimated Japanese growth for 1973 as a whole at 11 per cent (in real terms), but at only 1.4 per cent for the crisis quarter of October to December. Estimates for 1974 range from zero to 2.5 per cent. These indicators follow a 20-year period in which gross national product increased by 8–12 per cent a year, while energy use rose by over 500 per cent and oil consumption by some 2 300 per cent in all. For the future, the Institute of Energy Economics has revised figures. It assumes an average growth in real GNP of 7.5 per cent for 1970–75, 6.6 per cent for 1975–80, and 6 per cent for 1980–85. These figures reflect, among other things, improved efficiency in use of energy, a decline of the share of oil in the total energy budget, an increase of the share of natural gas, and an increased use of nuclear power – providing 12.5 per cent of the electricity in 1985. [242]

Japan has a very advanced scientific and technological basis, however, which it will use for the development of new energy sources and methods, either by its own efforts or in cooperation with other countries. Japan is scheduled to have its first synthetic natural gas power plant in operation within a couple of years. [243] Cooperation has already begun with the United States in developing solar energy, and discussions with the Soviet Union about Japanese participation on a barter basis in the exploitation of the oil reserves of western Siberia are currently under way. Part of this cooperative agreement would provide for the building of transport facilities from the Tyumen fields to the Pacific Ocean, either as a 7 000-km pipeline or railway or a combination of the two. Whatever the solution, it has security implications for China, since such a pipeline or railway would add to the military potential of the Soviet Union in a very sensitive border area. The Japanese government is therefore known to be proceeding with these discussions with the Soviet Union with great caution. There is another security aspect involved in these discussions, since the Soviet Union has expressed an interest in Japanese assistance in building an oil refinery at Nakhodka on the Sea of Japan. An oil refinery here would be an important asset to the Soviet Navy, which operates from Vladivostok. [244]

China

Only limited information is available as to oil consumption, production and reserves in the *People's Republic of China*: China's oil consumption probably roughly equals its production, since China is self-sufficient and its *per capita* consumption of oil is very low. In recent years China has even had some room for exportation. While less is known about China's plans for future oil consumption, it is evident that the required oil resources would be enormous if China aspired to achieve the same lifestyle of high *per capita* energy consumption as that prevailing in the industrialized world today, bearing in mind that China has a population of 700 million. [245] However, China's ambitions are probably more limited in a quantitative sense.

A few years ago Premier Chou En-lai disclosed that Chinese production of crude oil in 1970 amounted to 400 000 b/d (20 million t/y). In January 1974 he was reported to have disclosed that production in 1973 had risen to 1 million b/d (50 million t/y). [246—248] Other estimates (like that of British Petroleum) have been more conservative, however, and have assessed the production in 1973 to be about 800 000 b/d (39 million t/y).

In 1973, China exported one million tons to Japan, and smaller amounts to Hong Kong and Thailand. Exports to Japan in 1974 are reported to be in the range of 67 000 b/d (3 million t/y) to 100 000 b/d (5 million t/y). [249] China has also been exporting oil to North Korea and North Viet-Nam for some years. [250]

In recent years oil fields have been discovered and developed in northeast and northern China, these being well located in relation to centres of consumption and available transportation. The Ta-Ching oil field, in the province of Heilungkiang in northeast China, where development began in 1960, now accounts for half of China's production of crude oil. [239, 251—253] Other major areas of production are Shengli in Shantung; Karama, Turfan and Tarin in Sinkiang; Yumen in Kansu; the Tsaidam Basin in Tsinghai; Yenchang in Shensi; and the Szechuran Basin. Offshore production has also started in the Pohai Bay and Taku, near Tientsin, and the Shengli field has also been extended offshore. [254] Prospects for offshore discoveries in the Pohai Bay are described as promising; [255] offshore drilling has now been started on a fairly large scale, some of the equipment being imported from such industrialized countries as Japan, the USA and Denmark. [256—257] Most of the smaller ocean basins forming the western margin of the Pacific are also promising areas (the Bering Sea, the Sea of Okhotsk, the Sea of Japan, the Yellow Sea, the East China Sea and the South China Sea). [258] To date, there has been no exploration in the extensive shelf-basin area extending 2 600 miles along the Pacific coast and outward from 100—3 000 or more miles. [239] According to one expert study, China is assumed to have recoverable crude oil reserves in established oil-bearing areas of 19.6 billion barrels (2 700 million tons). [255]

China's alternative energy resources focus primarily on coal, which accounted for about 90 per cent of all the primary energy available in China as of 1970. [259] China is third in the world after the United States and the Soviet Union, in terms of total coal reserves. For many years, China has had a limited production of shale oil, estimated to be 20 000 b/d (1 million t/y). [236] With regard to developing other energy sources and methods, China is in a much less favourable situation than the above-mentioned industrialized countries because of its less advanced technological base. However, an experimental geothermal power station is now being built in the province of Huailai about 90 km from Peking. [260] On the other hand, because of the substantial contribution of productive manual labour by its vast population, and the highly developed energy-recycling discipline in the society, China is probably less dependent upon the development of new sources and methods and comparatively less vulnerable to restrictions of supplies.

The third world

The situation of the countries in the third world varies widely. Some of them have large populations and only limited oil reserves (Bangladesh, Brazil, India and Pakistan). Others have large populations and substantial oil supplies, although in some cases hardly sufficient to meet the needs of the countries themselves, much less to cover the energy needs of other countries with fewer oil resources in the same region, if they are to progress far in the pattern of modern industrialized welfare states (Algeria, Indonesia, Iran, Iraq, Nigeria and Venezuela).

Those countries which combine large reserves of oil with limited populations are of course in a much more favourable situation. Most such countries are situated in the Arabian/Persian Gulf area.

Southern Asia

India, with a population of close to 600 million inhabitants, has a yearly consumption of 460 000 b/d (22.9 million t/y), which is less than that of, for instance, high *per capita* consuming Sweden (with only 8 million inhabitants). India has an oil production of its own of 150 000 b/d (7.2 million t/y). Its imports therefore amount to about 320 000 b/d (15.9 million t/y), of which practically all stems from the Middle East − notably Iran. [261−262]

The recent oil price increases will hurt India particularly, and the goals set in its fifth five-year development plan, beginning in April 1974, are now much in doubt. The cost of the oil imports in 1973 is estimated to have been $460–$500 million, a figure which is likely to be more than doubled in 1974, if 340 000 b/d (16.9 million t/y) are imported as planned. This would mean that oil imports would consume 30–50 per cent of India's export earnings, compared with 20–30 per cent in mid-1974. [263−265] The annual target of 5.5 per cent real growth is therefore likely to turn into a probability that 1974 will be a year of minimal or zero growth. [241a]

In view of its serious oil situation, India is likely to increase its efforts to find new land and offshore oil reserves. Proven reserves total 779 million barrels (106 million tons). The Indian government has formulated a "crash programme" to increase indigenous production by about one million tons this year and to curb consumption of crude and refined products by about four million tons. The aim is to establish reserves of 65 million tons by quick exploration of potentially good areas both on land and offshore. [264] In its first attempt at offshore drilling, the

Indian government has recently struck promising oil sources at a point called Bombay High in the Gulf of Cambay, some 180 km north of Bombay. [265] India is also pursuing the line of securing as many concessions for overseas exploration as possible and is already a partner in a multinational project in Iran. [266] It has also acquired substantial concessions in Iran, and in April 1973 India entered a 12-year agreement with Iraq for the supply of 820 million barrels (11.2 million tons) of oil beginning in 1976. [267] Also, the Soviet Union has agreed to supply India with 60 000 b/d (3 million t/y) during 1974. [268] Finally, India has concluded an agreement with Iran on very favourable terms; Iran is understood to have promised to deliver 40 000 barrels (2 million tons) in 1974 at a price of $3.50 a barrel. [269]

Coal is India's most important energy asset but the quality is poor and production could not be raised fast enough to make it a significant substitute for oil in the foreseeable future. The other basic energy resource is water, of which the major untapped potential lies in the rivers of the north, fed from the Himalayas. A striking feature of the Indian energy economy is, however, that non-commercial energy sources – cow dung, firewood and vegetable wastes – provide a considerable part of the total consumption. [241b] In the search for substitutes during the recent oil shortage, a 30-year-old experiment with "Gobar gas" plants was brought to life again on a wide scale. A Gobar gas plant produces methane gas for fuel and lighting and, as a byproduct, nitrogen-enriched manure for crops. The gas plant is very simple in construction; a plant sustained by five cows and costing $200 in India, produces gas enough to provide cooking fuel and light for a family of four. The Indian government has ordered 20 000 Gobar gas plants to be built. [270]

Bangladesh (population over 60 million) has no significant proven oil reserves on its territory and hence no production of its own. On the other hand, Bangladesh has considerable reserves of natural gas. The country's consumption of oil is low in relation to the size of its population (around 20 000 b/d [1 million t/y]). [271] As in India, the huge rise in oil prices has dealt a serious blow to the ambitious five-year economic plan, which took effect during the autumn of 1973 and aims at an annual growth rate of 8.8 per cent over the 1972–73 level. Oil imports, though small, will now consume more than 30 per cent of the foreign exchange earnings of Bangladesh, compared with 8 per cent before the raise in price. The effect on the already crippled Bangladesh economy will be disastrous. [272]

Pakistan (population over 53 million) is more fortunate in that it has both oil and gas resources, although these are limited as far as oil is concerned. Pakistan's oil fields are concentrated in the Potwar Basin in the north of the country. Pakistan's total indigenous production is approximately 8 000 b/d (400 000 t/y) which meets only 12 per cent of the demand of 70 000 b/d (3.5 million t/y). The shortfall is made up by imports, mainly from Iran. [271, 273]

Sri Lanka (population 13 million) also will be seriously affected by the oil crisis and the country may have to pay nearly half its export earnings in 1974 to import crude oil. [274] Sri Lanka has no oil production nor any known reserves of its own. In recent years, however, there has been interest in petroleum prospecting offshore, particularly in the Palk Straits.

Indonesia is an important PE-country. Its oil production has tripled since 1967 and amounted to 1.3 million b/d (64.2 million t/y) in 1973. According to statements by the state oil company Pertamina, Indonesia has the potential to double this output within the next few years. Most of the oil produced, which is mainly light and has a low sulphur content, comes from Sumatra. Intensive offshore exploration is currently under way, since the first oil discovery was made in 1970 in the Java Sea. The offshore fields discovered off the coasts of Java and Kalimantan (ex-Borneo) are expected to add considerably to the Indonesian output of crude oil. Reserves are estimated at somewhat above 10 billion barrels (1.4 billion tons) or roughly 1.6 per cent of world reserves.

For the present, Pertamina has decided to export as much of its crude oil as possible. Japan took almost three-quarters of Indonesia's oil exports in 1973. But Indonesian domestic consumption is expected to rise considerably – the present *per capita* consumption among Indonesia's 120 million inhabitants is very low – and at some point the choice between continuing to export or conserving oil for future domestic consumption will have to be made. [275–276]

As regards other areas in *South East Asia*, attention was focused on the South China Sea in 1966 when a United Nations aerial magnetic survey indicated that the prospects for finding oil in the sedimentary layers off South Viet-Nam's coasts were very good. In the summer of 1973 the government of South Viet-Nam signed contracts with four multinational oil companies for offshore concessions south and southeast of the coast near Saigon. It is hoped that commercial oil may possibly start flowing from these expected oil reserves by 1976. [277]

Drilling for oil is presently also going on in the Gulf of Siam, off the coasts of the Khmer Republic (Cambodia) and Thailand, but so far without any significant result. The Thai sector of the Gulf of Siam is expected to become one of Asia's most active areas of exploitation during the next year, however. [277–278]

The most promising exploitation results in the South China Sea have so far been made in the Malaysian sector (the Federation of Malaysia includes Malaya, Sarawak and Sabah), both off the coast of the Malay Peninsula and off Sarawak and Sabah in northern Borneo. These discoveries may enable Malaysia to become a fairly large exporter of oil, and also of gas, by 1980. [277, 279]

Exploration for oil reserves is also going on in the Philippines, where hopes have recently been expressed of finding substantial oil and gas reserves southwest of Cebu Island. [280]

North Viet-Nam is also exploring the prospects for finding oil reserves in the Tonkin Gulf, and is reportedly negotiating with Japanese, Italian and French companies for assistance in these endeavours. [281–282]

Although Singapore has practically no oil production of its own, the oil sector is of paramount interest to its economy and trade because of the great number of refineries situated in Singapore, the majority of which are owned by multinational oil companies, notably Shell. With their capacity of over 1 million b/d, they make Singapore the third largest refinery centre in the world (after Houston and Rotterdam). The crude oil is imported almost totally from the Middle Eastern area and re-exported as oil products, primarily to Japan, South Viet-Nam, Thailand and Hong Kong. [283]

While describing the situation in this region of the world, *Australia* deserves particular mention. Its production amounts to 390 000 b/d (19.4 million t/y) and it holds oil reserves estimated to be 2.3 billion barrels (313 million tons). The currently producing fields are Moonie and Alton in Queensland, Barrow Islands in

Western Australia and the Bass Strait (between the Australian mainland and Tasmania). [222c] Australia is also fortunate as far as other fossil fuels are concerned. According to recent studies it will not have used more than 13—18 per cent of its coal reserves and not more than 75 per cent of its natural gas reserves by the year 2000. Moreover, Australia possesses 20—30 per cent of the world's known uranium reserves. [284] Finally, a recent research study under the auspices of the Australian Academy of Sciences suggests that, by the year 2000, solar energy may cover as much as 25 per cent of Australia's total energy demand — half of which would be in the form of low-grade heat, and half synthetic fuel. Generally speaking, Australia enjoys more sunshine than almost any other of the world's highly industrialized countries. [285] However, Australia has so far been fairly dependent on foreign supplies of oil, a fact which is regarded as a particular drawback because of the uncertainty of sea lanes and the attraction of tankers as targets in case of war. [286]

Latin America

Among countries with substantial oil reserves, but also large populations, mention should first be made of some of the countries in Latin America.

Brazil (population 100 million) has fairly substantial oil reserves on its territory, particularly in the northeast. However, because of Brazil's rapid economic growth, its indigenous production is far from sufficient, covering less than one-third of Brazil's annual requirements. Since production in 1973 amounted to 165 000 b/d (8.1 million t/y) and consumption to over 700 000 b/d (or 35 million t/y), there was a substantial need for imports. [287] The Brazilian state oil company Petrobras (Petroleo Brasileiro S.A.) is in fact the world's largest single buyer of crude oil. Brazil's crude oil import bill could amount to $2 billion in 1974, which is more than twice the 1973 figure and equivalent to nearly a quarter of expected foreign exchange earnings in 1974. [288] In 1972 Petrobras created a subsidiary, Braspetro (Petrobras Internacional S.A.), for the express purpose of searching abroad for oil. Braspetro has since signed exploration and drilling agreements in Colombia, Iraq, Madagascar and Egypt. [289—290]

The largest oil producer among the Latin American countries is *Venezuela* (population 11 million); its production of crude oil in 1973 amounted to 3.5 million b/d (178.8 million t/y). The main oil-producing area is the Cuenca de Maracaibo in the west, an area including almost all of the state of Zulia, Lake Maracaibo, and stretching into Colombia. Three-quarters of Venezuela's crude oil output is extracted from over 4 000 active wells there. [158]

Under present Venezuelan law, the foreign oil companies present in the country are scheduled to begin handing back concessions and installations to the government in 1983. However, recent statements by government officials and the appointment of a special commission to consider all aspects of a planned takeover indicate that this reversion will take place in the near future. [291—292]

Venezuela's exports of crude oil and refined products in 1973 amounted to 3.1 million b/d (154 million t/y), of which about half went to the United States and close to 15 per cent to Canada.

Both production and exports have been declining during the 1970s, however, as have the proved oil reserves in the country — from almost 20 billion barrels (2.7 billion tons) at the end of 1967 to 14 billion barrels (1.9 billion tons) at the end of 1973. [293] At present production levels, these reserves would be exhausted in little more than 10 years, a prospect that increases the pressures in Venezuela for conservation of its most valuable and irreplaceable resource. A decision was consequently taken in April 1974 to reduce crude oil production by 15 per cent. [292] However, sucessful exploitation of the heavy oils in the Orinoco belt, which stretches north of the Orinoco river, could add substantial new reserves. The belt is estimated to contain over 700 billion barrels (95.2 billion tons) of very heavy viscous crude oil of fairly high sulphurous content (4 per cent). It is estimated that, with available technology, up to 10 per cent of this heavy oil could be recovered and upgraded, which would represent 70 billion barrels (9.5 billion tons) or five times Venezuela's present proved reserves. [293] France has taken an interest in participating in the development of these heavy oils. [294]

Table 2A.1 shows other Latin American countries which have substantial oil reserves and production.

Table 2A.1. Oil production, oil reserves and populations of selected Latin American countries, 1973

Country	Production thousand b/d	Reserves bn barrels	Population mn people
Mexico	550	3.6	53.0
Argentina	420	2.5	24.0
Colombia	200	1.4	22.5
Ecuador	193	5.7	6.5
Trinidad & Tobago	165	2.2	1.0
Peru	68	1.0	14.5

Source: BP Statistical Review of the World Oil Industry, 1973 (London, the British Petroleum Co. Ltd., 1973).

In November 1973, 22 Latin American and Caribbean nations, both oil exporters and importers, established the Latin American Energy Organization (OLADE), the aim of which is to promote the integration, protection, conservation, rational utilization, commercialization and defence of the region's energy resources.

The agreement states, *inter alia*, that one of the prime objectives of the new organization is to further

individual or collective defence against all forms of action, sanctions or coercion which may be brought to bear against any member as a result of measures which may have been adopted to preserve and utilize its resources, and to put these resources at the service of its development plans. [295]

The possibilities for this kind of broad cooperation within OLADE will be heavily influenced by the future oil realities in these countries. The United Nations Economic Commission for Latin America (ECLA) has recently published a study on the Latin American oil sector, in which forecasts are made for the oil production and consumption of the Latin American countries in 1974 and 1980, indicating the need for imports and potentials for exports. (See table 2A.2.)

Table 2A.2. Projected oil production and consumption of Latin American countries in 1975 and 1980

b/d, thousand

Country	1975			1980		
	Production	Consumption	Balance	Production	Consumption	Balance
Argentina	520	590	− 70	694	772	− 78
Bolivia	62	15	+ 46	87	21	+ 66
Brazil	278	694	− 416	434	954	− 520
Colombia	260	139	+ 121	347	182	+ 165
Chile	43	135	− 92	43	174	− 131
Ecuador	260	40	+ 220	434	56	+ 378
Mexico	625	642	− 17	781	833	− 52
Paraguay	–	7	− 7	–	10	− 10
Peru	87	139	− 52	121	182	− 61
Trinidad & Tobago	174	43	+ 131	208	64	+ 144
Uruguay	–	45	− 45	–	59	− 59
Venezuela	4 163	191	+ 3 972	4 684	243	+ 4 441
Others	3	278	− 275	4	347	− 343
Total	**6 475**	**2 959**	**+ 3 516**	**7 837**	**3 897**	**+ 3 940**

Source: "Latin America Prospects", *Petroleum Economist*, January 1974.

Africa

In Sub-Saharan Africa, *Nigeria* has rapidly become a substantial oil producer after production started on a commercial basis in the mid-1950s. During 1973 production amounted to 2 million b/d (100.1 million t/y) which was about four times the production in 1969 – the first year after the Nigerian Civil War when production figures seemed to have been normalized. Prospects for further increases are good, given the government's declared policy of raising production as rapidly as possible, with the purpose of boosting revenue for the development of other economic sectors of the most populated country in Africa (80 million inhabitants), and also given the urgent demand for Nigeria's nearly sulphur-free oil. Its relative proximity to some large emerging areas and the continuing success in the discovery of new crude oil reserves are additional advantages. [296] It is estimated that Nigeria's known oil reserves (20 billion barrels [2.6 million tons]) are good for at least 25 years at the present rate of production, but new discoveries will probably increase these figures considerably. The majority of Nigerian oil exports (about 50 per cent) goes to Western Europe.

Although Nigeria heavily dominates oil production in *West Africa,* a steady growth in production along the coast south of the equator, particularly offshore, is beginning to gather impetus, notably in Gabon, the Congo and Angola. There is still no commercial production in Zaïre, although several promising discoveries have been made; offshore production is planned to start in mid-1975. [297–298] Oil deposits are also reported to have been found off the coasts of Liberia, Cameroon and Ghana as well as in Chad and Niger, even if the estimated quantities are not yet sufficient to be financially feasible. [297, 299] The continental shelf off most of West Africa is narrow, but favourable geological characteristics of the coastal sedimentary basins continue down under the deep water of the continental slope. As a result, there has been greater interest by companies in acquiring ultra-deep offshore concessions off West Africa than anywhere else in the world. [300]

Of special interest is oil production in *Angola* because of the armed conflicts between the Portuguese forces and the liberation movements there. In 1973, production amounted to approximately 150 000 b/d (7.5 million t/y) most of which came from Cabinda Gulf Oil Company's numerous offshore fields in the enclaved province of Cabinda. However, it is believed that a decline may be registered towards the end of 1974, unless substantial new fields are discovered in the near future. [301]

In November 1973 it was reported in the London *Observer* that Cabinda Gulf had discovered a major new oil field west of Cabinda, comparable in size to some of those in the Arabian/Persian Gulf area. Cabinda Gulf was reported to have kept this information secret because it did not want to reveal its recent oil discoveries in an area where the MPLA guerillas were active. The contents of this report were later denied by Cabinda Gulf, however. [302]

Most of Cabinda Gulf's production has been exported, mainly to Canada, the United States, Trinidad and Japan. [303] A limited part has gone to Portugal (about 7 per cent of Cabinda Gulf's production), but this situation evidently changed during the Arab oil embargo against Portugal at the end of 1973, when some reports indicated that Portugal's share of Cabinda Gulf's exports rose to over 40 per cent, making Portugal the largest importer of Cabinda oil. [304]

In Angola proper, where production is at present limited to relatively small onshore fields operated by Belgian-owned Petrofina affiliates in cooperation with the Portuguese government (the joint company is called Petroangol), a number of new fields are being put into production, while a good deal of exploration work is being undertaken both on- and offshore by, among others, affiliates of Texaco and Compagnies Françaises des Petroles. [301]

Total oil reserves in Angola, including Cabinda, have been estimated to be 1.5 billion barrels (204 million tons).

South Africa is in a precarious situation as far as oil is concerned. The search for oil has so far been fruitless. In the eight years of prospecting up to 1973, 90 of the 91 holes were dry. Since South Africa is practically isolated from potential sources of oil in the rest of Africa, it has had to rely on imports, amounting to about 260 000 b/d (13 million t/y). The majority of the imported oil has stemmed from countries in the Middle East, notably Iran, but also Saudi Arabia and others.

During the 1973 oil embargo, deliveries of oil from OAPEC countries were discontinued. However, South Africa had long planned for such an embargo and vast strategic reserves had reportedly been stored in disused gold mines. In addition, South Africa possesses the largest coal reserves in the southern hemisphere and has mastered an advanced technology for the liquefaction and gasification of oil (see further appendix 3, p. 91). South Africa is therefore able to limit its reliance on imports of oil to 21 per cent of its total energy requirements. [305]

Rhodesia is in a much more vulnerable situation, although so far it has managed to maintain limited supplies — not least through cutting consumption by 50 per cent. [305]

The Middle East and North Africa

The most abundant oil reserves in the world are concentrated in certain areas of the Middle East, primarily in the Arabian/Persian Gulf region, and, to a lesser extent, North Africa, The Middle East holds about two-thirds of the world's known proved reserves of oil. About half of the world's reserves are in fact found in an area 800 km by 500 km around the Arabian/Persian Gulf, a small part of the Middle East and a minute fraction of the world's surface. [306] The prospects for the discovery of large-scale accumulations of oil in North Africa were never considered high until exploration was eventually successful in the Algerian Sahara in 1956. The Algerian discoveries drew attention to the potential of the neighbouring sedimentary basins and further spectacular success was soon achieved in Libya where, within a remarkably short time, a country with no known oil reserves had been transformed into one of the world's major oil producers and exporters.

The Gulf crude oil has high API gravities (that is, they are mainly light oils). They have high per-well productivity and are found in relatively shallow fields. They are therefore easily accessible and comparatively cheap to exploit. On the other hand, the generally high sulphur content of the crude oils and the distance of the producing fields from their markets are adverse economic factors when compared with other oil-producing areas, such as Libya and Nigeria.

So far, these countries, or rather the multinational oil companies operating in them, have been steadily increasing their output of oil. In 1973 the countries in the

Table 2A.3. Oil production, oil reserves and populations of the Middle East and North Africa regions: selected years, 1972–80

	Production mn barrels/day				Reserves bn barrels	Populations mn people
	1972	1973	1975[a]	1980[a]	1973	1972
Middle East						
Abu Dhabi	1.0	1.3	(2.3)	[4.0]	21.5	0.75
Iran	5.0	5.9	(7.3)	[10.0]	60.0	30.55
Iraq	1.5	2.0	(1.9)	[5.0]	31.5	10.07
Kuwait	3.0	2.8	(3.5)	[4.0]	64.0	0.91
Saudi Arabia	5.7	7.3	(8.5)	[20.0]	132.0	8.20
Other Arabian/Persian Gulf	1.8	1.8	(1.8)	[2.0]	38.9	8.77
Total Middle East	**18.0**	**21.1**	**(25.3)**	**[45.0]**	**347.9**	**59.25**
North Africa						
Algeria	1.1	1.1	(1.2)	[1.5]	7.6	15.27
Libya	2.2	2.2	(2.2)	[2.0]	25.5	2.08
Other North Africa	0.4	0.4	(0.4)	[0.4]	6.8	56.05[b]
Total North Africa	**3.7**	**3.7**	**3.8**	**[3.9]**	**39.9**	**7.34**
Total Middle East and North Africa	**21.7**	**24.8**	**29.1**	**[48.5]**	**387.8**	**66.59**

[a] The figures are based on those presented in 1973 by J.E. Akins of the US State Department. In Akins' survey (which, incidentally, gave no estimates for "Other North Africa" and therefore these figures were estimated to be unchanged) it was noted that projected future production figures were unrealistically high in some cases, particularly the 20 million b/d projected for Saudi Arabia in 1980. Iran's declared intention to level off production at 8 million b/d, and Kuwait's decision to keep production at 3 million b/d, were also noted. More recent events clearly indicate that projections may have to be revised downward even more drastically.

[b] Of which, 34.84 for Egypt.

Source: Akins, J.E., "The Oil Crisis: This Time the Wolf Is Here", Foreign Affairs, Vol. 51, No. 3, April 1973, pp. 479–80.

Middle East produced 21 million b/d (1045.2 million t/y) or 37 per cent of total world production. The countries in North Africa produced 3.6 million b/d (174.3 million t/y) or 6.3 per cent of the world total. In 1972 Saudi Arabia overtook Iran as the largest oil producer in the region. The production figures for 1973 for the main producers, the estimates of their production in 1975 and 1980, estimated reserves and the population of each country are indicated in table 2A.3.

Thus, the Middle East and North Africa are well able to support a large increase in production for several years to come, but in some cases their importance as PE-countries will probably begin to decline around the mid-1980s, given the trends so far in worldwide production and consumption. For some of the Arabian/Persian Gulf states, notably Saudi Arabia and Iran, prospects are brighter in view of their enormous proved reserves, which, in addition, are constantly being revised upwards. These two states are therefore likely to continue to provide the bulk of the expected increasing demand in Western Europe, Japan and the United States. A third supplier of significant potential for these countries is Abu Dhabi. Kuwait is not expected to increase its production above the present level. In Qatar only one field has been found onshore, and while prospects offshore are more encouraging, production will never be likely to rise above 1 million b/d. Iraq is still not very well explored and it is possible that the country may contain reserves second only to Saudi Arabia. Apart from the Soviet Union, some western countries are likely to benefit from the Iraqi oil supplies in the future. Finally, Libya and Algeria may play a relatively significant role in supplying very light, low sulphur crude oils, but the limited reserves will not allow these two countries to become massive exporters of oil. [12c] One thing all these countries have in common, however, is that they have no immediate oil supply problems with regard to their own economic and military security.

Finally, because of its special position, mention should be made of *Israel's* oil situation. Oil was discovered in Israel in 1955. Although about 35 wells in Israel are now producing, their output is only about 2 000 b/d (100 000 t/y). The current level of production in Egyptian territory occupied by Israel is about 100 000 b/d (5 million t/y), estimated to be worth roughly $80 million before the increased oil prices. Some estimates of potential production in Sinai ranged as high as 800 000 b/d (40 million t/y). [12d] During the winter of 1973–74, production in the Sinai oilfields temporarily declined not only due to the Arab-Israeli hostilities, but also because a misdirected Israeli missile started an offshore well blaze at the Abu Rhodeis oilfield (see further note 37). In peacetime, Israel consumes about 140 000 b/d (7 million t/y). [307] Israel obtains the balance from undisclosed sources, but Iran is reported to be a main supplier of this balance. Israel also exports some oil; Romania and Italy have been mentioned in the press as countries receiving Israeli oil.

The short blockade of the Bab-el-Mandeb strait during the 1973 October War prevented oil supplies coming to Israel via the port of Eilat, most of which is normally passed on through the pipeline to Ashkelon on the Mediterranean. Israel is said unofficially to have fuel stocks for four months. [308]

Appendix 3.

Energy sources

I. *Existing energy sources*

Wood

Wood is of negligible importance as far as its industrially directed use is concerned. However, because of the energy bound in plants through photosynthesis, forests and green plants can become an important source for the production of other energy forms (mainly methane gas). [309] (See page 101.)

Coal

Coal has had a long history of use. Mining of coal on a large scale began some 150 years ago when it became a prerequisite for the subsequent industrial revolution. About one-half of the total coal mined has been mined during the last four decades. Experts predict that the Earth's coal supplies are still sufficient to serve as a major source of industrial energy for two or three centuries and many of them regard a shift from an oil back to a coal economy as necessary within a fairly short time particularly as the technology for converting coal into synthetic crude oil and synthetic natural gas makes further progress. [310]

Such a shift, however, will be both expensive and difficult, as there are many problems associated with the use of coal. In the United States, which has abundant coal reserves, the chief reasons for a lack of expansion in the utilization of coal have been the following: (*a*) the low cost, convenience, and ready availability of natural gas; (*b*) the convenience of oil and the availability of low-sulphur oil; (*c*) the inability of power companies to obtain assured long-range supplies of the low-sulphur coal that will be required in the near future as clean-air regulations become effective; (*d*) uncertainty regarding practicability – the high cost of processes which could make the readily available high sulphur coals usable by removing sulphur from coal or from power plant stack gases; (*e*) increasingly stringent environmental and health-and-safety regulations affecting the mining of coal; and (*f*) recurrent transportation problems. However, these problems are likely to be mitigated by new techniques in sulphur removal, automation, underground gasification and so on. [311]

In addition to these new techniques, the abundant availability of coal in certain parts of the world also favours further exploitation. In general, it can be said that the major deposits of coal are fairly well documented on a worldwide basis. [312] These identified coal reserves plus additional hypothetical resources total about 15 200 billion tons, the distribution of which is indicated, continent by continent, in table 3A.1.

The Soviet Union, the United States and China have the largest coal deposits and between them account for some 88 per cent of total reserves; the United Kingdom, FR Germany, Australia, India, Canada, South Africa and Poland all have significant reserves and account for another 8 per cent of total reserves. [313]

Table 3A.1. World coal resources, 1973

Tons, bn

Region	Identified resources	Hypothetical resources	Estimated total resources
Asia and European USSR	6 300	3 600	9 900
Total USSR	*5 900*	*2 700*	*8 600*
North America	1 600	2 600	4 200
Europe	560	190	750
Africa	72	140	212
Oceania	54	63	117
Central and South America	18	9	27
Total coal resources	**8 600**	**6 600**	**15 200**

Source: Brobst, D.A. and Pratt, W.P., eds., *United States Mineral Resources*, Geological Survey Professional Paper No. 820 (Washington, 1973).

Oil

The more technically correct word for oil is rockoil or petroleum (from the Latin: *petra* = rock and *oleum* = oil).

Petroleum, in its raw state called crude oil or crude, is a mixture of hydrocarbons, containing varying amounts of sulphur and traces of other elements (vanadium, titanium). The sulphur content is quite significant since it determines the type of refining that is necessary.

For instance a "sweet" or "low-sulphur" crude oil is defined as one which contains less than 0.5 per cent by weight of sulphur compounds. With more sulphur than this the crude is termed "sour" or "high-sulphur" and a special refining operation is needed to remove the sulphur compounds, which would otherwise produce unacceptable corrosion and pollution effects. Most Middle East crudes are "sour" whereas those in Libya, Nigeria and Indonesia have low-sulphur contents.

Many types of hydrocarbons exist in crude oil, as a result of the large number of isomeric forms of the hydrocarbons (that is, compounds having the same molecular formula). Relatively few, however, actually occur in any significant proportions in any particular batch of crude oil.

Crude oil can be separated into different fractions. These fractions are known as refined products and they can be used for many well-known purposes. The word petroleum therefore covers a host of different compounds and mixtures ranging from ethane and methane, which are gases at normal temperatures, to solid derivatives or bitumen.

There are three main groups of hydrocarbons present in crude oil. The most important of these comprises the paraffins, whose basic formula is C_nH_{2n+2}. The second important group of hydrocarbons comprises the cycloparaffins or naphthenes with the molecular formula C_nH_{2n}. Crudes containing large proportions of naphthenes leave a residuum of asphalt on distillation. The third major hydrocarbon group comprises the benzenoid or aromatic hydrocarbons with the formula C_nH_{2n-6}, which usually makes up less than 10 per cent by volume of most crude oils.

In addition to being a primary fuel, petroleum gains further importance by also being the basis of the petrochemical industry. Petrochemicals may be defined as chemicals which can be produced in one step from a petroleum feedstock. From these primary products an enormous range of further products can be obtained, including solvents, detergents, plastics, agricultural chemicals, synthetic rubber, and a variety of other products.

One of the newest and most interesting applications of petroleum is as a raw material for protein synthesis. It has been found that many micro-organisms can live and develop in hydrocarbon mixtures and can produce protein concentrates which are analogues to animal proteins. From a ton of normal paraffins it is technically possible to obtain a ton of protein concentrate containing nearly 50 per cent protein. During the last few years, test production of petroleum-derived proteins, as for example high-protein yeast, has started in several countries. It seems likely that such proteins will be of increasing importance in feeding the future population of the world — perhaps initially as an animal feed ingredient and later as a means of fortifying conventional foodstuffs. [232b]

Petroleum is found, and is thought to be formed, in the rock which makes up the earth's crust. In fact its occurrence is generally limited to rock which has been formed at the bottom of ancient seas, so-called sedimentary rock. Furthermore, it exists only under quite specific conditions — an adequate thickness of bedrock, marine source rocks and reservoir rock to hold the oil and cap rock with suitable geometry to prevent its escape are required. Considering these specifications, the distribution of oil across the face of the Earth is, not surprisingly, extremely patchy and although approximately half the world's land area is occupied by sedimentary basins, only a very small number of these have provided reserves on a large scale. Half of the world's presently known oil reserves of 673 billion barrels are found in an area of 800 km by 500 km around the Arabian/Persian Gulf.

Because the hydrocarbons in liquid oil break down at higher temperatures, there are downward limits to exploration imposed by the gradually rising temperatures found at greater depths. It is therefore impossible to continue indefinitely to find additional oil by deeper drilling even where sediments are thick enough. The process of "cracking" comes into operation naturally and destructively. Every sedimentary basin has its individual downward limit, most commonly 4 000 — 10 000 metres. [306a]

In general, the rate at which a well can produce oil depends on a number of factors — the initial reservoir pressure, the porosity and permeability of the reservoir rock, the thickness of the productive section, the oil viscosity, the degree of gas saturation, and so on. In practice, however, wells seldom produce at their maximum capacities during the early history of an oilfield, but usually only at some fraction of this — the Maximum Economic Rate (MER) — which is calculated to result in the maximum output of primary oil over the lifetime of the oilfield, normally assumed to be 20 years. "Primary" oil is thus the volume of oil that can be produced at the surface by the unaided natural energy of the reservoir. It will amount to only a fraction of the original volume of oil-in-place; between 75—80 per cent of the original oil content of the reservoir will be left unproduced when the gas pressure has declined so much that it can no longer propel oil up the wells to the surface.

When the flow of primary oil has eventually terminated pressure, maintenance operations (for instance the introduction of high-pressure gas or water flooding) may be inaugurated to stimulate the "second recovery" process.

Processes which seek to recover additional hydrocarbons from a reservoir after the completion of normal primary and secondary production operations are called tertiary processes. They involve the use of vapour from various miscible solvents introduced into the reservoir (mostly hydrocarbon, carbon or water miscible methods) or the controlled combustion of some of the residual crude oil *in situ* to produce an advancing hot "front" or "thermal flood" to sweep out some of the residual crude oil still retained in the reservoir rock (thermal method). As much as 8 per cent of the current US production comes from oilfields where tertiary recovery techniques are being used. [313]

In most sedimentary basins on land, at least some exploration has already taken place. Although very large fields may remain to be discovered, they will most probably not be comparable to the Middle East area. It is true that the continental shelves are less known. The sea-bed is estimated to hold about 18 per cent of the world's proved reserves and it is generally accepted that a continuously increasing percentage of the world's petroleum energy will have to come from the sea-bed. [258] Although there are probably more areas comparable to the North Sea to be discovered — of enormous value to the owner nations — they are not likely to be as abundant or easily accessible as the Middle East area. The only area which has not yet been sufficiently explored to substantiate such estimates is Siberia, particularly northern Siberia and its continental shelf, which is the broadest in the world. [306a]

For more details on known oil reserves and their exploitation, see appendix 2.

Natural gas

Natural gas is a valuable energy source: it is cheap, versatile and fairly clean. Natural gas, like oil, is quite unevenly distributed throughout the world. The largest resources of gas are found in the Middle East, North Africa, the Soviet Union (where the sedimentary basins seem to hold the greatest potential for discovering further large quantities of natural gas) and the United States. It is most often found in the same sedimentary areas as those which yield oil (associated gas, in contrast to non-associated gas which occurs in structures which are essentially non oil-bearing); the ratio of the ultimate amount of natural gas to crude oil is almost constant (6 400 cubic feet per barrel oil). The potential energy — on a thermal basis — of all existing natural gas is difficult to estimate but it is considerably lower than that of oil — perhaps two-thirds of it. Thus, because its capacity to serve the industrialized world would last only a few decades, natural gas cannot substantially replace oil as an energy source. [314]

If some of the present plans for the exploitation of Siberian reserves are realized, the reserves of natural gas in the Soviet Union may become of significant importance not only to the Soviet Union, but also to the United States, Japan and a number of other countries. According to these plans, natural gas from the Tyumen fields is to be transported in pipelines to Murmansk, from where the liquefied form can be transported in special carriers to terminals on the east coast of the United States. Similarly, natural gas from the Yakutsk fields is to be transported to the port of Nakhodka (near Vladivostok) from where liquefied natural gas can be transported both to the west coast of the United States and to Japan.

Gas transport, however, is more expensive than the transport of oil. This is certainly true of the intercontinental transport of gas in liquefied form in special carriers, but it is also true of the transport of gas in pipelines since gas has a low thermal density compared with oil; a given pipeline can, for example, carry only one-fifth the quantity of gas on a thermal basis as it can oil.

The development of larger-diameter, high-pressure pipelines, made possible by better steels and improved welding techniques, will probably lower the costs of gas transport on the basis of economies of scale. Also, recent advances in submarine pipeline technology and laying techniques have enabled gas found under continental shelf sea-beds to be brought ashore from deep water and over long distances. Developments in this field have already facilitated, or will in future lead to the transport of gas by pipeline from the North Sea or across the Mediterranean. [306b]

Hydroelectric power

The utilization of hydroelectric power stands as the paramount example of the successful tapping of cheap and renewable energy. While most of the potential capacity for hydroelectric energy is already taken up in the industrialized world, Africa, South America and South East Asia still have great potential to develop, to the benefit of their own industrialization. Nevertheless, the share of hydroelectric power in most countries' energy budgets is limited to only a few per cent. Of total world primary energy, hydroelectricity provides only 2 per cent. [70b]

Nuclear energy (fission)

Nuclear power was once believed to be the solution to mankind's energy needs as fossil fuels gradually became depleted. To date, however, nuclear energy accounts for less than one per cent of total world energy production and for about 2.5 per cent of total world electricity generating capacity. Nuclear fission has doubtless many substantial advantages over traditional sources of energy. The basic materials for the production of nuclear energy, uranium and, for future use, thorium, are found in fair abundance in the Earth's crust.

But concern over the problems involved in the use of nuclear fission energy have increasingly caused rethinking as to the overall advantages of the use of such energy. The problem of long-term storage of radioactive wastes remains unsolved; plutonium with a half-life of 24 390 years is an outstanding example. There is also the problem of reactor operating hazards such as the chance of serious accidents or radioactive leakage. There are finally the problems associated with the safeguarding of fissionable materials used as reactor fuel, or produced in the reactors, and the risks that such material may be illegitimately diverted and used in the production of nuclear weapons or to achieve some coercive goal. (See reference [315].)

95

II. New energy sources and technologies

Oil shale

Oil shale is a fine-grained sedimentary rock occurring in large masses throughout the world, particularly in the United States, Brazil, Europe and West Africa. The Rocky Mountain area of the United States alone (Utah, Colorado and Wyoming) is estimated to hold enough oil shale to produce 1 400 billion barrels of oil — to be compared to the 43 billion barrels of present proved reserves of conventional crude oil in the United States and the world total of 673 billion barrels.

The oil shale rock contains a tar-like organic material called kerogen which is a solid and a mixture mainly of hydrocarbons. When heated to 450–600°C, kerogen releases vapour that can be converted to raw shale oil which can, in turn, be refined into petroleum products. The processing costs are high, however, since more than one and a half tons of rock must be processed for each barrel of oil produced. One estimation of the cost per barrel shale oil is $4.50–$5.50 which could serve as an indicator of the profitability of importing oil. Disposal of the processed rock, furthermore, could create great damage to the environment. [70c]

At the beginning of 1974, the US Department of the Interior offered six tracts of public land in Colorado, Utah and Wyoming for use in a prototype oil-shale leasing programme. The programme could provide up to 250 000 b/d by 1981, but more importantly it would test whether the estimated shale-oil reserves can be developed at acceptable economic and environmental costs. [316]

One of the most interesting aspects of the programme will be to test the *in situ* method, developed by the Occidental Petroleum Corporation, of extracting oil from shale. It consists, essentially, of blasting a chamber inside the rock formation and then injecting natural gas which, when burning at a very high temperature, separates the oil from the rock. This oil can be pumped out from the bottom of the chamber. The advantages of this method can be outlined as follows: it does not require, as in conventional methods, the use of great amounts of water; it produces low-sulphur oil; it requires lower capital investment and will have lower operating costs than conventional mining; and since the process takes place underground, it entails minimal surface disturbance and produces no above-ground dumps of shale after mining. [317]

Tar sand

Tars are viscous liquids rather than solids whose principal distinction from crude oil is that they cannot be extracted from the ground by means of wells. Tar sands are sands impregnated with heavy crude oil. The best known deposits of tar sand, and possibly the world's largest, are in the province of Alberta, Canada, particularly in northern Alberta (the Athabasca tar sands). Venezuela and Colombia also hold considerable reserves of tar sand.

There are estimated to be over 600 billion barrels of oil in the Athabasca sands, of which half may be ultimately recoverable. The amounts recoverable by presently available techniques, however, are much smaller, ranging from 26 billion to 80 billion barrels. By comparison, it can be noted that present proved reserves of conventional crude oil in Canada amount to 10 billion barrels and in the United

States to 43 billion barrels. Some limited production of oil from the tar sands in Athabasca is already taking place. By the mid-1980s, production targets of 1.5–2 million b/d are projected – to be compared with a 1973 production of conventional oil in Canada of 2.1 million b/d, or in the United States of 10.9 million b/d. The Canadian tar sands therefore do not seem to offer any realistic large-scale solution to the immediate (or short-range) energy problem on the North American continent, much less to any parts of the world outside this continent; but their long-range potential seems very favourable. Production of oil from tar sand furthermore involves high costs and the price of the final product has been estimated to be around $6 a barrel, a cost which seems much more reasonable in 1974 than it had previously in view of the huge price increases of conventional oil. [223] The same reasoning, of course, applies to oil shale as well.

Coal liquefaction and gasification

The production of oil from coal has been the subject of study throughout most of this century. Because of the easy availability of cheap crude oil during the last few decades, interest in processes for converting coal into oil has been minimal, however.

The Fischer-Tropsch synthesis process, developed during the 1930s, is the best known method for making *synthetic crude* (syncrude) from coal. Already during World War II there were commercial installations in Germany operating on the basis of this process. Since 1955, a plant at Sasolberg, South Africa, owned by the South African Coal, Oil and Gas Corporation has been using the same process to produce oil from coal at ever increasing efficiency. This plant is now reported to produce over 5 000 b/d, or 12–15 per cent of South Africa's total consumption of oil. [318–319]

In the Fischer-Tropsch process employed at Sasolberg, carbon monoxide and hydrogen react in the presence of a catalyst to yield a large range of pure petroleum hydrocarbons. The first step, the gasification of coal, involves the production of raw synthesis gas in Lurgi pressure gasifiers using steam and oxygen. This is then passed through a gas purification plant. The pure gas is the raw material for the two Fischer-Tropsch synthesis processes used at Sasolberg, the Arge (Lurgi) process and the Synthol process. The combination of the Arge and the Synthol processes yields the full range of products normally derived from crude oil and also a number of others usually manufactured in petroleum chemical plants, such as raw materials for the manufacture of synthetic ammonia fertilizers, butadiene, styrene, ethylene and so on. [306c]

Tentative estimates from US research suggest that the production of one ton of synthetic crude oil will require upwards of 2.5 tons of coal, with a maximum yield of perhaps three barrels of oil from a ton of coal. [70d]

The production of *synthetic natural gas* (SNG) from coal is, as a process, closely allied to syncrude production, both involving the same gasification and purification steps but differing from each other in the synthesis step – SNG requires only methane as the highest hydrocarbon.

There are five major processes for coal gasification, but only one, the West German Lurgi process, has been commercialized and then only in Europe. Several

SNG-from-coal plants using the Lurgi processing steps are planned for the USA, however. [70e, 320]

The development of coal gasification and liquefaction entails numerous engineering problems and substantial capital costs. Also, the health hazards and the environmental damage associated with the use of coal are still problems defying easy solution.

Nuclear energy (fusion)

A considerable amount of energy is released when atoms of heavy isotopes of hydrogen, deuterium or deuterium and tritium, fuse together. The energy released in the explosion of a hydrogen bomb is due to an uncontrolled fusion reaction. Over the past 20 years research has been concentrated on the controlled fusion reaction so that nuclear fusion reactors could be constructed. Such reactors would enormously increase the world's energy supply, since deuterium exists naturally in all water. Tritium, the heaviest hydrogen isotope, is made from lithium, an element at present found mostly in North America and Africa, and also in sea water.

To realize a nuclear fusion reaction, deuterium or deuterium and tritium mixtures must be heated to very high temperatures (of the order of tens of millions of degrees) so that the nuclei of the elements will have sufficient velocity to collide. At these temperatures, matter exists only in a state of full ionization, called plasma. Such hot plasma forms the new nuclear fuel for fusion reactors. Initially then, extremely high temperatures are produced and subsequently the hot plasma is confined within a restricted space for a long enough time to allow fusion to occur and produce a useful net gain of energy. At these temperatures special non-material containers must be devised to contain the hot plasma. Considerable research has been done on the use of intense magnetic fields for such confinement.

In recent years the use of lasers has been investigated as another method of bringing such nuclei together. Lasers have been utilized in order to compress pellets of deuterium to high densities. Calculations show that by such a method it would be possible to compress deuterium sufficiently for fusion to take place.

Unfortunately, reactors based on deuterium-deuterium or deuterium-tritium fuel cycles require the handling of large quantities of tritium, a radio-nuclide of hydrogen which decays by emitting beta-rays with a half-life of 12.3 years. This factor could constitute a potential health hazard. Moreover, a considerable amount of very high energy neutrons are produced as a result of the fusion reactions occurring within such fuel cycles. These neutrons interact with the structural materials of the reactor and the impurities within these materials produce new radioactive nuclides. The management of these radioactive substances will present problems similar to those encountered in the structural material of the fission reactors.

Because of the technical complexities associated with fusion energy, the costs involved in fusion research and development and large-scale application will be quite substantial. Opinions differ widely among scientists as to when commercial applications may become operable on a reasonable scale. Few predict that this will take place before the year 2000, and some doubt that fusion reactors will be commercially used until many decades later – if ever. [70f, 321]

Geothermal power

The Earth's heat is a potentially valuable source of energy, the use of which is still in its infancy. Nonetheless this resource has already been proved practical in some areas of the world (for example in California, Iceland, Italy and New Zealand).

The resource may be divided into three types: steam, hot water and hot rock. Although the first two are available in only a few, scattered locations, their usefulness is well-proven.

The hot rock method is being developed at, among other places, the US Atomic Energy Commission's Los Alamos Scientific Laboratory (LASL) in New Mexico. The basis of the method appears to be a hydrofracturing technique, where large cracks have to be created in a bed of hard rock in order to expose a large area of hot rock. Subsequently, a circulating flow of pressurized water is pumped down one well and up another to extract the heat from the rocks. At the top of the well the heat may be transferred to a secondary fluid before being delivered to a turbine.

According to many scientists, the Earth's heat could be used to generate substantial amounts of electricity in the near future, but estimates of the resources available vary widely and substantial technical problems remain to be solved. The prevailing scientific view seems to be that the total feasible potential from this source does not promise to be larger than a small fraction of the world's future power requirements. According to sources within the US Department of the Interior, geothermal energy could account for between one and 20 per cent of the nation's electrical generating capacity by the year 2000, with most estimates in the lower half of this range. [70g, 322–323]

Solar energy

Solar radiation is the most abundant form of energy available to man. Since sunlight is diffuse and intermittent, large areas will be required to collect sufficient amounts of energy and store it for the production of power. Despite its abundance, solar energy has only been exploited in a limited way. The technologies that would allow more widespread use are not commercially available, one reason being that solar energy systems so far have been more expensive to develop and use than other systems. For some applications, however, disparity in cost could rapidly disappear as solar technology improves and as costs of fossil fuel soar.

Solar energy could be converted to electricity by a thermal cycle, in which solar heat drives a turbine, or by the direct conversion of light to electricity by photovoltaic cells. One application where solar energy could be obtained almost as cheaply as conventional power is home heating, where the solar collector would be the roof of the house. Solar energy offers an ideal means of cooling buildings, because it operates most effectively at the very times that conventional systems impose peak loads on the electric supply, that is, when the sun is at its hottest. The most promising short-term application of solar energy, proponents agree, lies in this kind of heating and cooling of buildings.

Plans for more ambitious applications exist: for instance, to place gigantic solar collectors (satellite solar-power stations or SSPS) in geostationary orbits. Night and day they would collect the sun's rays and transfer their energy uninterruptedly back to earth as microwave beams which would be picked up and converted to electricity.

No one knows yet how extensive a contribution solar energy is destined to make to national energy budgets. Countries which have tropical meteorological conditions are obviously better suited for the use of solar energy than those which have not. There are large areas of the world (for example, the desert areas in West Africa) where a wide use of conventional-fuel-free and maintenance-free "solar pumps" could be of vital importance for water distribution.

In the case of the United States, a joint report in 1973 by the National Science Foundation and the National Aeronautics and Space Administration (NASA) suggested that by the year 2020 solar energy could provide 35 per cent of the heating and cooling in buildings, 30 per cent of the nation's gaseous fuels, 10 per cent of its liquid fuels and 20 per cent of its electrical needs. The report therefore proposed an outlay of $3.5 billion on solar energy research over the next 15 years. [70h, 324]

Wind energy

Wind energy — caused by variations in the rate at which sunlight warms the air — is generally considered the energy source closest to being operational. Wind power is a great resource but it has not recently been used on a large scale. Different ideas have been launched for such large-scale use, but the costs and hazards involved have not been well determined.

At one time windmills were used extensively in northern Europe and the USA to produce energy. Modern propellers turned by the wind could be used to drive generators to produce electricity. The electricity could be used conventionally or to produce hydrogen from water, particularly at offshore installations (see page 101).

The principal disadvantages of wind power are the variations in wind speed and direction, which cause electrical output to fluctuate and increase capital costs. This fluctuating output means that wind generators must either be employed with other generating systems or have access to storage facilities to match supply with demand. Capital costs of wind systems are now estimated to be two to five times as high as conventional generating plants. [325]

Tidal energy

Tidal energy is a renewable source, caused by the gravitational force of the moon and the sun. A bay or an estuary that is filled and emptied by tidal power can be dammed and the flowing water can be used to turn turbines.

Tidal power has not turned out to be as economically successful as conventional hydroelectric power, one reason being that the capital costs of tidal power plants have been considerably higher. Two full-scale modern tidal power plants have been built, one in France and the other in the Soviet Union. Only about 20 places in the world seem to have the right combination of tidal range and geography to make a tidal power scheme at all practicable. [70i]

100

Ocean thermal differences

This method uses the great temperature differences that exist between the surface and the ocean depths in tropical waters. It has, for instance, been calculated that, theoretically the heat being carried by the Gulf Stream through the Florida Straits between Miami and the Bahamas could be harnessed to produce all the electricity now used by the United States; the effects of such a tapping of energy from the Gulf Stream on the heat load it carries to the European continent are less known, however. The electricity produced by ocean thermal differences could be transmitted directly to the mainland or used to electrolyze sea water to produce hydrogen.

Much research must be done, however, to investigate such basic fields as those relating to the possible benefits of a floating *versus* a stationary installation, the type of engine best suited to the process and the uses of the generated electricity. Extensive transmission systems will be needed to carry the power from the offshore stations to the consuming centres. If the electricity is used instead to produce hydrogen, new pipelines will be needed to transport it. Capital costs are estimated to be equivalent to those of current nuclear reactors. [325−326]

Bioconversion

This term encompasses the use of organic materials, produced by photosynthesis, to make usable fuels. The principal methods now being studied include converting urban wastes and animal manure to methane gas, burning crops specially chosen for their fuel yield and using green plants and the enzyme hydrogenase to produce hydrogen from water.

The technology for bioconversion systems is not generally as well demonstrated as that for wind power. Most advanced is the production of methane from organic wastes. Feasibility studies are being made on potential crop yields, while basic research still remains to be done on producing hydrogen through photosynthesis.

Bioconversion processes suffer from relatively low efficiencies. According to critics, even if satisfactorily developed, they could supply only a small percentage of the world's power needs.

Nevertheless, it has been pointed out that the energy value of the refuse generated every year in the United States alone is equivalent to 290 million barrels of low-sulphur fuel oil, or 800 000 b/d, the equivalent of 5 per cent of the present US domestic consumption. [325, 327]

Hydrogen

Some of the primary energy forms mentioned above (mainly nuclear and coal power and possibly solar power) could serve as a valuable source of a secondary general-purpose fuel, namely hydrogen fuel. It should, however, be noted that the production of hydrogen fuel entails the use of large amounts of primary energy and the high cost of manufacture by electrolysis makes it uncompetitive as a fuel. Current world production of hydrogen is about 20 million tons a year.

A most important characteristic of hydrogen is its versatility in being able to serve both electrical and other energy demands although the overall cost of electricity produced from hydrogen is comparatively high due to the high costs of transmission and distribution. It can be substituted for petroleum and coal in almost all industrial processes which require a reducing agent, such as in steel factories and other metallurgic operations. Hydrogen can also be easily connected to a variety of fuel forms, such as methanol, ammonia and hydrazine. Hydrogen can be transported easily and stored without much difficulty, enabling it to be used for aircraft and road vehicle propulsion. The combustion of hydrogen is generally not considered to result in polluting emissions, since there is only one end-product — water. This has been questioned by some scientists, however, who have pointed out that this reaction favours the production of hydrogen peroxide (H_2O_2) which, if produced in large quantities could become a potential hazard to the environment. [328]

A considerable amount of research is therefore required in hydrogen production before the use of hydrogen energy can be made economically attractive. It must again be emphasized that the use of hydrogen fuel does not solve the dependence on some other primary energy sources. Among methods studied to produce hydrogen energy, one deserves special mention; use of some chemical reactions at very high temperatures can be made for synthesizing hydrogen from water. One method of obtaining the required high temperature is the use of high-temperature nuclear reactors (HTR). It is based on the rise of nuclear process heat from high temperature reactors in order to drive novel high-temperature chemical reactions. Research on this method has been undertaken at, for instance, Euratom's joint research centre at Ispra. In addition, high-temperature gas-cooled reactors (HTGRs) will eventually be built to produce hydrogen gas and other secondary fuels such as gasified coal, and it is thought that fast breeder reactors, while generating electricity, will have enough breeding gain to sustain the HTGRs.

A significant amount of operating experience has been acquired with hydrogen fuel cells; such cells have already been used successfully in automotive systems. [329–330]

Methanol

Methanol, CH_3OH, is another synthetic secondary fuel, which has been described as being superior to hydrogen in many ways and as providing an especially attractive alternative fuel to gasoline. It shares many of the virtues of pure hydrogen. It can be made from most other fuels — from petroleum, coal, oil shale, wood, natural gas, or gas obtained from farm and municipal waste — so that a methanol economy would be flexible and could draw from one or another energy source as conditions change. Methanol is easily stored in conventional fuel tanks and can be shipped in tank cars, tank trucks, and tankers; it can be transported in oil and chemical pipelines. Of greatest importance is the fact that up to 15 per cent of methanol can be added to commercial gasoline in cars now in use without it being necessary to modify the engines. As compared with the use of gasoline alone, this methanol-gasoline mixture results in improved economy, lower exhaust temperature, lower emissions, and improved performance. Furthermore, methanol can be burned cleanly for most other fuel needs, and it is especially suited for use in fuel cells for generating electricity.

The first, immediately apparent drawback of methanol is that facilities for producing it in adequate quantities to take the pressure off petroleum have not existed for the past half century; that is, from the time that the latter almost completely displaced it as a major fuel. There are also minor technical drawbacks associated with mixed fuel storage and gas-conversion energy loss; but the main obstacles to vastly expanded methanol production and use appear to be bureaucratic and politico-economic. Society is reluctant to accommodate the introduction of new fuels, shortages notwithstanding. [331–332]

Appendix 4.

Recent arms transfers to the Middle East

I. *Egypt*

Two main factors have influenced Egypt's arms procurement policy: the desire to be a modern, independent nation playing a leading role in the Arab world, and the conflict with Israel. Egypt has no indigenous arms industry of any major significance.

In the early 1950s, the Western powers used their capacity to supply or withhold arms as a lever to persuade Egypt to join a Western alliance. Their pressure led Egypt, in 1955, to sign an arms deal with Czechoslovakia. The deal marked the end of the Western monopoly over arms supplies to the region. Since then, Egypt has become almost exclusively reliant for arms on socialist countries (mainly the Soviet Union).

After the setbacks suffered in the June War of 1967, Egypt felt the need to replace equipment which had been destroyed or captured by the Israelis. Of its major Soviet-delivered weapons, Egypt had lost most of its MiG fighters, all of its Tu-16 medium bombers and Il-28 light bombers and the large majority of its tanks. By the second half of 1968, Egypt confirmed the completion of its replacement programme. Deliveries comprised mainly the same types of weapon as those lost. In addition, Egypt received a number of Su-7 supersonic fighter-bombers and improved radar equipment from the Soviet Union.

Throughout 1968 and 1969, fighting across the Suez Canal intensified, precipitating new arms supplies to both Egypt and Israel. Most of the Egyptian acquisitions were designed to improve its air defence system. A new military assistance agreement was signed in August 1968. Additional Su-7s, MiG-21s and SA-2 "Guideline" missiles were supplied during 1969. In addition, Egypt received about 800 T-54/55 tanks during this period.

The Israeli offensive against SA-2 batteries at the end of 1969 and in January 1970 prompted the Soviet Union to agree to supply new defensive equipment to Egypt, in particular the SA-3 "Goa" anti-aircraft missiles, useful against low flying aircraft. In addition, a number of MiG-21 "Fishbed Js", a radar-equippped, all-weather version for night interception, were delivered. The effectiveness of the air defence system thus obtained — believed to be partly Soviet-operated — brought a halt to Israeli deep penetration raids into the Nile Valley, but raids across the Suez Canal continued until a temporary ceasefire began on 7 August 1970.

On 27 May 1971, the Soviet Union formalized its relations with Egypt with the signing of a Soviet-Egyptian Treaty of Friendship and Cooperation, pledging military assistance to Egypt for the next 15 years. In October 1971 President Sadat visited the Soviet Union. The joint communiqué issued at the end of this visit implied a Soviet promise of further military aid, but there was no immediate increase in arms supplies to Egypt. It is likely that the MiG-25 "Foxbat" fighters and perhaps the Tu-16 "Badger" medium bombers, which appeared in Egypt during the autumn of 1971, were exclusively operated by Soviet military personnel and only on reconnaissance missions.

Soviet aid to the Middle East underwent a dramatic change in 1972. Since 1967, the Soviet Union had attempted to maintain a delicate balance in the Middle East with the object of supporting the Arab states in their conflict with Israel and at the same time preventing the outbreak of a new war and lessening tension in the area. This policy meant that, on the one hand, the Soviet Union supplied Egypt with a variety of equipment, accounting for 75 per cent of Soviet major arms exports to the Middle East in 1965–71, and on the other hand, excluded specifically offensive weapons, despite repeated requests for such weapons by Egypt. It was this Soviet reluctance which prompted the Egyptian move of July 1972, in which the Soviet advisers and experts who had been assisting in military training and operations – generally assumed to number between 15 000 and 20 000 – were asked to leave the country, a move which temporarily stemmed the flow of major new Soviet weapons. Indeed, the Soviet Union also withdrew a number of its defensive missiles. However, considerable numbers of the MiG-21s, along with SA-3 missiles and anti-aircraft guns, were left behind.

During the autumn of 1972, Egyptian-Soviet relations improved again, and new arms deliveries were subsequently started, when Moscow delivered more than 100 modern T-62 tanks and over 60 SA-6 missiles. Another missile delivered during this period, which also made its first appearance on the Arab-Israeli battlefield during the 1973 October War, was the SA-7 "Strela" infantry-operated missile. The Egyptian losses during this war were substantial, but these have partly been made up by replacements from the Soviet Union.

During the spring of 1974, President Sadat initiated a sudden and novel move in Egypt's arms procurement policy. On 18 April he announced that Egypt had decided to end more than 18 years of almost exclusive reliance on Soviet arms supplies and to seek armaments from other sources. President Sadat declared that he had made his decision after the Soviet Union had failed in the last six months to act on his request for arms deliveries. However, he did not name the countries that he hoped would become new suppliers. [333] The US Secretary of Defense reacted to this statement a few days later by indicating that the United States would examine the possibility of selling arms to Egypt. [334] According to later reports, however, such arms transfers will not take place. [335] It seems clear that whatever country Egypt chooses as a substitute arms supplier, it will face great problems in integrating new types of weapons and undertaking the necessary retraining of personnel within its present military organization.

II. *Israel*

Israel's motives for having a strong defence are more or less self-explanatory, given the fact that it has been under external threat and military pressure since its very creation. As a relatively advanced industrial state, Israel has been able to build up an armaments industry of its own. It is self-sufficient in small arms and claims to be able to produce 25 per cent of its total weapon requirements. It can overhaul, maintain and repair most of its weapons, and Israeli engineers have been very successful in modifying weapons purchased or captured from abroad (for example, the T1-67 from Soviet-built T-54/55 tanks captured in the 1967 June War). The domestic defence effort has intensified since the June War, but Israel is nevertheless still dependent on imports for major items of equipment.

Since 1954, Israel's two main suppliers have been France and, later, the United States. With the end of the Algerian War, however, France began making persistent attempts to improve its relations with the Arab countries. During the 1967 June War France imposed an arms embargo on the Middle East, which primarily affected Israel. Thus Israel has become reliant mainly on the United States. The French embargo, made total in 1969, has been progressively lifted, but no major items have been supplied.

Before 1965, the United States had preferred to leave the supply of Israel's imported arms to European nations for fear of jeopardizing relations with Arab states. The only exceptions to this policy were some Hawk missiles supplied to Israel in 1963. The deal was justified by the argument that an imbalance had been created by the movement of weapons from the Soviet Union into the area, particularly of Tu-16s.

In early 1966, the United States agreed to supply A-4 Skyhawks to Israel. The sale was defended on the grounds that Israel had failed to find equivalents of the required sophistication in European markets and that it needed the aircraft "to avoid serious arms imbalances that would jeopardize area stability" — the kind of argument which was to be repeated several times during the ensuing years.

In June 1967, the USA imposed an embargo on the Middle East which was lifted in October for Israel and certain selected Arab countries. Prime Minister Eshkol visited the United States in January 1968, and requested F-4 Phantoms and additional Skyhawks. The US government was reported to be delaying its decision for several reasons, one being that it was trying at this time to come to some agreement with the Soviet Union for a settlement on arms limitation in the area. Nevertheless, in November 1968 a deal was announced for 50 Phantoms and 25 additional Skyhawks.

In September 1969, Prime Minister Golda Meir visited the United States and requested additional Phantoms and Skyhawks as well as other military equipment. No decision on the aircraft was made, but it appears that six Phantoms shot down during the bombing raids on the Suez Canal in 1970 were replaced from the US Air Force inventory.

When US Secretary of State Rogers put forward his proposal for a temporary ceasefire in June 1970, the United States agreed at the same time to supply military assistance worth $500 million to Israel. The agreement was announced in October 1970 and authorized by the US Congress in January 1971. The aid package included 36 additional Phantoms and Skyhawks (18 of each), Shrike air-to-surface missiles and Walleye glide bombs for use against SAMs, additional Hawks, 180 tanks (including M-60 main battle tanks), helicopters and other equipment. The aid package was followed by the reopening of the Jarring peace talks, which had been suspended since March 1969. When the Jarring talks broke down again in June 1971, the United States suspended further deliveries of such military aircraft as Skyhawks and Phantoms to Israel.

On 15 November 1971, the US administration declared that the balance in the

Middle East was unchanged. It was not until Prime Minister Meir's visit in December that the United States agreed to proceed with the deliveries of 80 Skyhawk bombers and, a few weeks later, of 42 additional Phantoms. Deliveries took place during 1972 and 1973.

In March 1973, Prime Minister Meir once again visited Washington. The final agreement on Israel's new arms purchases was not settled until a few months later. In June it was reported that the United States had agreed to sell 48 additional Phantom and 36 Skyhawk fighter-bombers.

During the 1973 October War the Israeli Air Force suffered heavy losses. According to estimates by the US Department of Defense, the Israeli Air Force lost 105 aircraft including 52 A-4 Skyhawks and 27 F-4 Phantoms. It has been reported, however, that the United States more than made up Israeli air losses in its air-lift resupply effort in October. The Soviet anti-tank missiles are believed to have been the major cause of the Israeli tank losses of over 800.

III. *Syria*

The political background to Syria's arms procurement policy is extremely complex. The dominant theme has been the Arab-Israeli conflict, since Syria has been actively hostile towards Israel from the beginning. In addition to meeting Syria's military requirements, the acquisition of arms has also had an important political function, namely, as the decisive element in the trials of strength between the different factions contending for the leadership of the country.

From 1954 onwards, Syria developed close ties with the Soviet Union. After some fluctuations, their relations were strengthened, particularly in the middle of the 1960s. A new arms supply agreement was signed in 1966, which was reported to be worth $200 million and to include MiG-21s and SA-2 "Guideline" missiles.

During the 1967 June War, Syria lost over half its air force and substantial quantities of army equipment. After the war, Syria's losses, mainly of MiG-17s, MiG-21s and T-54 tanks, were all replaced by the Soviet Union. However, by 1969 a rift had appeared in the Soviet-Syrian relationship. The same year it was reported that Syria had received a gift of Chinese arms worth between $10 million and $15 million. Later that year, however, a new arms deal worth $200 million was concluded between Syria and the Soviet Union. The deliveries included MiGs, Su-7 fighters and helicopters. A new arms agreement with the Soviet Union was signed in July 1972, and a substantial amount of weaponry was delivered to Syria throughout the autumn of that year. Because of the strain in the relationship between Egypt and the USSR at that time, Syria succeeded Egypt as the foremost ally of the Soviet Union.

In the spring of 1973, it was reported in the press that the Soviet Union had also delivered the highly effective shoulder-fired SA-7 "Strela" anti-aircraft missile. There were also reports of additional deliveries later in the spring, consisting of 40 MiG-21 jet fighters, an unspecified number of SA-2 and SA-3 missiles and two mine-sweepers. In all, Israel claimed to have destroyed 60 Syrian aircraft during the period since the June War of 1967: 48 MiG-21s with the remainder made up of MiG-17s and Su-7s.

The Syrian losses during the October War of 1973 were substantial, but the Soviet Union replaced these, both during and after the war.

Unlike Egypt, Syria will reportedly not seek to diversify the sources of its arms supplies — the Soviet Union will continue to be its major supplier of arms. [336]

IV. *Jordan*

The Arab-Israeli conflict, and particularly pressures from the large numbers of Palestinians in Jordan, have been the major factors in the shaping of Jordan's military procurement policy.

The United States assumed the responsibility for providing military aid to Jordan in 1957. On the whole it has been reluctant to supply arms, however, because of its relationship with Israel. On successive occasions, when it appeared that the monarchy might either be overthrown or at least be giving way to pressure from the Palestinians and from other Arab states to acquire weapons from the Soviet Union, the United States has agreed to increase arms deliveries. These deliveries have usually been accompanied by increased deliveries to Israel as well.

After the 1967 June War, Jordan's traditional suppliers, the United States and the United Kingdom, were initially unwilling to replace Jordanian losses. But repeated threats to turn to the Soviet Union for arms, combined with increased internal pressures, finally led to substantial British and US arms supplies. The USA started delivering the long awaited F-104 Starfighter aircraft in 1968, together with Patton tanks and other equipment, while the UK delivered additional Hunter aircraft and Centurion tanks. The UK also agreed to supply Tigercat surface-to-air missiles in a $36 million deal financed by Saudi-Arabia.

In 1970, civil war broke out between the army and the Palestinians. The US response followed the pattern of its behaviour in previous Jordanian crises. The US Sixth Fleet was deployed off Jordan and US troops in FR Germany were flown to Turkey. After the conflict, the USA agreed to an additional $30 million in aid for fiscal year 1971 and a $200 million military aid package for the next five years. When King Hussein visited Washington in February 1973, an agreement was made that the United States would supply Jordan with some 24 F-5E supersonic fighters.

In the 1973 October War Jordanian forces took part on a limited scale only, suffering losses of probably not more than 20 tanks.

V. *Iraq*

Supplies of major weapons to Iraq have been substantial. Some of the factors affecting Iraq's demand for weapons have been purely political and connected with that country's ambition to wield influence within the Arab world. Another factor has been Iraq's indirect participation in the conflict with Israel; although it did not take an active part in the 1967 June War, it lent aircraft to Jordan and later stationed troops in Jordan and Syria. Since 1961, Iraq has also been fighting an internal war — broken by an occasional armistice — against the Kurds in northern Iraq, who demand autonomy. The peace settlement with the Kurds announced in March 1970 lasted no more than four years. Finally, Iraq's interests in the

Arabian/Persian Gulf area have been a factor affecting arms supplies. In this context, Iraq's territorial conflicts with Kuwait and Iran should be mentioned, and also Iraq's reported deliveries of arms to insurgents in Dhofar in Oman. In most of the negotiations with potential arms suppliers — as indeed in most of Iraq's foreign relations with major powers — the question of oil has played an important role.

The pattern of supplies has changed considerably over the last 20 years. Until 1958, when the Iraqi monarchy was overthrown, Iraq continued to rely on Western countries for arms. After 1958 the relationship with the supplier depended on which faction of the Baath Party was in power. A series of coups, assassinations and other contingencies led Iraq to veer between cooperation and rivalry with the United Arab Republic, and between the UK and the Soviet Union as favoured arms suppliers. In 1970, France entered the picture as a weapon supplier (supplying armoured cars). In the preceding years, France and Iraq held parallel negotiations about the sale of Mirage aircraft in exchange for exploration and exploitation rights for French oil companies in the Rumailia oil fields. However, in April 1968 it was announced that Iraq would develop these oil fields itself, and the Mirage negotiations seem to have been suspended a few months later, when General Aref was overthrown by General Bakr.

During the past few years Iraq has bought its weapons mainly from the Soviet Union. A treaty of friendship including provisions for military cooperation was signed between the two countries on 9 April 1972. Following a visit to the Soviet Union by President Bakr in September that year, it was announced that the two countries had "agreed on special measures to further strengthen the defence potential of the Iraq Republic and to promote the preparedness to fight of the Iraqi forces". This coincided with the deterioration in relations between Egypt and the USSR in the summer of 1972.

Only a few days before the outbreak of the 1973 October War, there were reports in the press, based on information from the US Department of Defense, that the Soviet Union had sent about 12 Tu-22 Blinder supersonic jet bombers to Iraq. If this information is correct and if the bombers are to stay in Iraq, neither of which is certain, it would be the first time that the Soviet Union has exported aircraft of this type.

Iraq took part in the 1973 October War with aircraft, tanks and troops. Its losses were estimated to have amounted to 21 Hunters and MiG-21s and 125 tanks.

VI. *Saudi Arabia*

Saudi Arabia was one of the few Arab countries to escape European rule. The monarchy was strongly traditionalist and, until recently, relied on troops made up of Bedouin tribesmen for defence and support. In the past seven years, Saudi Arabia has vastly expanded and modernized its armed forces; of particular significance is the sophisticated air defence system which has been developed.

The increased demand for weapons in Saudi Arabia has depended on several main factors. First, the expansion of the oil industry created strong pressures for modernization, primarily affecting the armed forces. Second, Saudi Arabia is concerned with protecting its interests in the Arabian/Persian Gulf area, where it has been involved in a number of disputes including a long-standing dispute with the Yemen, resulting in Saudi Arabian support for the Royalists during the Yemeni Civil War. Another dispute, now more or less resolved, arose from Saudi Arabia's claim to the Buraimi Oasis, which is jointly possessed by Abu Dhabi and Oman. Third, Saudi Arabia is committed to the Arab cause in the conflict with Israel; Saudi troops have been stationed in Jordan since the 1967 June War and have been involved in fighting with Israel. Finally, Saudi Arabia has a special position as guardian of the Muslim faith and custodian of the holy city of Mecca, which is one reason why Saudi Arabia has from time to time competed with Egypt for leadership of the Islamic world. The traditional monarchy's animosity towards communism is also a factor to be taken into account.

Saudi Arabia's main arms suppliers are the United Kingdom and the United States. The United States had base rights in Saudi Arabia until 1962. Relations with these two countries have periodically been under strain, however, mainly because of US support for Israel. The past few years have seen Saudi Arabia establishing closer military relations with France and Pakistan.

At one stage in 1963, Saudi Arabia expressed the need for a sophisticated air defence system to protect the supply lines to the Royalists in the Yemen, and after intricate negotiations lasting two years, the Saudi Arabians agreed upon British Lightning fighters and US Hawk missiles.

The British deal was part of an offset arrangement with the United States, because Britain needed these extra exports to balance major British purchases of the F-111 from the US aircraft industry. The total deal with Saudi Arabia was worth around $300 million and was facilitated by easy credit terms. It took several years to deliver and install the equipment and to train Saudi Arabians to operate it. In 1966, the UK agreed to an interim deal, known as "Operation Magic Carpet": second-hand aircraft and missiles operated unofficially by British personnel.

Saudi Arabian relations with the United Kingdom and the United States deteriorated after the 1967 June War. In 1968 Saudi Arabia unexpectedly purchased armoured cars from France, rather than from the UK. At the same time it was announced that British mercenary pilots would be replaced by Pakistanis. Already in 1967, Pakistan had signed an agreement in which it undertook to train troops and provide technical assistance.

In 1968 Saudi Arabia ordered helicopters from France and Italy and later placed large orders with the United Kingdom, including patrol boats and hovercraft. From 1973 on, Saudi Arabia received about 50 Northrop F-5 fighters and trainers from the United States (of which 30 are of the F-5E version), worth about $130 million in all. Orders for another 70 F-5s, to be delivered over a three-year period, are anticipated, but no formal agreement has yet been concluded.

In May 1973, Saudi Arabia signed a contract with the UK worth around $630 million, to be paid over five years. Under the agreement, buildings and infrastructure, air and technical training, spares and maintenance will be provided to keep the air defence system fully operative.

Also in May 1973, it was disclosed that Saudi Arabia had opened discussions with the United States for the purchase of what was originally reported to be military equipment worth $500 million consisting of ships, military communications equipment and training assistance. Later the actual quantity of the purchases of F-4 Phantoms discussed was referred to by US officials as only "a handful or two". In July it was reported that France was also very much in the picture, offering to sell its Mirage-3E. French Defence Minister Galley visited Saudi Arabia in September and on 1 October *Le Monde* reported that Saudi Arabian purchases of 38 Mirage-3Es were practically finalized. No official confirmation was then given, however.

Amid a flurry of unclear and contradictory statements, it was reported in the beginning of January 1974 that France and Saudi Arabia had concluded what seemed to be an "arms-for-oil" agreement in December 1973, in accordance with which Saudi Arabia was to supply France with nearly 200 million barrels (27 million tons) of crude oil during a period of three years (40 million barrels in 1974, 65 million barrels in 1975 and 90 million barrels in 1976). In French part of the deal was reported to be the 38 Mirage planes mentioned above, but also an unspecified quantity of missiles, AMX-30 tanks, frigates and minesweepers. Concurrently there were reports that a more important agreement was also under way and discussed during French Foreign Minister Jobert's visit to Saudi Arabia at the end of January 1974. According to this proposal, France was reportedly prepared to provide equipment, ground services and technical know-how for Saudi Arabia's industrial development in exchange for the guaranteed supply of 5 900 million barrels (800 million tons) of crude oil over 20 years at a steady rate of 800 000 b/d (40 million t/y). [337–341]

On 9 June 1974 the United States and Saudi Arabia signed a wide-ranging military and economic agreement that both sides said "heralded an era of increasing close cooperation between the two countries". Under the terms of the agreement, two joint commissions were established: one on economic cooperation and the other on Saudi Arabia's military needs. The military commission will review programmes already under way for modernizing Saudi Arabia's armed forces in the light of this country's defence requirements, especially as they relate to training. At the signing of the agreement, US officials said that they hoped that the new accord would provide Saudi Arabia with incentives to increase oil production and would serve as a model for economic cooperation between the United States and other Arab States. [342]

The current US presence in Saudi Arabia consists of a growing military and aerospace involvement in the country. The evolving activities are spearheaded by the US military services, partly through resident military assistance groups, and by several aerospace companies, with the encouragement or acquiescence of the US military. In addition to the developments indicated above, the US Air Force is assuming an active role in advising the Saudi government and assisting US companies in participation in a possible new Saudi air defence system, which would supplement the air defence network purchased from the UK. The US Navy is actively advising the Saudi government on ships, facilities, operations and training for an expanded Saudi Navy to protect the country's long and exposed coastline along the Red Sea and the Arabian/Persian Gulf. [343]

According to a US Department of Defense representative, five US firms with defence-related contracts operated in Saudi Arabia in mid-1973 (Lockheed, Raytheon, Bendix, AVCO and Northrop) employing about 700 civilians. [114d] *Aviation Week & Space Technology* reports that US aerospace companies employ an estimated 2 500–3 500 in Saudi Arabia working under contracts to the Saudi government for various kinds of operations, maintenance and training on military and civil aerospace equipment. In addition to its support contract for radar and navigational aids, Lockheed plays a key role, providing various kinds of facilities and technical guidance for Saudi aviation. [343] Another company, Raythenon, has 60 US and 50-60 Saudi nationals running an air defence training school and performing basic Hawk missile system maintenance. Moreover, in April 1974 it was reported that Raytheon had won a $200 million contract for the modernization of Saudi Arabia's aerial defence missile system. [344]

VII. *Kuwait*

Kuwait became a fully independent state in 1961. The same year an agreement was signed with the United Kingdom under which the latter undertook to assist the Kuwaiti government if it requested such assistance. The agreement was annulled in 1968, following the announcement that the UK would withdraw from the Arabian/Persian Gulf by 1971.

During the 1950s and 1960s the Kuwaiti armed forces grew rapidly. One reason given for this was that Kuwait had to build up its own defence to compensate for the British withdrawal. A second was that Kuwait faced external threats, mainly from Iraq. A third reason could be the intention of the traditional rulers, the Sabah clan, to use the army to consolidate its hegemony, particularly in view of the large number of foreigners living as immigrants in Kuwait. Finally, the defence build-ups in Iran and Saudi Arabia and the ambitions of these countries in the area must also have spurred the arms build-up in Kuwait.

An air force was established in 1961, and in 1966 Kuwait ordered Lightnings armed with missiles from the United Kingdom, all of which were delivered by 1969. Kuwait also purchased a number of armoured vehicles, patrol boats and anti-tank missiles. In 1969, it went on to purchase Italian helicopters.

In May 1973, there were reports that Kuwait was expected to order from the United States more than $500 million worth of military matériel, such as 160 M-60 tanks, 32 F-8 Crusader fighters, about 1 800 TOW anti-tank guided missiles, more than 150 anti-aircraft missiles of the improved Hawk type, and some light helicopters. Official US representatives also disclosed that the United States had received inquiries from Kuwait regarding the willingness of the USA to sell the F-4 Phantom, a matter which was being actively considered by the US administration. This arms deal would considerably augment the equipment of Kuwait's current armed forces. There has been no confirmation of such a deal since those reports, however.

Concurrently, both the French Mirage F-1 and the Anglo/French Jaguar were under consideration. After a visit to Kuwait by French Foreign Minister Jobert in January 1974, it was reported that an arms agreement had been concluded between France and Kuwait according to which France was to provide 16 Mirage fighters, a number of helicopters and other French weapons. [345] Later the Minister of Defence of Kuwait announced that a contract for the purchase of French helicopters had been signed. [346] Finally, in April it was officially announced that Kuwait and France had signed a contract for a number of Mirage F-1s (assumed to be about 30). Deliveries of this plane will take place in 1974 and 1975. The Defence Minister of

Kuwait was reported to have stated that the agreement had been concluded on a government-to-government basis with no restrictions whatsoever on Kuwait's right to use the planes as it deemed fit. He also said that the Mirage F-1 was the most highly perfected military aircraft presently in service, that it could carry out offensive operations and that it was equipped with air-to-air and air-to-surface missiles. According to Kuwaiti press reports, the total value of the deal with France amounted to $85 million. [347]

It was reported in the press in January 1974 that the Defence Minister of Kuwait had commented to the effect that Kuwait was prepared to buy weapons from East European countries also, if it suited his country's needs. [348]

VIII. *Iran*

Iran has received more major weapons since 1950 than any other Middle East country, except Egypt. In recent years there has been a rapid increase both in defence spending and in imports of major weapons. The value of major weapon imports has grown from a yearly $8.5 million in the early 1960s to an average of $156 million a year from 1968 on. The main supplier has been the United States.

There are various explanations for Iran's high defence expenditures and large supply of armaments: (a) the armed forces play an important role in structuring and developing the society; (b) US military aid has been given high priority because of Iran's pro-Western policy and strategic situation; (c) Iran has been, and still is, at odds with some of the other countries in the Arabian/Persian Gulf area; and (d) since the United Kingdom announced its withdrawal from the area, Iran has expressed a very keen interest in playing a dominant role in the Arabian/Persian Gulf area.

Up to the mid-1960s, Iran was mainly dependent on US military supplies. Major items of equipment supplied included F-84 fighters and M-47 Patton tanks. By the mid-1960s, the Shah was beginning to make attempts to reduce his dependence on the West. In 1967 an arms deal with the Soviet Union was announced, which consisted of $100 million worth of "non-sensitive" military equipment – armoured troop carriers, trucks and anti-aircraft guns. The deal was a barter arrangement and the Iranian component consisted primarily of supplies of natural gas after the completion of a Soviet-built pipeline. The Iranian-Soviet arms deal was a significant event and a clear gesture of independence, since it was the first time that a country actively participating in a Western military alliance had acquired Soviet arms. Since then, however, no further Iranian-Soviet arms deals have been reported. The negotiations with the Soviet Union were probably the main factor in increasing the readiness of the United States to supply arms and in 1966 the United States agreed to supply F-4 Phantoms, of which the first 32 were delivered in 1968–69.

In 1968 the United States agreed to supply $100 million of arms on easy credit terms. The request was to be reconsidered every year. During the next few years, Iran purchased considerable amounts of military equipment, including British fast frigates and hovercraft. A vast helicopter build-up was also undertaken. For its air defence system, Iran has acquired the British Rapier low-level surface-to-air missile system at a cost of $113 million. In addition, a multimillion dollar radar contract was signed with Marconi radar systems. The system is said to be among the most powerful and advanced ever produced.

In 1970, Iran began a five-year plan for the modernization of its forces. Under this programme, Iran received 32 Phantoms and 30 Lockheed C-130 Hercules aircraft, worth a total of $200 million. Its helicopter strength also grew considerably after being augmented by deliveries from Italy. During the first years of this plan, Iran purchased 800 Chieftain tanks from the United Kingdom, which is the largest tank deal known to have been concluded by a third world country. The navy, too, received substantial additional strength by purchases of destroyers, frigates and hovercraft from the United States and the United Kingdom. The build-up in missiles was also very substantial during this period after purchases or orders from the United States (Sidewinder, Sparrow, TOW, Hawk and Maverick), France (SS.11 and SS.12), the United Kingdom (Rapier, Seacat and Swingfire) and Italy (Sea Killer).

In February 1973, it was reported that Iran had contracted in recent months to buy more than $2 billion worth of military equipment from the United States over the next five years. It was described by US officials as the largest single arms deal ever arranged by the Department of Defense. Officials also said that the purchase would include such equipment as the most modern Bell helicopter (Isfahan) and Sea Cobra gunships, 140 Northrop P-5E interceptors, 180 Phantom F-4 fighter bombers and Lockheed C-130 Hercules transports. The Shah had reportedly also expressed interest in the F-15 Eagle, a new air force interceptor not yet in production. From sources in the US Senate, it may be assumed that laser-guided bombs would also be part of the purchase. It was also understood that the United States would station an unusually large detachment of 300 military personnel in Iran to train Iranians in the use of the new weapons (technical assistance field teams or TAFTs).

In January 1974, it was reported that the Iranian government had officially undertaken to buy 30 Grumman F-14A fighters from the United States at a total cost of $900 million. [349] The first 24 of these swing-wing fighters are to be delivered in 1976 and the remaining six in 1977. F-14 Tomcats, which are designed to carry Phoenix missiles, are so modern that they have only recently been procured by the US Navy as its most modern aircraft. In June 1974, it was reported that an additional 50 F-14s had been agreed upon, bringing the total to 80. [350]

With regard to US defence industry interests in Iran, a representative of the US Department of Defense reported in mid-1973 that there were approximately 30 US firms with defence-related contracts utilizing about 900 US civilian employees operating in Iran. [114d] The number of contractor personnel was expected to increase in the year ahead as some programmes gathered momentum. The firms were providing a wide spectrum of assistance to the military services of Iran primarily related to instruction, training and maintenance in connection with the equipment purchased from the United States.

As far as other suppliers are concerned, British deliveries are continuing: in January 1974 Iran ordered air-defence radar equipment from the British Aircraft Corporation to the value of $150 million. [351]

There have also been press reports that the Federal Republic of Germany will supply three armaments factories to Iran and provide training for its armed forces.

The German government has announced the training programme for Iranian military personnel but has denied the sales of weapon factories. [352–353] France has also entered this market recently: the Iranian government ordered six French La Combattante-2 gunboats armed with Exocet missiles in February 1974. [354] In this context it should be added that on 9 February 1974 Iran and France concluded an agreement on a vast industrial cooperation programme for the two countries, reportedly worth up to $5 000 million over ten years. From the Iranian side it was *inter alia* stated that Iran intended to order from France a group of nuclear-power plants with a total production of 5 000 megawatts. The agreement also provides for cooperation in petrochemical and gas liquefaction development projects in Iran, and foresees French oil exploration in Iran and joint exploration in third countries. In addition, France has offered to build a natural gas pipeline from Iran to Europe as well as an Iranian fleet of gas tankers. The agreement makes no specific arrangements for crude oil deliveries to France. [355]

Appendix 5.

Recent economic and technical agreements between oil-producing and oil-consuming countries

France—Iran   Agreement signed for vast long-term cooperation in energy development and industrialization. The deal may include an order for five nuclear power stations from France. Value: $4.5–$5 billion. 9 February 1974. [355]

France-Libya   Agreement signed providing for the exchange of Libyan oil for French nuclear power plants, refineries, harbours, telecommunications and other joint investments – including the joint financing of projects in France, Libya and third countries. Estimated value: $5 billion. 19 February 1974. [356–357]

France—Saudi Arabia First deal comprising the delivery by Saudi Arabia of about 27 million tons of crude oil in exchange for such equipment, goods and services as are designed to assist Saudi Arabia's programme of industrialization. Value: not known. Beginning January 1974. [337]
An even larger deal involving as much as 800 million tons of crude oil over 20 years is under discussion. Value: not known. End January 1974. [340–341]

Federal Republic of Germany—Iran Decision in principle between the two governments providing for FR Germany to build an oil refinery and petrochemical complex in Iran, which will be the world's largest. Part of the project is expected to be financed through the sale of natural gas by Iran to FR Germany, possibly transported in pipelines via the Soviet Union. Long-term oil supplies, in return for the West German contribution, have also been discussed. Value: $2.2 billion. End January 1974. [358]

Italy—Libya   Agreement concluded under which Libya will supply Italy with 30 million tons of oil a year – to be compared with 23 million tons for 1973. Italy's contribution will be goods and services for the industrialization of Libya. Value: not known. 25 February 1974. [359]

Italy—Saudi Arabia Saudi Arabia has agreed in principle to supply Italy with an additional 20–30 million tons of oil in the next three years under an economic, technical and industrial agreement between the two countries. Value: not known. Beginning February 1974. [360]

Japan—Iran   Proposal made by Japan to Iran involving loans and credits to be earmarked for the construction of a refinery, a

116

	petrochemical plant and a cement plant. Value: $1 billion. 10 January 1974. Later reports indicate, however, that Iran cancelled the deal on 4 March 1974. [361–363]
Japan—Iraq	Agreement signed under which Japan will receive 160 million tons of crude oil and oil products over 10 years in return for undertaking petrochemical refining and other industrial projects. Value: $1 billion. 17 January 1974. [364]
Sweden—Libya	Agreement reached for a 10-year cooperative programme under which Libya will deliver 2 million tons of crude oil a year to Sweden in exchange for steel, timber, paper and cement. In addition, Sweden will build tankers and merchant carriers for Libya. The two countries will also investigate the possibility of Libya helping to finance the construction of an oil refinery in Sweden. Value: not known. 6 March 1974. [365]
United Kingdom —Iran	Agreement providing for Iran to exchange about 5 million tons of crude oil for British deliveries of textile fibres, steel, paper, petrochemicals and other industrial goods. Value: $240 million. 25 January 1974. [366]
United States — Iran	Tentative agreement between the Iranian government and five US refining companies for the joint construction and operation in Iran of what could be one of the largest refineries in the world (with an output of 500 000 b/d). Value: $500–$750 million. 8 November 1973. [367]
United States —Saudi Arabia	Agreement in principle reached between the two governments on more active US support in the industrialization of Saudi Arabia and in the supply of its requirements for defensive purposes. Value: not known. 5 April 1974. [368]
	Agreement, signed on 9 June 1974, provides for the establishment of two joint commissions, one on economic cooperation and the other on Saudi Arabia's military requirements. Four working groups have been created: industrialization; manpower and education; technology research and development; and agriculture. These are to prepare recommendations for the Economic Commission. The two governments agree to consider setting up an economic council for the private sector, to foster further cooperation. [342]

Appendix 6.

Official texts related to the 1973 oil embargo

I. *Text of the resolution arising from the 1973 Arab decision to use oil as a political weapon, 17 October 1973*

The Oil Ministers of the member States of the Organization of Arab Petroleum Exporting Countries (OAPEC) held a meeting in the city of Kuwait on the 21st of Ramadan 1393 A.H., corresponding to the 17th of October, 1973 A.D., to consider employing oil in the battle currently raging between the Arabs and Israel. Following a thorough discussion of this question of the Oil Ministers,

Considering that the direct goal of the current battle is the liberation of the Arab territories occupied in the June 1967 war and the recovery of the legitimate rights of the Palestinian people in accordance with the United Nations resolutions;

Considering that the United States is the principal and foremost source of the Israeli power which has resulted in the present Israeli arrogance and enabled the Israelis to continue to occupy our territories;

Recalling that the big industrial nations help, in one way or another, to perpetuate the status quo, though they bear a common responsibility for implementing the United Nations resolutions;

Considering that the economic situation of many Arab oil producing countries does not justify raising oil production, though they are ready to make such an increase in production to meet the requirements of major consumer industrial nations that commit themselves to cooperation with us for the purpose of liberating our territories;

Decided that each Arab oil exporting country immediately cut its oil production by a recurrent monthly rate of no less than 5 % to be initially counted on the virtual production of September and thenceforth on the last production figure until such a time as the international community compels Israel to relinquish our occupied territories or until the production of every individual country reaches the point where its economy does not permit of any further reduction without detriment to its national and Arab obligations.

Nevertheless, the countries that support the Arabs actively and effectively or that take important measures against Israel to compel its withdrawal shall not be prejudiced by this production cut and shall continue to receive the same oil supplies that they used to receive prior to the reduction. Though the cut rate will be uniform in respect of every individual oil exporting country, the decrease in the supplies provided to the various consuming countries may well be aggravated proportionately with their support to and cooperation with the Israeli enemy.

The Participants also recommended the countries party to this resolution that the United States be subjected to the most severe cut proportionately with the quantities of crude oil, oil derivatives, and hydrocarbons that it imports from every exporting country.

The Participants also recommended that this progressive reduction leads to the total halt of oil supplies to the United States from every individual country party to the resolution. [369]

II. *Text of the communiqué of a meeting of the Organization of Arab Petroleum Exporting Countries in Kuwait, 4 November 1973*

The Arab Oil Ministers met for the second time in Kuwait on 4–5 November 1973 and studied the method of implementation of their first decision and its effects. They took decisons, among them that the reduction in oil production in each Arab country which is a party to the first decision shall be 25 per cent of the September production, including quantities deducted as a result of the embargo on oil supplies to the U.S. and the Dutch market. A further reduction amounting to 5 per cent of the November output will follow in December provided that such reduction shall not affect the share that any friendly state was importing from any Arab exporting country during the first nine months of 1973.

It was also decided to send the Algerian Minister of Energy and the Saudi Arabian Minister of Petroleum and Mineral Resources to Western capitals to explain the Arab point of view regarding the two meetings held by the Arab Ministers of Oil.

It was further decided that meetings will be held from time to time in future, as the need arises, to follow up on the implementation of the decisions and their effects. [370]

III. *Text of the EEC Foreign Ministers' resolution on the requisites for a just and lasting peace in the Middle East, 6 November 1973*

The nine Governments of the European Community have continued their exchange of views on the situation in the Middle East. While emphasizing that the views set out below are only a first contribution on their part to the search for a comprehensive solution to the problem, they have agreed on the following:

They strongly urge that the forces of both sides in the Middle East conflict should return immediately to the positions they occupied on Oct. 22 in accordance with resolutions 339 and 340 of the Security Council. They believe that a return to these positions will facilitate a solution to other pressing problems concerning prisoners of war and the Egyptian Third Army.

They have the firm hope that, following the adoption by the Security Council of resolution No. 338 of Oct. 22, negotiations will at last begin for the restoration in the Middle East of a just and lasting peace through the application of Security Council resolution No. 242 of 1967 in all its parts.

They declare themselves ready to do all in their power to contribute to that peace. They believe that those negotiations must take place in the framework of the United Nations. They recall that the Charter has entrusted to the Security Council the principal responsibility in the making and keeping of peace through the application of Council resolutions Nos. 242 and 338.

They consider that a peace agreement should be based particularly on the following points:

1 The inadmissibility of the acquisition of territory by force.

2 The need for Israel to end the territorial occupation which it has maintained since the conflict of 1967.

3 Respect for the sovereignty, territorial integrity and independence of every State in the area and their right to live in peace within secure and recognized boundaries.

4 Recognition that in the establishment of a just and lasting peace account must be taken of the legitimate rights of the Palestinians.

They recall that according to resolution No. 242 the peace settlement must be the object of international guarantees.

They consider that such guarantees must be reinforced, among other means, by the despatch of peace-keeping forces to the demilitarized zones envisaged in article 2 (c) of resolution No. 242. They are agreed that such guarantees are of primary importance in settling the overall situation in the Middle East in conformity with resolution No. 242 to which the Council refers in resolution No. 338. They reserve the right to make proposals in this connexion.

They recall on this occasion the ties of all kinds which have long linked them to the littoral States of the south and east of the Mediterranean. In this connexion they reaffirm the terms of the declaration of the Paris summit of Oct. 21, 1972, and recall that the Community has decided, in the framework of a gobal and balanced approach, to negotiate agreements with these countries. [371]

IV. *Text of the statement issued by the Arab Oil Ministers on 8 December 1973, making the lifting of the embargo conditional upon Israeli withdrawal*

The Arab Oil Ministers and their representatives, signatories to this resolution, met in Kuwait City on Saturday, 14th Dhul Qi'da 1393 corresponding to 8.12.1973; and after perusal of their resolution of 23.10.1393 corresponding to 18.11.1973 concerning the suspension of the 5 per cent cut in oil production in December in relation to the countries of the European Economic Community except Holland, provided that the decrease continues afterwards for all non-excluded countries at the rate of 5 per cent for January compared to the December production level; have decided as follows:

First: If agreement is reached on withdrawal from all territories occupied in 1967, foremost of which is Jerusalem, in accordance with a time-table signed by Israel and guaranteed by the United States, the embargo on the United States shall be lifted as soon as implementation of the withdrawal time-table starts. At that time the general reduction ratio shall be determined so as not to go beyond or below the actual rate at the time of the embargo lifting for the provision of oil to consuming countries. The same ratio applied then to Europe and the rest of the world shall be applied to the United States.

Second: When agreement is reached as to the withdrawal time-table, the Oil Ministers enforcing this resolution shall meet to lay down a schedule for the gradual restoration of oil production to its September 1973 level corresponding to the stages of withdrawal.

Third: African, Muslim and friendly countries shall be supplied with all the amounts of oil for which they have contracts even though this requires raising production by a rate that ensures meeting their local needs, provided that it is ascertained that oil is not re-exported to countries under embargo. [372]

V. *Text of the Arab Oil Ministers' communiqué on the progress of their oil-restrictive policy, issued after their meeting in Kuwait, 24-25 December 1973*

At their meeting in Kuwait, the Arab Oil Ministers heard a report by Shaikh Ahmad Zaki Yamani, the Saudi Arabian Minister of Petroleum and Mineral Resources, and Mr. Abdesselam Belaid, the Algerian Minister of Industry and Energy, on their tour of certain Western capitals, the impressions they formed during this tour, the outcome and effects arising from it, and the proposals they have put forward as a result of all of this.

The assembled Ministers studied the real aim of the oil measures adopted in their previous decisions, which is to convey to the world the real injustice inflicted on the Arab nation through the occupation of its territories and the uprooting of an entire people — the Palestinian people — without allowing this to cause the economic collapse of any nation or nations of the world. They reaffirmed once again their previously announced decision of 17 October that these measures should not affect friendly countries and that there should be a clear differentiation between those who side with the Arabs, those who side with the enemy, and those whose position is in between.

The assembled Ministers took note on the one hand of the change in Japan's policy towards the Arab cause, which has been demonstrated by various means including the visit of the Japanese Deputy Prime Minister to the Arab countries, and on the other hand of the deteriorating economic situation in Japan, and they decided to accord Japan special treatment which would not subject it to the full extent of the across-the-board cutback measures, out of a desire to protect the Japanese economy and in the hope that the Japanese Government, in appreciation of this stand, will continue to adopt just and fair positions vis-à-vis the Arab cause.

The assembled Ministers, in recognition of the political stand of Belgium, also decided to lift the cutback on oil supplies to that country and to permit oil supplies to reach its territory via Holland, after receiving sufficient guarantees that such supplies will reach Belgium in full. They also decided to supply certain friendly countries with their actual oil requirements, even in excess of the level of their imports for September 1973, on condition that Arab oil does not find its way beyond their borders or replace non-Arab oil which they would have imported. In implementation of all this, the Ministers decided to raise production in their countries by 10 per cent of September production so that the percentage reduction becomes 15 per cent instead of 25 per cent, and not to apply the further reduction for January.

The Ministers noted with satisfaction the gradual change which has begun to become evident in American public opinion, since a significant segment of it has begun to recognize the reality of the Arab problem and Israel's expansionist policy. This has been particularly evident in the adoption by a number of American senators and congressmen of objective and unbiased attitudes towards the Arab-Israeli question.

The assembled Ministers hope that the desire of the US Government to participate in the search for a just and peaceful settlement of the problem will be fruitful and will lead to results beneficial to the peoples of the world and in particular to bilateral relations between the Arab and American peoples. However, the embargo on both America and Holland will continue.

The Ministers will meet again in Tripoli in the Libyan Arab Republic after the end of the second part of the tour of the two Ministers representing them, unless the situation calls for an earlier meeting. [373]

VI. *Text of the statement issued after the OAPEC conference in Vienna, 17-18 March 1974*

The Arab Oil Ministers held a series of meetings during the period of March 13 and the 18th at Tripoli and Vienna, during which they heard the report presented by Shaikh Ahmad Zaki Yamani, Minister of Petroleum and Mineral Resources of the Kingdom of Saudi Arabia, and by Sayed Belaid Abdesselam, Minister of Energy and Industry of the Algerian Popular Democratic Republic, concerning the results of the second part of their trip which included Spain, Italy, West Germany and Japan.

The ministers studied the political analysis presented by the two said ministers which was based on their talks with the officials of the respective countries they visited.

The ministers re-evaluated the results of the Arab oil measures in the light of its main objective, namely to draw the attention of the world to the Arab cause in order to create the suitable political climate for the implementation of the Security Council Resolution 242 which calls for the complete withdrawal from the Arab occupied territories, and for the restoration of the legitimate rights of the Palestinian people.

The ministers took cognizance of the fact that the said measures made the world public opinion aware of the importance of the Arab world for the welfare of world economy, and consequently it became receptive to the legitimate rights of the Arab nation which led to the gradual isolation of Israel and paved the way for the assumption of political stances which openly condemn Israel's expansionist policy.

Indicative of such stances were the clear change of policy of the European Community represented by its joint declaration of November 6, 1973, the positions assumed by Belgium, Italy, West Germany and Japan which were even more just and clear: And also the signs which began to appear in various American circles calling (in various degrees) for the need of an even-handed policy vis-à-vis the Middle East and the Arab world.

It appeared to the ministers that the American official policy as evidenced lately by the recent political events assumed a new dimension vis-à-vis the Arab Israel conflict.

Such a dimension, if maintained, will lead America to assume a position which is more compatible with the principle of what is right and just towards the Arab occupied territories and the legitimate rights of the Palestinian people.

The Arab Oil Ministers are aware of the fact that oil is a weapon which can be utilized in a positive manner in order to lead to results the effectiveness of which may surpass those (results) if the oil weapon was used in a negative manner.

Therefore, they came out with resolutions in which the oil weapon was used in a positive manner, the purpose of which was to encourage the countries which showed readiness and willingness to work for a just remedy to the cause which would lead to the complete termination of the Israeli occupation and to the restoration of the legitimate rights of the Palestinian people.

Israel alone will bear the dangerous responsibility if the forthcoming events lead to the undertaking of more severe oil measures, in addition to the other various resources which the Arab world can master in order to join the battle of destiny.

Israel alone is to be blamed for the effects suffered by the countries which came under the embargo or which suffered as a result of the reduction of the oil production, and it (Israel) remains responsible today for the maintaining of the production of Arab oil at the level which is below the needs of the market.

In the light of the principles, facts and objectives mentioned previously the Arab Oil Ministers decided at the conclusion of their meetings the following:

First: To treat Italy and the Republic of West Germany as friendly countries to meet their petroleum needs.

Second: To lift the embargo on oil supplies to the United States, it being understood that this decision as much as all the other decisions shall be subject to the review on the occasion of the meeting to be held by the Arab Oil Ministers on the 1st of June, 1974 in Cairo.

The ministers emphasized their support for all the Arab countries in their just struggle and to the Syrian Arab Republic at the present time during which it endeavours to reach the means which would eventually lead to the full liberation of its territory and to the complete liberation of all the Arab occupied territories, first of which comes Jerusalem.

For its part, the Syrian Arab Republic did not give its assent to the decision to lift the embargo.

For its part, Libya did not give its assent to the decision to lift the embargo or to any increase in production.

For its part, Algeria makes it clear that the lifting of the embargo is provisional in nature, limited to the period expiring June 1, 1974. [374]

Appendix 7.

*The Washington Energy Conference
of 11–13 February 1974*

I. *Text of the final communiqué*

Summary Statement

1. Foreign ministers of Belgium, Canada, Denmark, France, the Federal Republic of Germany, Ireland, Italy, Japan, Luxembourg, the Netherlands, Norway, the United Kingdom, the United States met in Washington from February 11 to 13, 1974. The European Community was represented as such by the President of the Council and the President of the Commission. Finance ministers, ministers with responsiblity for energy affairs, economic affairs and science and technology affairs also took part in the meeting. The ministers examined the international energy situation and its implications and charted a course of actions to meet this challenge which requires constructive and comprehensive solutions. To this end they agreed on specific steps to provide for effective international cooperation. The ministers affirmed that solutions to the world's energy problem should be sought in consultation with producer countries and other consumers.

Analysis of the Situation

2. They noted that during the past three decades progress in improving productivity and standards of living was greatly facilitated by the ready availability of increasing supplies of energy at fairly stable prices. They recognized that the problem of meeting growing demand existed before the current situation and that the needs of the world economy for increased energy supplies require positive long-term solutions.

3. They concluded that the current energy situation results from an intensification of these underlying factors and from political developments.

4. They reviewed the problems created by the large rise in oil prices and agreed with the serious concern expressed by the International Monetary Fund's Committee of Twenty at its recent Rome meeting over the abrupt and significant changes in prospect for the world balance of payments structure.

5. They agreed that present petroleum prices presented the structure of world trade and finance with an unprecedented situation. They recognized that none of the consuming countries could hope to insulate itself from these developments, or expect to deal with the payments impact of oil prices by the adoption of monetary or trade measures alone. In their view, the present situation, if continued, could lead to a serious deterioration in income and employment, intensify inflationary pressures, and endanger the welfare of nations. They believed that financial measures by themselves will not be able to deal with the strains of the current situation.

6. They expressed their particular concern about the consequences of the

situation for the developing countries and recognized the need for efforts by the entire international community to resolve this problem. At current oil prices the additional energy costs for developing countries will cause a serious setback to the prospect for economic development of these countries.

7. *General Conclusions.* They affirmed, that, in the pursuit of national policies, whether in the trade, monetary or energy fields, efforts should be made to harmonize the interests of each country on the one hand and the maintenance of the world economic system on the other. Concerted international cooperation between all the countries concerned including oil producing countries could help to accelerate an improvement in the supply and demand situation, ameliorate the adverse economic consequences of the existing situation and lay the groundwork for a more equitable and stable international energy relationship.

8. They felt that these considerations taken as a whole made it essential that there should be a substantial increase of international cooperation in all fields. Each participant in the conference stated its firm intention to do its utmost to contribute to such an aim, in close cooperation both with the other consumer countries and with the producer countries.

9. They concurred in the need for a comprehensive action program to deal with all facets of the world energy situation by cooperative measures. In so doing they will build on the work of the OECD. They recognized that they may wish to invite, as appropriate, other countries to join with them in these efforts. Such an action program of international co-operation would include, as appropriate, the sharing of means and efforts, while concerting national policies, in such areas as:

The conservation of energy and restraint of demand.

A system of allocating oil supplies in times of emergency and severe shortages.

The acceleration of development of additional energy sources so as to diversify energy supplies.

The acceleration of energy research and development programs through international cooperative efforts. (1)

10. With respect to monetary and economic questions, they decided to intensify their cooperation and to give impetus to the work being undertaken in the IMF, the World Bank and the OECD on the economic and monetary consequences of the current energy situation, in particular to deal with balance of payments disequilibria. They agreed that:

In dealing with the balance of payments impact of oil prices they stressed the importance of avoiding competitive depreciation and the escalation of restrictions on trade and payments or disruptive actions in external borrowing. (2)

While financial cooperation can only partially alleviate the problems which have recently arisen for the international economic system, they will intensify work on short-term financial measures and possible longer-term mechanisms to reinforce existing official and market credit facilities. (3)

They will pursue domestic economic policies which will reduce as much as possible the difficulties resulting from the current energy cost levels. (4)

They will make strenuous efforts to maintain and enlarge the flow of development aid bilaterally and through multilateral institutions, on the basis of international solidarity embracing all countries with appropriate resources.

11. Further, they have agreed to accelerate wherever practicable their own

national programs of new energy sources and technology which will help the overall world-wide supply and demand situation.

12. They agreed to examine in detail the role of international oil companies.

13. They stressed the continued importance of maintaining and improving the natural environment as part of developing energy sources and agreed to make this an important goal of their activity.

14. They further agreed that there was need to develop a cooperative multi-lateral relationship with producing countries, and other consuming countries that takes into account the long-term interests of all. They are ready to exchange technical information with these countries on the problem of stabilizing energy supplies with regard to quantity and prices.

15. They welcomed the initiatives in the U.N. to deal with the larger issues of energy and primary products at a world-wide level and in particular for a special session of the U.N. General Assembly.

Establishment of Follow-On Machinery

16. They agreed to establish a coordinating group headed by senior officials to direct and to coordinate the development of the actions referred to above. The coordinating group shall decide how best to organize its work. It should:

Monitor and give focus to the tasks that might be addressed in existing organizations;

Establish such ad hoc working groups as may be necessary to undertake tasks for which there are presently no suitable bodies;

Direct preparations of a conference of consumer and producer countries which will be held at the earliest possible opportunity and which, if necessary, will be preceded by a further meeting of consumer countries. (5)

17. They agreed that the preparations for such meetings should involve consultations with developing countries and other consumer and producer countries. (6)

(1) France does not accept point nine in its entirety.
(2) (3) (4) In point ten France does not accept these paragraphs.
(5) France does not accept point 16 in its entirety.
(6) France does not accept point 17 in its entirety.

II. *Views expressed by the participants at the Washington Energy Conference**

The nature and scope of the problem

The United States. The energy crisis constitutes an unpredicted challenge to the prosperity of most nations and to the entire structure of international cooperation. The challenge will remain for at least the rest of the 1970s and perhaps beyond this period.

* These summaries are based on official statements made by representatives of the countries concerned at the Washington Energy Conference.

The European Economic Community. The exceptionally grave situation on the energy market affects the world economy as a whole, though not all countries and regions to the same extent. The oil shortage and its economic and monetary aspects, particularly the price trends, are of basic importance for the maintenance of growth, full employment and the foreign trade equilibrium of national economies.

Japan.. What is being tested by the oil crisis is international solidarity, or the concept of "one-world".

Security aspects

The United States. Security and economic considerations are inevitably linked and energy cannot be separated from either. The energy crisis raises fundamental questions about the hope to achieve global stability. Failure to resolve the energy problem would threaten the world with a circle of competition, autarchy, rivalry and worldwide depression.

The European Economic Community. We must be guided by a spirit of cooperation, not of confrontation.

France. The participants in the Washington Conference must not appear before the world as unilaterally seeking to define a "new course" which would inevitably lead to a confrontation or a conflict with the PE-countries and possibly with all the developing countries.

Multilateral *versus* bilateral approaches

The United States. The energy problem is still manegeable multilaterally. Concerted international action is imperative among major consumer nations, among developed and underdeveloped countries, and among producer and consumer nations.

Isolated solutions are impossible. Countries such as the United States and Canada are capable of solving the energy problem by largely national means but even they would suffer from the impact of a world economic crisis.

The dilemmas facing all countries cannot be avoided through exclusive bilateral arrangements. The United States does not dispute the right of sovereign nations to make individual arrangements. It is essential, however, that these arrangements follow agreed rules of conduct and only occur under the umbrella of international cooperation. Unrestrained bilateralism is certain to produce disastrous political and economic consequences. Narrowly competitive approaches have traditionally ended in conflict – economic or military or both.

Cooperation rather than confrontation must guide relationships with the PE-countries. The ultimate goal must be to create a cooperative framework within which producers and consumers will be able to accommodate their differences and reconcile their needs and aspirations. The PE-countries must be given a secure stake in an expanding world economy and the IC-countries a secure source of supply.

The European Economic Community. The worldwide nature of the problem requires treatment transcending a regional context. In a spirit of worldwide cooperation, the EEC is resolved to collaborate in achieving constructive solutions.

Isolated responses cannot be anything but inadequate when the balance of world

127

economy is at stake. It must be ensured that international economic relations are not seriously disrupted by unilateral measures. Some countries are more prone than others to adopt a beggar-my-neighbour attitude. The strengthening of cooperation between PE- and IC-countries must be founded on a fair balance of interests.

France. It is important to initiate a dialogue and to develop cooperation between IC- and PE-countries without distinction. All bilateral or multilateral contacts seem useful, but it is undesirable to plan or establish a system of preliminary consultations between the large consuming entities only.

Cooperation in every aspect between Europe and the PE-countries, especially Arab countries, seems to fit the current situation. Europe intends to establish real cooperation with them.

Japan. Harmonious relations between PE-countries and IC-countries should be established in order to bring about a fundamental solution to the oil problem. A cooperative international community, which embraces the PE-countries, must be promoted and developed. Japan responds to and sympathizes with the oil-producing countries' aspirations to build up their countries. They are expending keen efforts toward development of their countries, but are hindered by severe environmental conditions and a feeling of insecurity about the future depletion of oil resources. At present and in future, Japan will direct as much effort as possible toward promoting friendly and cooperative relations on a broad basis for the advancement of industrialization in, and the development of human and cultural exchanges with these countries.

Prices

The United States. Price levels in February 1974 are simply not sustainable. The effects of these prices will be disastrous to the IC-countries, and particularly to the developing countries. Nor can the PE-countries escape the effect of global deflation, mounting restrictions in world trade and monetary systems and the political tensions of unbridled competition. Excessive prices will also call for massive investments in alternative energy sources, which raises the prospects of lower prices and diminished export markets for the PE-countries in the future.

The European Economic Community. Depending on their degree of dependence on imported oil, the IC-countries will feel the increase in oil prices in very different ways. Given continued high prices (the February 1974 level) the PE-countries will receive additional revenues of a magnitude that will result in a worldwide upheaval in trade and capital flows. Appropriate economic measures must be taken on a world scale to ensure that the requisite adjustments are carried out along orderly lines.

Japan. The Japanese economy is one of the economies hardest hit by a cut in supply or hike in price.

Japan considers it appropriate to initiate a study, together with oil-producing countries, on an oil price-setting mechanism, including the question of price levels, that would give a stable supply of oil commensurate with the total effective demand for oil and which would insure price predictability.

Oil-poor underdeveloped countries

The United States. The underdeveloped countries must be quickly drawn into consultation and collaboration. Their futures are the most profoundly affected of all. Unable to meet present prices for oil and fertilizers, they face the threat of starvation, abandoned hopes for further economic development, political tension, social turmoil and human despair. The richer countries must not permit this to happen; they should not cut their aid programmes to the underdeveloped countries in response to balance-of-payments problems. The PE-countries should show special understanding towards the underdeveloped nations.

The European Economic Community. Energy-importing underdeveloped countries are the hardest hit by the rise in oil prices. It is essential that these countries can also take part in the discussions and cooperation on energy matters.

Japan. The heavy impact of the present oil crisis is being felt especially in the non-oil-producing underdeveloped countries. The effects of a sharp increase in oil prices, compounded with rises in the prices of imported materials, will create a serious crisis in the already weak international balance-of-payments position of these countries. In addition to these direct impacts, the stagnation of industrial production in advanced countries is causing a reduction in materials supplied to the underdeveloped countries, as well as a decrease in the rate of imports from these nations. There is also a danger that stagnation of industrial production and deterioration in the international balance of payments in the industrialized countries may decrease the ability of these countries to extend aid to the underdeveloped countries. These direct and indirect impacts raise the threat that the promotion of economic and social development in the underdeveloped countries, an indispensable condition for international stability, may be seriously hampered in future. The developing countries in Asia in particular are strongly affected by the impact of the oil crisis, *inter alia*, by the stagnation of Japan's economy.

The oil embargo

The United States. The oil embargo carries profound worldwide implications – the possibility of manipulation of raw material supplies in order to prescribe the foreign policies of IC-countries.

Emergency sharing

The United States. The United States is willing to share available energy in times of emergency or prolonged shortages. It is prepared to allocate an agreed portion of the total US petroleum supply, provided other IC-countries with indigenous production do likewise.

The European Economic Community. Work on questions concerning the allocation of energy resources in the event of supply difficulties has been under way within the OECD for some time, but stands in need of a fresh impetus.

Cooperation in R&D efforts

The United States. The United States is prepared to make a major contribution, backed by its most advanced energy research and development (R&D), to a broad programme of international cooperation in energy matters. It is also prepared to examine the sharing of uranium enrichment technology (diffusion and centrifuge).

Such a multilateral enrichment effort could be undertaken within a framework of assured supply, geographic dispersion and controls against further proliferation.

The European Economic Community. The basis for cooperation among industrialized countries must be strengthened in those fields which affect those countries most closely. Research and development is such a field. In this sphere, participation by other interested countries should be welcomed. For the sake of efficiency, use should be made of such organizations as the OECD.

France. France is prepared to embark on such a programme of technological cooperation as would increase the supply of conventional or new energy sources, and which could be extended to different industrialized countries. The normal framework for such cooperation should be that of the OECD.

Financial cooperation

The United States. There is a crucial congruent interest between the PE-countries and the IC-countries in the field of financial cooperation and an urgent need for cooperative solutions. The United States recommends, *inter alia: (a)* new mechanisms to facilitate the distribution of international capital flow from oil revenue surpluses; (*b*) a design for cooperation between producers and consumers to build confidence in investment policies and in the integrity of investments; and (*c*) steps to facilitate the fuller participation of producing nations in existing international institutions and to contribute to the urgent needs of the developing consumer countries.

The European Economic Community. Dangerously conflicting policies must be avoided. Competitive devaluation is not a remedy and must be avoided. The same applies to overbidding and commercial protectionism.

France. There is no reason why economic and monetary problems resulting from the new oil situation should not be dealt with in the existing international institutions which normally deal with them, such as the OECD and the IMF.

Japan. At no time has it been more necessary than at present for international cooperation and mutual understanding regarding economic policies, in order to cope with the domestic economic situation and balance-of-payments position.

The institutional framework

The United States. Some tasks can be carried out by existing international institutions. A coordinating group should be established to relate defined tasks to such existing bodies, to undertake those tasks for which there are presently no suitable bodies, and to prepare for a new meeting. Another conference of IC-countries should then be called, which could include representatives of the developing countries. This meeting would lead to a third conference of IC- and PE-countries. The entire process should be completed by 1 May 1974.

The European Economic Community. It would be undesirable for the "Washington Conference", particularly in its original composition, to become a permanent institution; it is not inconceivable, however, that suitably composed working parties be set up in the short term to deal with a number of questions, the membership of these being open to both IC- and PE-countries. Nor should a new form of international cooperation be set up in which only the highly developed countries are represented and which usurps some of the functions of existing international organizations. Instead a fresh impetus should be given to the work of already existing organizations, for example the OECD and the IMF. It is important to consider the ways in which groups of countries which have so far not participated in this work should become involved in it.

Concerning the proposal by the French and Algerian governments to convene a worldwide meeting under the auspices of the United Nations to discuss energy and raw material problems, the EEC considers it important to decide on a procedure which would ensure that such a meeting achieved rapid results.

The "Washington Conference" should be the first step towards a comprehensive dialogue between the developed IC-countries, the underdeveloped IC-countries and the PE-countries, to begin by 1 April 1974 at the latest.

France. France is prepared to participate in an exchange of views on several aspects of the energy problem, but it does not want to institutionalize, in any manner, the IC-countries independently of the underdeveloped countries and PE-countries, be it in the form of working groups, an action or coordinating group, or more or less regular conferences with similar participation as in the "Washington Conference".

Flexible exchanges of information could possibly be envisaged between the IC-countries within, for example, the framework of the OECD.

A world consensus regarding the organization of relations between IC- and PE-countries can only be brought about at a conference held under the auspices of the United Nations.

Although its objective is broader than the one envisioned by France since it involves all matters dealing with raw materials, the Algerian initiative does not seem incompatible with the French proposals in this respect.

Japan. Japan anticipates that the Washington Conference will be the first step in building a harmonious relationship between the PE- and the IC-countries. It is of primary importance to realize, as early as possible, a constructive dialogue with the PE-countries, in view of the urgent nature of the problem.

Appendix 8.

Territorial disputes

I. *East Asia*

In 1968 the Emery Report was commissioned by the UN Economic Commission for Asia and the Far East (ECAFE): it found that the potential for commercial oil from the thick deposits of oil-bearing sediment all along the western rim of the Pacific was excellent, some of the most promising areas being situated at some distance from the coastal borders of the Asian nations. [376] The question of which nation has the right to explore and develop these vast riches of the sea-bed is being raised with growing urgency and has since caused an increasing number of disputes between the bordering coastal powers.

An area of conflicting claims where oil exploration is already under way lies 100 miles northeast of Taiwan, surrounding the Senkaku islands. The uninhabited Senkaku islands, claimed by Japan as part of the Ryukyu group, are also claimed by China and Taiwan and are thought to be in the middle of the richest potential zone for oil. [377] Intensive exploration of the area has been hindered by the dispute over exploration rights. In the spring of 1972, Japanese protests to the US firm Pacific Gulf Oil, which had received a concession to explore the area from Taiwan, resulted in the withdrawal of a West German vessel doing a seismic survey. Pacific Gulf Oil had stopped using its own vessel in the area after the US State Department had warned a year earlier that it would not be advisable to explore for oil in the disputed area. [378–379] No progress appears to have been made in resolving the conflicting interests.

Conflicting claims to exploration and development rights in the northern part of the East China Sea became an open source of friction between Japan and South Korea in 1969 when Japan granted an oil concession in a disputed area to Nippon Oil. In 1970 South Korea countered by granting a concession covering much of the same acreage to Korean-American Oil, operator for the US Wendell Phillips Oil Co. The controversial area, designated block VII by South Korea, covers 60 000 sq km and lies south of the South Korean Cheju Do island and west of the Japanese island of Kyushu. South Korea's claim is based on the water depth and the projection of the continental shelf southwards from the Korean peninsula. Although a belt of deep water separates block VII from Japan's continental shelf, Japan can claim the area on the basis of the median-line principle, with the line drawn through the Korean Straits.

When serious negotiations finally started in September 1972, survey work by the two countries' competing concessionaires was broken off. After ten months of negotiations, during which several reported settlements proved illusory, the representatives of Japan and South Korea succeeded in producing two documents outlining the general terms of a settlement. These documents were initialled by the negotiating teams on 4 July 1973. Further work resulted in more specific operative terms which, together with the July documents, were reformulated in a 50-year pact and signed in Seoul on 30 January 1974 by South Korea's foreign minister and Japan's ambassador.

According to the terms of the agreement, the joint development zone includes all of the controversial block VII and two additional large slices of sea-bed to the west and east of this block. The zone is subdivided into nine smaller blocks, each of which is to be explored and developed by a joint concession to two companies, one authorized by Korea and the other by Japan. Costs and production profits are to be equally shared by the companies, but taxes and royalties are paid at the prevailing domestic rates to the country which authorized the share in the concession. Thus companies authorized by South Korea will pay 12.5 per cent of sales in royalties and 50 per cent of net profits to Seoul. The corresponding rates for companies authorized by Japan are 1 per cent and 42 per cent. [380] Both South Korea and Japan have given preference to those companies which held concessions when the area rights were under dispute. The agreement also established a joint governmental commission to supervise operations, control the division of production and mediate in disputes between concessionaires.

The method worked out by Japan and South Korea to resolve their conflicting claims is unique. The agreement delimits for the first time a block of acreage which the two countries will explore and develop jointly and defines the terms and administrative structure for a joint sharing of costs and profits. In addition, the agreement provides firm lines of demarcation between other areas where Japan and South Korea will work separately. [381–382]

Although this agreement has not yet been proven as a smooth-functioning arrangement, it might have been hoped that at least one area in the disputed Asian waters had been removed from contention. This is not so: shortly after the agreement was signed, China voiced a protest claiming that it was an "infringement" of its sovereignty over the continental shelf extending from the mainland, and warned that Japan and South Korea "must bear full responsibility for all the consequences" of their action. [377]

China's hesitancy in the past over the active pressing of its claims in the China Seas may be partly interpreted as a tactical decision to wait until it had established sovereignty over Taiwan, a decision China could afford since its oil and gas needs are still more than met by domestic production. But the rush for potential oil reserves caused by the Middle East crisis, and the growing realization of the prospect of global energy shortages may press China into a more frontal policy. However, China may also not wish to commit itself too actively until the Law of the Sea Conference scheduled for 20 June–28 August 1974 in Caracas. [376]

II. South East Asia

Spratly and Paracel Islands

The potential oil reserves in the sedimentary basin beneath a number of tiny atolls and reefs in the South China Sea are almost certainly a major cause of the recent flare-up of the long-standing dispute over the sovereignty of these islands. Known to Western geographers as the Reed-Nansha-Tizard Block or Spratly

Archipelago (after the British geographer who mapped the area in the 1960s), and to the Chinese as the island groups Nansha (Spratly), Hsisha (Paracel), Chungsha and Tungsha, [383] the islands extend over 250 000 sq km of the South China Sea. There are an estimated 150 waterless islands, devoid of all resources except guano used for fertilizer, none more than a mile long and none ever inhabited. Claimants of the islands in the past have included France, Malaysia, the Philippines, Nationalist China, the Republic of Viet-Nam and the People's Republic of China.

The recent military confrontation was precipitated by the Republic of Viet-Nam formally incorporating Spratly (Nansha) Island and ten others in the Nansha group into the coastal province of Phuoc Thuy in September 1973, shortly after having granted its first concessions for drilling in its coastal waters. On 11 January 1974, the Chinese Foreign Ministry denounced the Viet-Namese annexation and reasserted the Chinese claim to all four island groups and the sea areas around them. Manoeuvres of Viet-Namese and Chinese naval power in the area surrounding the Paracel (Hsisha) islands finally erupted in a two-day armed confrontation on 19–20 January 1974 involving MiG jet fighters and ships armed with missiles. The conflict ended with the Chinese in possession of the islands and the South Viet-Namese in retreat. The Republic of Viet-Nam appealed to the Paris Conference on Viet-Nam and the UN Security Council and expressed interest in referring the dispute to the International Court of Justice at the Hague. Following the forced withdrawal of the South Viet-Namese from the Paracel Island group, President Thieu is reported to have sent a reinforcement of 120–200 men to the Spratly group, 540 miles south of the Paracels. Nationalist China and the Philippines also reportedly have small troop contingents in the archipelago and are engaged in talks with the Republic of Viet-Nam concerning a peaceful solution to their conflicting claims of sovereignty. South Viet-Nam has stated that it would welcome the support of Nationalist China and the Philippines "in opposing foreign countries' plots of encroachment on Viet-Namese territory". [384] In response to South Viet-Nam's sending naval vessels to the Spratly group, Peking issued a statement accusing South Viet-Nam of "a new military provocation" and repeated that China would tolerate no infringement of its territorial integrity. [385]

Since China supports the 200-mile "economic zone" or "patrimonial sea" concept, in claiming the four groups of islands it also claims the right to exploit the sea-bed in a 200-mile arc surrounding them. According to geologists, some of the best oil prospects lie in the outer reaches of this arc in areas which the "rim" countries, Malaysia, the Philippines and South Viet-Nam, might interpret as natural extensions of their continental shelf. The Soviet Union hinted support of Saigon in its news coverage of the dispute by dismissing China's actions as an exhibition of its expansionist tendencies. [386]

The conflict potential of the dispute is increased by the Provisional Revolutionary Government's (PRG) denial of legal validity to concessions granted by the Saigon government. Following a meeting on 5–6 February 1974, the PRG Minister of Foreign Affairs issued a communiqué affirming that natural resources "are the sacred and inviolable property of the population: only a body formed by general free and democratic elections organized by the National Council of Reconciliation ... is competent to treat problems concerning resources". The PRG considers that the Saigon administration is only "an instrument of American neo-colonialism" and that "all contracts passed by it with no matter what country, no matter what society or foreign enterprise, are without value". [387]

The South China Sea and the Gulf of Siam

South Viet-Nam

In May 1973 the National Petroleum Board of South Viet-Nam issued its first invitations to bid for offshore oil concessions to 27 foreign oil companies. Thirty search blocks covering 230 000 sq km in the South China Sea and Gulf of Siam were offered. Of these 30, only 12 blocks were completely clear of conflicting territorial claims by South Viet-Nam's southern and western neighbours. [388] Of the 111 000 sq km in dispute, 19 000 sq km are claimed by Thailand, 62 000 sq km by the Khmer Republic, 2 000 sq km by Malaysia and 28 000 sq km by Indonesia. In addition, some 15 000 sq km of the 80 000 sq km reserved for future offshore exploration is claimed by Indonesia. [389] The 11 blocks in the Gulf of Siam subject to counter-claims by the Khmer Replublic, Thailand and Malaysia did not draw any bids. In fact, because of the disputed exploration rights, only eight blocks covering 59 800 sq km of sea-bed between 15 and 120 miles south and southeast of the Saigon coastal area attracted bidders. Two of these eight blocks are among those subject to boundary disputes with Indonesia. [389–390] The contracts signed with four firms (Mobil, Exxon, Pecten Vietnam [a wholly owned subsidiary of Shell Oil], and Sunningdale Co. of Canada) in September 1973 required the concessionaires to spend a total of $59.3 million on exploration and to start seismic work within six months and drilling before September 1975. [389] The National Petroleum Board stated its intention of re-offering the unawarded 22 blocks within the next year. [390]

A delegation was sent to Cambodia to discuss continental shelf limits in May 1973. [388]

The Khmer Republic (Cambodia)

In July 1973, the Khmer Ministry of Mining awarded an 18 548 sq km concession to Marine Associates of Hong Kong. The southern half of the concession overlaps the offshore area claimed by South Viet-Nam. [390]

Thailand

The government of Thailand has also granted concessions in disputed areas and allowed wildcat drilling to begin. Following a promising gas and oil strike by the US Tenneco Co. in a well 160 miles offshore, Thailand requested Tenneco to withhold test rate information since the strike lies near acreage claimed by both the Khmer Republic and South Viet-Nam. Negotiations among the three governments were begun. The 1974 published limits of the Thai continental shelf in the Gulf of Siam also conflict with the western limits of the Khmer claims. Discussions among the countries concerned has so far failed to produce any agreement. [389–390]

The Malacca Straits

Malaysia and Indonesia have declared that the Malacca Straits connecting the Andaman Sea with the South China Sea is not an international waterway but within Indonesian and Malaysian territorial waters. Singapore also rejects international management of the Straits but, along with Indonesia and Malaysia, accepts shipping on the basis of "innocent passage". [391] A trilateral agreement between Thailand, Indonesia and Malaysia was signed late in 1971 delimiting their respective rights in the northern part of the Malacca Straits. [392]

The Andaman Sea

The agreement signed by Indonesia and Thailand in December 1971 on the demarcation of their offshore borders [392] was apparently not conclusive. Negotiations between these countries on the demarcation of the deep water area at the southern end of the Andaman Sea off the coast of northern Sumatra opened again in September 1973, [393] and were reported to have been concluded during the spring of 1974. [394]

III. *The Gulf Area*

In the Arabian/Persian Gulf area several territorial disputes related to the existence of oil have been settled, although some still remain unresolved, a matter treated further on page 49. Other territorial conflicts in this area have been based on factors other than oil but have been complicated by the existence of oil in the area. A typical example of this has been the conflict between the Iraqi government and the Kurdish population in northern Iraq.

In 1961, a considerable section of this minority population rose in rebellion under General Mulla Mustafa Barzani, the leader of the Democratic Party of Kurdistan, and proclaimed an independent Kurdish state. Military operations in the following years tended to follow a regular pattern — a spring and summer offensive by the government forces, with the ground then won being lost again to the Kurds in the autumn and winter. A settlement was not reached until 1970 when a peace plan was accepted by both parties; it conceded *inter alia* that the Kurds should participate fully in the government.

On 11 March 1974 President Bakr put forward a proposal for autonomous rule in Kurdistan and gave the Kurds 15 days to accept the proposal, [395–396] but they rejected it and the decree for autonomous rule was issued on 26 March without Kurdish consent. The main point of disagreement was the Kurdish demand that the oil-rich Kirkuk area should be included in the autonomous region. [397] In an interview on 31 March, General Barzani said he would unilaterally declare autonomy for Kurdistan, or take even more drastic measures if the crisis worsened. [398]

After the government's announcement on 11 March fighting broke out, in which oil installations reportedly became targets of attack. On 4 May there were confirmed reports that Kurdish guerillas had blown up oil and gas tanks in the Kirkuk region in retaliation for the bombing of four Kurdish towns. If true, this attack was the first of its kind and would represent a shift in Kurdish tactics. [399]

During the fighting General Barzani appealed for support from the West suggesting that oil might be the reward for such help. [400] The Iraqi government claimed that the Kurds had received military aid from the United States, [401] but this claim was immediately denied by the US State Department. [402] There were also press reports that the Kurds received military or financial aid from a number of other countries (Iran, Turkey and Israel). [400—404]

It should also be noted in this context that already in June 1973 the Kurdish leader, General Barzani, said in an interview that he would have opposed Iraq's nationalization of the Kirkuk oil fields in June 1972 if he had been consulted by the government.

We are ready to do what goes with American policy in this area if America will protect us from the wolves. If support were strong enough, we could control the Kirkuk field and give it to an American company to operate. It is in our area, and the nationalization was an act against the Kurds. [405]

IV. *Northern Europe*

In Europe, the area giving rise to the most territorial problems has been the North Sea. There the area south of the 62nd parallel has been settled in accordance with the principles for the division of the continental shelves laid down in the 1958 Geneva Convention, supplemented by a decision taken by the International Court of Justice (ICJ) in the Hague.

The 1958 Convention, which came into force in 1964, laid down rules by which the continental shelf areas could be equitably divided among the coastal states concerned. The principle employed was that, where two or more states have coasts opposite each other, the boundary of their continental shelf sovereignty is determined by application of equidistance measurements, that is, the boundary is the median line equidistant from the nearest points on the base lines (low-water lines) from which the breadth of the territorial seas is measured.

These principles enabled a number of agreements to be made which delineated the different North Sea sectors, but in some cases disputes still arose about these boundary delimitations. In particular, West Germany maintained that the definition quoted was unacceptably disadvantageous in view of the inward-curving coastline of that country. The dispute with its neighbours was taken to the ICJ, which ruled in 1969 that the German-Dutch and German-Danish offshore sector boundaries should be revised. [232c]

For practical reasons, a border was drawn in 1964 across the continental shelf along the 62nd parallel. As to the area north of this parallel, no production licences have yet been granted but concessions are expected to be allotted in 1975. [406] Geographically speaking the Norwegian continental shelf can be roughly divided into (a) the North Sea area extending to 62°N (off Stadt, where the Norwegian trough goes out into the Atlantic Ocean); (b) the mid-Norwegian shelf from Stadt to Lofoten; (c) the Norwegian shelf from Lofoten round the North Cape to the Soviet frontier; and finally (d) the Svalbard shelf lying to the north of the deep channel south of Bjørnøya. [407] However, the final boundaries for the Norwegian shelf have not yet been decided, nor has an agreement been negotiated with the

Soviet Union defining the border between the Norwegian and Soviet continental shelves in the Barents Sea.

The official Norwegian view of the consequences to their foreign relations of petroleum finds in the Norwegian continental shelf was stated in a report to the Norwegian parliament in 1971:

When appraising matters connected with the opening of the northern Norwegian Continental Shelf regions for economic operations, and particularly when determining the order of priority for exploitation of the various parts in these regions, foreign relations aspects must be kept in mind.

Royal Decree of 31st May 1963 gave Norway sovereignty over the Continental Shelf in as far as concerns exploration for and exploitation of natural resources and as far as the depth of the sea permits – but not beyond the median line in relation to other nations. This is in conformity with the international concept which has grown up.

The Ministry of Foreign Affairs has assumed that – as stated in Report No. 95 (1969–70) to the Storting – these wide areas of the Shelf which have for the said purpose been place under Norwegian sovereignty, would only gradually be opened for economic operations.

One matter to be considered is that no borders have as yet been fixed for the Norwegian Continental Shelf areas north of 62° N. Lat.

As mentioned in Report No. 95, principles with regard to the Continental Shelf limits out towards the deep ocean are currently being considered by the United Nations. In its Continental Shelf policies Norway should adopt a line which makes allowance for the work being done on an international arrangement of these matters.

With regard to borders between Russian and Norwegian Continental Shelf areas, preliminary discussions of these matters were started in Oslo in October 1970, although negotiations proper have not yet commenced.

One consequence of further appreciable petroleum finds on the Norwegian Continental Shelf will be that Western Europe will be less dependent upon supplies of crude oil from other parts of the world. On the other hand, it is to be anticipated that such oil deposits will create heightened interest in our coastal regions. The finds hitherto made in the North Sea have not resulted in altering the factual and political circumstances which are of significance for our foreign relations. Should these finds be supplemented by big commercial finds farther north, we must be prepared for this to lead to increased political interest in our country.

Generally speaking the Ministry of Foreign Affairs has recommended that one should seek to find principles for Norwegian Continental Shelf policy in the North, which aim at gradual utilization of resources to be found there, giving due consideration to other nations' legitimate interests in these areas, where the borderlines for the continental shelves of other nations, have still not been definitely fixed.

Making an overall appraisal of the possible foreign relations aspects of any big petroleum finds north of 62° N. Lat., the Ministry of Foreign Affairs states that it will be especially important to ensure that the exploration for and exploitation of petroleum resources is under Norwegian management and control. [408]

The prospect of finding oil in the archipelago of Svalbard gives rise to additional problems because of the special status of these islands. Svalbard is an archipelago, of which the main islands are Spitsbergen, Nordaustlandet, Edgeøya, Prins Karls Forland, Bjørnøya, Hopen, Kong Karls land, Kvitøya, and many small islands. By an international treaty, signed on 9 February 1920 in Paris, Norway's sovereignty over the archipelago was recognized by some 40 countries. On 14 August 1925 the archipelago was officially incorporated into Norway. However, the Paris treaty also recognized the right of all countries to exploit the natural resources of Svalbard (article 3). [409]

Coal is the principal resource, and is exploited by a Soviet community (between 3 000 and 4 000 people) and a Norwegian community (about 1 000 people). [410]

Svalbard consists partly of sedimentary rocks, which implies the possibility of finding petroleum on land. A number of desultory explorations have been made off the islands of Spitsbergen, Edgeøya, Barentsøya and Hopen, but so far, according to the Norwegian Ministry of Industry, no commercially exploitable finds have been made. [411] The Soviet Union has now announced that it will undertake new drillings on Soviet concessions on Svalbard. [406]

Pursuant to the Svalbard Treaty (article 9), Norway undertakes not to create nor to allow the establishment of any naval base in the Svalbard archipelago, nor ever to construct any fortification in this territory which may be used for warlike purposes.

The Soviet Union demanded as early as 1944 that Norway relinquish its sovereignty over Bjørnøya south of Svalbard. Also it suggested that the Svalbard Treaty should be abrogated and that a common Soviet/Norwegian defence system should be installed on the island. The discussions were postponed until after World War II. When this suggestion was again presented by the Soviet Union in 1946 it was rejected by Norway. [412–413]

Preliminary discussions regarding the delineation of this area were started in Oslo in October 1970, but actual negotiations have not yet commenced. When the Norwegian Premier, Bratteli, visited Moscow in March 1974, it was decided that negotiations on the border lines in the Barents Sea should start in the autumn of 1974, that is, after the International Law of the Sea Conference in Caracas in the summer of 1974. [414]

Norway contends that the boundary of the continental shelf should be determined by the application of the principle of the median line. The Soviet Union already in a decree of 1926 declared that the sector principle should apply, according to which each nation bordering the Arctic draws a line to the North Pole from its eastern and western extremities on the Arctic coast. [415]

The point at issue with regard to Svalbard is whether the area's potentially oil-rich sea-bed forms part of Svalbards's continental shelf – which would give some 40 signatory states exploiting rights and most probably introduce the international oil companies to the area, thus giving rise to complex strategic problems – or whether the whole area between the North Cape and Svalbard is under Norwegian jurisdiction. Norway claims that the latter is the case, [411a] and the Soviet Union is likely to prefer this situation to opening up the Svalbard continental shelf to other signatories.

It is assumed that several years will pass before the final borders are fixed for the whole of the continental shelf north of the 62nd parallel.

Generally speaking, this part of the Arctic region is a very sensitive one, not only because of the unsettled territorial questions and the concomitant right to exploit the underlying reserves. This is not surprising when it is considered that a strategically vital Soviet naval base is situated in this region, at Murmansk which is only 100 km from the Soviet-Norwegian border. This is the largest naval base area in the world in terms of the number of naval ships it supports, and it is by far the largest submarine base in the world. Murmansk boasts a strategic eminence unmatched by any other Soviet port, since it is the only Soviet port with ready wartime access to the world's oceans. In winter, there is still open water in the Norwegian Sea, and normally the Denmark Strait between Greenland and Iceland is also open. In the other direction, beyond the ice-free Murmansk coast, the entire Siberian coastline merges into the Arctic pack ice as does the Bering Strait. The Northern sea route can be used for only 130—150 days each year and even then only with the assistance of icebreakers. [415] The Soviet Northern Fleet stationed in Murmansk comprises about 500 ships of all kinds and 100 000 men; there are also 40 000 other troops stationed in the region. Several hundred aircraft and helicopters form an integrated part of the Northern Fleet. About 180 of the ships are submarines of which 70—80 are nuclear powered (or about 75 per cent of the USSR's total nuclear submarine force). Of the nuclear submarines, about half are provided with Submarine Launched Ballistic Missiles (SLBMs), while the other half have Anti Submarine Warfare (ASW) functions. [413]

The NATO forces have a standing naval force, STANAVFORLANT (Standing Naval Force Atlantic), operating in the North Atlantic and the Norwegian Sea. It normally consists of six to eight destroyers and frigates on a rotation basis from various countries. Norway has four submarines and 15 smaller surface ships stationed in the waters outside northern Norway. The nearest major US naval fleet designated for this area is the Second Fleet (Atlantic), based in Norfolk, Virginia, which is about 6 000 km from the gap between Greenland-Iceland and the Faroe Islands. In addition, the United States has bases in Greenland and Iceland. [413]

Because the sea lane from Murmansk swings through the Norwegian Sea out into the Atlantic Ocean, both the Soviet Union and the NATO countries attach great strategic importance to this area, the latter for surveillance of Soviet naval activities and for blockading the Soviet sea-routes in case of war. If installations for oil exploitation are introduced into the area, a crucial question for the coastal states will be whether such installations can also be used militarily, for the surveillance of Soviet naval activities. It is doubtful, however, whether such surveillance equipment could even marginally improve the facilities already possessed by the United States and the Soviet Union for monitoring each others' naval activities. [416]

V. *The Aegean Sea*

At a time when the Cyprus conflict had shown some promise of a settlement, the historical rivalry between Greece and Turkey was fed new fuel in a conflict which continues to grow over their respective mineral rights in the Aegean Sea.

On 1 November 1973 the Turkish government awarded oil exploration concessions to the Turkish State Oil Co. at 27 places in the Aegean Sea which Turkey claims lie in its sector of the continental shelf. [417] Drilling was scheduled to begin in the summer of 1974. [418] Greece disputed this claim and immediately protested. According to the Geneva Convention ruling of 1958 the continental shelf is that area of the sea-bed extending from a nation's territory covered by not more than 200 m of water. Greece interprets this to mean that because of its island territories scattered in the Aegean, many of which lie quite close to the Turkish mainland and were taken from Turkey during World War I, Greece has virtual sovereignty over all the Aegean Sea apart from Turkey's territorial waters. Turkey, however, maintains that these islands cannot constitute the basis of a claim on the continental shelf; Greece is entitled to mineral rights within a six-mile territorial water limit surrounding each island but outside this limit jurisdiction over the continental shelf should be determined by a median line drawn between the mainland of the two states. [419]

The Greek discovery of oil and gas in commercial quantities off the island of Thassos, though not in a disputed area, has intensified the dispute by encouraging the prospects of commercial finds in other areas. Experts are reported to believe that the oil reserves in the Aegean are sufficient to meet Greece's domestic needs of nine million tons per year and still produce oil for export. [420] In June 1974, it was reported that the US company, Oceanic Exploration, as operator and majority shareholder in a four-company consortium, intends to bring recent North Aegean oil discoveries into production "as quickly as possible within the next two years". [421]

Throughout the spring the relationship between Greece and Turkey deteriorated. In April 1974 talks on Cyprus broke down over the Turkish demand for a federation but many analysts believe the motive for dissension on Turkey's part may have mainly been to strengthen its bargaining position on sea-bed rights. [422] Both nations increased their use of nationalistic rhetoric, brandished their military power and reinforced their military border units. [423—425] The tension rose significantly when Turkey sent a naval survey ship guarded by warships to search for oil on the Aegean sea-bed in the area off the Greek island of Lesbos. [426—428] While it has been pointed out that Greece and Turkey have new, unstable regimes which might wish to promote the fear of foreign aggression in order to consolidate power internally, tension over the outcome of the dispute would hardly be feigned in view of what is at stake.

The growing threat of a military encounter was viewed with alarm particularly in the West since Greece and Turkey, as members of the NATO alliance, are important strategic links in the West's defence structure. Pressure from the USA — reportedly interested in mediating between the two countries [429—430] — was most likely a significant factor behind the announcement by the Turkish Premier on 25 May that Greece had finally agreed to negotiate. [431—432] Talks would be held on 19—20 June in Ottawa where the Greek and Turkish foreign ministers would be attending the NATO Foreign Ministers' Council meeting. [433] The announcement of talks between the two countries apparently eased the crisis in the beginning of June. [434]

Not surprisingly, the renewed tension between Greece and Turkey has given new spurs to the arms race in the area. The first indication was Turkey's decision to set up a national strike force independent of NATO and to make undisclosed arms purchases. [424] Greece is reported to have placed orders, with France for 40 Mirage fighters, 125 AMX-30 medium tanks, and four gunboats equipped with Exocet surface-to-surface missiles. Concurrently, 38 F-4 Phantoms are being delivered from the United States and it has been reported that Greece hopes also to be able to order some medium-range bombers. [435—436]

Appendix 9.

The oil situation in Germany during World War II [437]

I. Supply and consumption from the outbreak of the war to May 1944

With the close of World War I, most of the industrialized nations were thoroughly aware of the problem of mineral supply. Germany became the leader in the adoption of measures to secure raw materials for war and peace purposes. Following World War I it began the intensive exploration and development of all domestic resources. Substitution, or the use of "ersatz" materials, was thoroughly investigated and in some cases introduced. Strategic minerals were imported in excess of current needs. The government took over the direction of nearly all efforts of this kind both in domestic development and in securing supplies from abroad.

Within its prewar boundaries, Germany had ample resources of, for instance, coal and artificial nitrates. It was devoid of high-grade iron ore, however, since Germany had lost the iron ores of Alsace as a result of World War I. For such elements as copper, nickel, sulphur, tungsten, titanium, tin, manganese, chromium, lead and bauxite, there was a shortage or complete absence of resources. [438]

In comparison with that of other world powers, Germany's oil supply at the outbreak of the war was at a low level. Its total production and imports of oil products and liquid fuels in 1938 amounted to a little more than seven million tons. The United Kingdom, with a much smaller population, imported 12 million tons during the same year. The United States and the Soviet Union, both nations with large crude oil resources, produced 164 and 29 million tons, respectively. Germany had accustomed its economy to this relatively small oil supply and had even planned its war strategy on this basis. War plans were based on *blitzkrieg* concepts, and on the assumption that oil requirements for successive short campaigns could be met in part by withdrawals from inventories.

The meagre oil supply to which Germany had become accustomed was seriously threatened at the outbreak of the war. In 1938 nearly 60 per cent of its total supplies were imported from outside the continent of Europe. On the other hand, Germany was the only country in the world to be producing synthetic oil products on a large scale, of which most was produced by the hydrogenation process and a smaller part by Fischer-Tropsch synthetic processes. By the outbreak of the war, seven hydrogenation, seven Fischer-Tropsch and a number of tar distillation and carbonization plants were in operation. Geographically the synthetic plants were concentrated near bituminous coal deposits in the Ruhr area and near brown coal deposits in Central Europe.

With its imports from overseas cut off by the blockade, Germany took three major steps to maintain its oil supply: (a) increased imports from within Europe, especially Romania and for a time the Soviet Union; (b) stepped-up production of domestic crude oil; and (c) expanded production of synthetic oil. These measures nearly offset the loss of overseas imports in 1940 and resulted in an oil supply for the years 1941–43 which was substantially greater than before the war.

The oil in the Caucasus was a major goal of Germany's 1942 campaign in the

Soviet Union. The Baku fields produced two-thirds of the Soviet Union's crude oil supply and two and a half times as much as all of Axis Europe — which had a production of approximately 12 million tons in 1941. With the failure to take Stalingrad, Germany's only hope of obtaining adequate oil resources was shattered.

In 1943, the Allies were able to put substantial production and transportation difficulties in the way of German imports from Romania. In a 15th air force raid on the Ploesti oil fields on 1 August 1943, some 50 000 tons of crude oil and refined petroleum products were destroyed along with 50 per cent of the refining capacity.

Nevertheless, Germany's achievement in the preceding years had been remarkable. Production of crude oil was tripled from 1938 to 1941 and increased further in the next two years. By the end of 1943, output was at a rate of almost two million tons a year, of which Austrian production accounted for nearly two-thirds. Moreover, the resources devoted to synthetic oil production were enormous, so that by the end of the period, 18 hydrogenation and nine Fischer-Tropsch plants were in production. (It is interesting to note, however, that while some German military and industrial leaders made determined efforts to construct an additional capacity as rapidly as possible, such groups as the manufacturers of hydrogenation compressors opposed the expansion of their own output since they wanted to avoid the creation of what in the post-war period would become excess capacity.)

The fact that the oil situation did not become critical for Germany before the systematic Allied bombing attacks on oil targets in 1944 was due to careful economizing and drastic restrictions on civilian consumption. Three major oil products were in drastically short supply, namely, aviation gasoline, motor gasoline and diesel oil. Requirements for aviation gasoline increased enormously with the outbreak of the war. Up to late 1941, the Luftwaffe had been able to stretch out the meagre production of aviation gasoline by drawing on stocks during relatively short campaigns. Beginning in 1942, however, the war of attrition on the Eastern Front and the defence of the Reich from air attacks of increasing ferocity brought about a great increase in the demand for aviation fuel. The shortage of aviation gasoline also severely affected Germany's air crew training programme.

Shortages of other oil products did not affect military operations so directly. Realizing that the supply of gasoline would not support it, Germany did not motorize its army to the extent that its opponents did. Even so, there were at the time of the invasion of the Soviet Union nearly 800 000 Wehrmacht vehicles consuming oil products. There is no evidence that the size of the tank procurement programme was ever affected by the fuel supply. It is true that the oil supply of the troops attempting to take Stalingrad was inadequate, but this appears to have been more a problem of transport over scorched earth than a lack of oil products in Germany.

Civilian consumption of motor gasoline was cut very steeply. In 1942 and 1943 about two-thirds of the German supply of motor gasoline was consumed by the Wehrmacht; half of the remainder was exported to allies and the rest, 0.3 million tons per year, was left for the civilian economy. Drastic cuts were also made in civilian consumption of diesel oil, while 40 to 50 per cent went to the Wehrmacht (chiefly to the navy).

In the spring of 1944, Germany's oil position was extremely tight. The Wehrmacht was not getting enough aviation gasoline to meet its minimum requirements, and its needs for motor gasoline and diesel oil were being met only by a ruthless stripping of the economy.

II. *The effects of bombing on supply.*

Prior to May 1944 the Allied aerial offensive against the oil target system of Axis Europe was sporadic and amounted to only about 4 000 tons of bombs. The only important raid during this period was the attack, referred to above, upon the Ploesti oil fields and refineries in 1943. Beginning in May 1944, heavy and sustained bombing of the petroleum resources of Germany and its allies was carried out by the 8th and 15th US Air Forces and the British RAF. In the 12-month period before VE-day, more than 200 000 tons of bombs were aimed at oil targets. By the end of September 1944, every important synthetic oil plant had been hit at least twice, and 69 refineries, numerous storage installations and a number of miscellaneous liquid fuel plants had also been attacked.

The effect of this campaign on the already precarious German oil supply was catastrophic. Total production and imports of oil products dropped by two-thirds between the first and the last quarter of 1944. The effects of the oil shortage on Germany's war effort were in fact greater than even the advocates of bombing oil targets had dared to predict. The extent of the shortage of aviation gasoline had been greatly underestimated. From September 1944 to the end of the war in May 1945, German consumption of aviation gasoline continued to decline. Only the consumption of jet fuel increased slightly. In February 1945, production of aviation gasoline was practically abandoned and it is known that in the last months of the war, most of the few German Air Force planes encountered were of the jet type.

The bombing of oil targets had the secondary effect of causing a drastic reduction in the output of a number of chemicals, including nitrogen, methanol and synthetic rubber, because of the interrelation between the synthetic oil and chemical industries. Methanol is the principal constituent of hexogen, which is a powerful explosive, the manufacture of which had to be abandoned in 1944 for lack of basic material. The force required to knock out this target was small in relation to the consequences of the oil loss on the German war effort. The more than 200 000 tons of bombs dropped on oil targets represented only about 15 per cent of all Allied strategic bombing in Europe.

Taking an overall view of Germany's wartime fuel situation, some experts have argued that the Allied forces should have concentrated more effort on the bombing of oil targets at an earlier date in order to achieve a quicker end to the war. Thus it has been noted that, on 25 July 1944, the RAF despatched a mere 135 bombers to the oil plant at Wanna-Eichel, whereas 550 were sent to bomb the city of Stuttgart. In the judgement of one authority, "Had the whole might of Bomber Command been placed against the oil and chemistry industry, and not sent off on further massive area assaults on the cities, there can be little doubt that the issue would have been settled there and then". [438] It has been suggested that too much attention was given by the Allied forces to the Fischer-Tropsch plants in that they produced little aviation fuel, while receiving 20 per cent of the bomb tonnage dropped. It is also surprising that more emphasis was not placed at an earlier date on the probable effect of bombing on aviation gasoline installations.

Whatever view is taken on these problems, there can be no doubt that the attack on oil had an immense effect on the course of the war. The defeat of Germany was due to a combination of pressures, but the attack on oil made a large contribution to the Allied victory. No doubt victory was certain, regardless of any German oil shortage, once the Allied armies had established themselves in France. Nevertheless, the final struggle would have been more difficult and more costly if the attack on oil had not reduced the mobility and efficiency of the German air force and the German army.

Notes

[1] The International Institute for Applied Systems Analysis in Laxenburg, Austria, is currently engaged in an Energy Systems Project, the aim of which is to study the role of energy in the ecosphere and in the society-technology complex. The basic concept of the project is that energy cannot be considered as an isolated problem, but as part of a system in which the production of energy is only one component. Thus the handling of energy and its position in the global and social complex in terms of ecology, economy, risks and resources are of similar importance. [1]

Another significant study on energy problems is that being undertaken by the Organization for Economic Cooperation and Development (OECD). Since 1972 this body has been carrying out an urgent reassessment of energy prospects for the period 1974—85, taking into account the broadest possible range of relevant factors. Among the latter are the complex interrelations between energy and the environment; the impact of the changing energy situation on balance-of-payments structures and the relations of OECD countries with the developing world; the role of technological innovations in meeting new requirements; and the possibility of more rational use of energy and other factors that could affect supply and demand within this time scale. The report is due to be published during the autumn of 1974. [2]

Other major energy research projects have usually been more nationally oriented. One such project aiming at a comprehensive analysis of national energy policy problems in the United States was announced by the Ford Foundation in August 1972. This so-called Energy Policy Project has given priority to five major areas of study: (a) the quality of life; (b) energy and lifestyles; (c) efficiency and conservation; (d) international outlook; and (e) scenarios of the future. [3]

[2] Although all countries are oil consumers, the mix of their roles as consumers, importers, producers and exporters differs widely. The United States, for instance, plays an important role as a consumer, a producer and an importer and, to a limited degree, also as an exporter. The Soviet Union is likewise an important consumer, producer and exporter, and, less significantly, an importer. Canada is a consumer, producer, importer and exporter and is fairly significant in all these roles. In this report, the importance of a country's exporting role in relation to its importing role, or *vice versa,* determines to which group that country belongs. Thus the terms PE- and IC-country refer only to the major roles played either as a producer-exporter or as an importer-consumer. The United States and Canada are therefore treated mainly as IC-countries. It should also be borne in mind that these variables are not static and may change in the longer perspective. (See the discussion in chapter 2 and appendix 2.)

[3] Opinions differ as to whether such cooperation is realistic or not. See, for instance, a series of articles in *Foreign Policy* 1973—74 on this question. [4—7]

[4] It is noteworthy, however, that the Organization for Economic Cooperation and Development (OECD), whose 24 members account for over 70 per cent of world oil consumption, has recently made the following observations in a review of the progress of its Long-Term Energy Assessment: "Apart from imbalances between oil refinery output patterns and demand structures in some areas, physical oil shortages are now rare. Governments are, however, confronted with new problems of a long-term nature resulting from the quadrupling of the FOB cost of crude oil to oil

146

companies in the space of a few months. Forecasts for 1980 and 1985 have now been made by OECD and checked with experts from national administrations. One preliminary result, highly relevant to policy decisions, is that, on one possible assumption, namely that international oil prices remain at or near present levels, the volume of oil imports of the OECD area in 1980 will not exceed that in 1973, a dramatic downward revision by 40 per cent from the pre-October 1973 forecasts. This result is due about equally to reductions in the growth of energy consumption in OECD countries, and to increases in production of indigenous oil and other energy supplies which are used as substitutes for oil imports.

In spite of this major shift in production and consumption patterns resulting from increased energy prices, this result should not encourage governments to believe that the market mechanism alone is going to solve all the problems related to the energy situation. There are a number of areas where policy decisions need to be taken to alleviate short- and long-term problems, and improve on the reduction in oil imports resulting from the operation of the market mechanism. Moreover, the supply and demand situation may remain tight in the years prior to 1980 and temporary or local shortages due to accidental causes or supply/demand adjustment difficulties are not unlikely.

The main areas where it is already clear that policy decisions could make a major impact are: (*a*) energy observations and demand restraint; (*b*) more rapid development of indigenous resources; (*c*) improved energy pricing policies; and (*d*) research and development." [2]

5 OPEC originally had five founders: Iran, Iraq, Kuwait, Saudi Arabia and Venezuela. The following countries have subsequently become members: Qatar (1961), Indonesia (1962), Libya (1962), Abu Dhabi (1967), Algeria (1969) and Nigeria (1971). In 1973 Ecuador was admitted first as an associate member and then as a full member. Gabon was admitted as an associate member in 1973. At its own request, Abu Dhabi's membership was aligned with that of the United Arab Emirates in 1974. Trinidad and Tobago have applied for membership. Seven of the members are Arab states.

6 The former Secretary-General of OPEC, Fuad Rouhani, has outlined the common characteristics of OPEC's founding members as follows:

1. They were developing countries.

2. They were large exporters of petroleum.

3. The financing of their development projects and the equilibrium of their budgets depended on the revenues of these exports.

4. They were not able to exploit their oil resources without the assistance of foreigners, and accordingly their oil industry was in the hands of the major oil companies.

5. The agreements governing the operation of their oil industry were to a large extent similar, so that the problems that presented themselves and the disputes that arose between the host countries and the operating companies were consequently often identical. [8]

7 One expert on OPEC activities, Zuhayr Mikdashi, has characterized the OPEC coalition and history in the following way: "The Organization of Petroleum Exporting Countries (OPEC) will probably be remembered in history as an outstanding example of relatively successful intergovernmental cooperation among developing countries. OPEC's achievements in raising the oil export income of members appear remarkable in view of the deep sociopolitical divisions among them — occasionally verging on armed conflicts. Nevertheless, OPEC countries have managed not to let these conflicts wreck their common interest in obtaining

substantially better terms from the international companies and from consumer countries. That OPEC countries could obtain better terms is not only the result of member solidarity but also of the relatively inelastic demand for petroleum. Another crucial factor favoring OPEC is that major consumer countries have been moderate in their drive to collectively countervail OPEC, except indirectly by allowing their international oil companies to join forces ostensibly in defense of consumers' interests. Major consumer countries have also declined so far to split forcefully the OPEC coalition. The continued existence of OPEC largely depends on (1) members' perception of gain outweighing sacrifices or frustrations of working together, and (2) the tolerance of major industrial importing countries." [9]

[8] In a resolution of December 1958, the General Assembly established the Commission on Permament Sovereignty over Natural Resources and instructed it to survey this subject "as a basic constituent of the right to self-determination". This commission prepared a draft resolution which came up before the General Assembly in 1962; the result was the resolution of 14 December concerning permanent sovereignty over natural resources. [10] On 25 November 1966, the General Assembly adopted a further resolution reaffirming and supplementing the principles of the previous resolution. [11]

[9] The founders of OAPEC were Kuwait, Libya and Saudi Arabia. They were later joined by Iraq, Abu Dhabi, Qatar, Bahrein, Egypt, Syria, Algeria and Dubai. Oman and Tunisia have applied for membership. Dubai withdrew at the end of 1972 after a dispute over the location of dry docks in the Arabian/Persian Gulf.

[10] Winston Churchill, in 1912, made a decision to involve the British government in the business of exploring for and producing oil. This decision allowed the government to invest funds in the then Anglo-Persian Oil Company, which was at the time very short of working capital, in order to safeguard supplies for the Royal Navy. [13]

[11] One oil expert, M.A. Conant, pointed out as late as 1973, that US dominance was likely to continue: "For the foreseeable future and despite the greater control by producing states over the disposition of their oil resources, it is likely to remain a fact that the companies which will continue to be the dominant factors in Saudi Arabia's growing production and truly immense reserves will still be American-owned. Iranian oil is next in importance in the Middle East and there the American share is now 40 per cent: in Kuwait it is now 50 per cent. If one adds British holdings to these percentages, the share of Middle East or 'Gulf' oil managed by American and British enterprises is for all practical purposes nearly total — and two-thirds of the world's known oil reserves lie in that region." [15]

[12] In a major research study on the changing patterns of country-company relationships since 1950, the following main developments were specified:

1. The revision of financial and geographical terms of the old concessions.

2. The setting up of the Organization of Petroleum Exporting Countries (OPEC) with worldwide membership through which countries can act jointly to promote their interests.

3. The entrance of new companies under new types of concession, partnership, or contract agreements.

4. The organization of national oil companies designed to participate in oil activities both on their own and/or in various forms of relationship to companies under the old concession agreements or under the various types of agreements with newcomers.

5. The setting up of the Organization of Arab Petroleum Exporting Countries

(OAPEC) to promote forms of joint action among a limited group of important oil-producing countries.

6. The as yet unfilled demand of some countries to be admitted to a participating ownership and management status in the old concessionaire companies. [16]

13 In an interview, OPEC Secretary-General, Dr Abderrahman Khene, expressed his views regarding the international oil companies in the following statement: "For the future, the oil companies have played out their role as intermediary traders. Nevertheless, there is a second aspect to be considered, namely the usefulness of these companies in the technical field. I have often emphasized that the companies in this sphere have a very important scope for the future. I would even say that it would be a pity to be deprived of their experience and abilities." [17]

14 One of the results of the energy crisis has been to focus public attention on the enormous power and potential to manipulate economies wielded by the major international oil companies. Through various kinds of investigation (hearings, and so on) the role of the oil companies is now being scrutinized by public bodies, for example, in the United States, Japan, FR Germany and Italy. The oil companies find themselves in an uneasy situation and find it particularly difficult to explain to the general public the *raison d'être* for their enormous profits reportedly earned during the oil crisis in the winter of 1973/74.

15 This special relationship has been commented on by one oil expert (Odell) in the following: "Notwithstanding the existence of such European-based companies, one must note that most of the oil used in Europe was — and still is — produced, transported, refined and distributed for foreign — mainly American — companies, over which, of course, in the final analysis political control rests elsewhere, and which also, in the event of crisis, could theoretically 'retire' to the other side of the Atlantic. Perhaps more realistically, given the existence of NATO and the OECD, with membership in both cases drawn from both sides of the Atlantic, one could reasonably suppose that necessary action required in Europe from such companies could be ensured through pressure exerted by the US government." [13]

Another interesting illustration of the relations between the three groups of interest was some revelations by Exxon Oil Co. officials at US Senate subcommittee hearings in April 1974. Exxon, as a partner in the Arabian American Oil Company (Aramco) and as the largest supplier of oil to the US armed forces, admitted that it had given Saudi Arabia confidential refinery data that was used to cut off oil to US military units during the Arab-Israeli October War. The data consisted of a detailed breakdown of how much Middle East crude oil was used by Exxon refineries around the world to meet US military needs. The Department of Defense had approved of the action, however. Senator Henry Jackson reportedly made the following comment on this subject: "The issue presented is this: What are the responsibilities of American-based multinational oil corporations to the United States government when the vital interests of the United States and the policies of the oil-producing nations these multinational corporations operate in are in a direct and fundamental conflict." [18]

16 The OPEC countries had managed to obtain several price increases in the preceding few years. At their meeting in Caracas in December 1970, the OPEC members decided to raise to 55 per cent the minimum level of tax on the net income of companies operating in the OPEC member states. Again, at meetings between the OPEC members and the oil companies in Teheran in January and February 1971, a five-year agreement between 23 international oil companies and the six producing countries in the Gulf was reached, after the OPEC members had threatened the oil companies with total embargo if the minimum requirements of the Gulf states were not met. At a meeting in Geneva in January 1972, the oil

companies agreed to adjust the oil revenues for six of the largest oil-producing countries of the Middle East caused by changes in exchange values of international currencies. In June 1973 a new agreement was concluded with the oil companies, under which the posted prices of crude oil were raised by 11.9 per cent and a mechanism was installed whereby prices should be adjusted monthly henceforth. [12a]

Concurrently, within less than two years, the PE-countries, led by the Gulf states, had forced through the beginnings of participation in the oil companies. Through a General Agreement on Participation, originally signed in New York on 5 October 1972, it was stipulated that, from 1 January 1973, host governments should acquire a 25 per cent participation in crude oil production from the concessions of foreign oil companies operating in their countries. This proportion would be increased to 51 per cent by 1 January 1982. The rules of the agreement changed quickly, however. Only Saudi Arabia, Abu Dhabi, Qatar and Oman signed individual participation agreements roughly in accordance with the model General Agreement. Kuwait announced in the summer of 1973 that it was seeking a new participating arrangement under which Kuwait would immediately acquire a 51 per cent holding in the joint companies' operations. In September 1973 Abu Dhabi took the same line but without giving a specific date for an earlier takeover. Later, in November, Saudi Arabia announced that it, too, was demanding an earlier attainment of 51 per cent participation. Still other countries such as Iraq, Libya and Nigeria have already achieved 51–55 per cent participation or complete nationalization. Retroactive to 1 January 1974, the Kuwait National Assembly on 14 May 1974 ratified a revised agreement by which the Kuwait government acquired a 60 per cent interest in the Kuwait Oil Company's operations. Qatar had earlier taken a similar decision. Iran, finally, initially took part in the participation negotiations but left them midway and on 24 May 1973 concluded a special 20-year agreement with the Western oil companies operating in Iran (the "consortium", in which British Petroleum is the main shareholder with 40 per cent). Under this agreement, the consortium will hand over the operation of all its facilities in Iran to the National Iranian Oil Co. (NIOC), and will in future act as technical advisers to the state oil company. In return, the consortium will be guaranteed long-term supplies of large quantities of crude oil. [19–21]

Indonesia's state oil company, Pertamina, has presided over an oil boom which has attracted more than 30 oil companies to Indonesia. Moreover, Pertamina claims that this expansion has been achieved without capitulating to foreign companies, since Pertamina has pioneered the production-sharing contract, a type of contract new to the oil world and which the oil companies accepted with great reluctance. Under production-sharing, Pertamina gains managerial control of oil operations and 65 per cent of all oil produced after a deduction from total output of up to 40 per cent for costs. Other countries in the region have tried to follow this example. Malaysia has passed a production-sharing law. Iran and the Philippines have adopted laws incorporating some of the principles of production-sharing. Burma and Bangladesh are expected to formulate laws on the Indonesian pattern. [22]

[17] Kuwait and Libya had by then announced decisions to cut their oil production for conservation reasons. Venezuela later made a similar decision on 9 April 1974. [23] At an international oil meeting in London on 18 April 1974, the Secretary-General of OPEC, Abderrahman Khene, warned that Qatar, Saudi Arabia and the United Arab Emirates — all of which have oil incomes far in excess of what they can absorb for their own economic development — might soon find it necessary to restrict their production. "Neither for the countries themselves, nor from a world point of view would it be wise to sustain production at a level which would exhaust known reserves in three decades", Mr Khene said. [24]

[18] For complete texts of the communiqués of 17 October, 4 November, 8

December and 25 December 1973, and of 18 March 1974, reference is made to appendix 6.

The account of the events related to the embargo is based on various articles in the major newspapers. Another source is *Keesings Contemporary Archives,* 26 November–2 December 1973, pp. 26224–28.

19At a news conference on 22 January 1974, Secretary of State Kissinger was reported to have said: "Failure to end the embargo in a reasonable time would raise serious questions of confidence in our minds with respect to the Arab nations with whom we have dealt on this issue". [36] In a speech on 6 February, Kissinger warned Arab governments against trying to force an Israeli withdrawal by the "blackmail" tactic of an oil embargo against the United States. He noted that the United States had been almost entirely responsible for the events that had brought about a ceasefire and troop disengagement agreement between Egypt and Israel. [37]

20 With the lifting of the embargo against the United States, Saudi Arabia authorized the Arabian American Oil Co., which controls 95 per cent of the Saudi Arabian crude production, to increase production immediately by 1.1 million b/d, raising Saudi Arabia's total daily production to about 8.2 million barrels, the pre-embargo level. [38–39] In future, Aramco would also be allowed to expand its current production and export capacity by about 2 million b/d to 11.2 million b/d by the end of 1975, although the actual level of production at any time would depend on what is allowed by the government. [40]

21 At a meeting with the Foreign Ministers of the Organization of African Unity (OAU) on 21 November 1973, the OAU recommended its members not to resume relations with Israel until it had withdrawn from all the occupied Arab territories and the legitimate rights of the Palestinian people had been restored. The OAU also requested the Arab countries which had not yet done so, as well as Iran and other oil-producing countries, to extend the oil embargo to South Africa, Portugal, and Rhodesia until these countries adhered to the UN resolution on decolonization. [41]

22 The Saudi Arabian Minister of Petroleum, Sheikh Ahmed Zadi Yamani, admitted in January that the oil boycott against the United States and the Netherlands had been ineffective. [42] At the beginning of March it was reported that crude oil supplies to Rotterdam never fell much below 60 per cent and had reached nearly 80 per cent of the pre-crisis level by the end of January. The corresponding figures for oil products were 77 per cent and 96 per cent, respectively. [43]

Finally, oil shipments from the Arabian/Persian Gulf (including Iraq and Iran) in December 1973 were about 7.4 per cent below the September level, according to a study commissioned by the International Longshoremen's Association in order to estimate the efficacy of the Arab oil embargo. Furthermore, increases by such non-Arab countries as Nigeria and Indonesia contributed to holding the overall world cutback to around 5 per cent. [44]

23 In a report released on 9 April, the US Department of Commerce revealed that several million barrels of oil had flowed into the United States during the embargo period from various OAPEC countries, some of which came from "boycott leaks" and some of which represented oil that had left the boycotting nations, but had not arrived in the United States when the embargo began. The report showed that Saudi Arabia was the major country of origin of most of this oil (25.8 million barrels imported during the period). [46] On 12 April, the Arabian American Oil Co. (Aramco) and two of its owners, Texaco Inc. and Mobil Oil Corp., denied that any US-destined oil had been loaded in Saudi Arabia after the embargo began in October 1973. [47]

The Shah of Iran was suggesting already in February that the United States had imported at least as much oil as it had before the Arab embargo was imposed. [45] This was immediately refuted by US officials who affirmed that the embargo was fully effective, [49] a view which was once again assailed by Iran. [50]

Interestingly enough, the Soviet Union also reportedly continued to supply the United States with limited shipments of oil, in spite of official Soviet support of the Arab oil embargo. [51—53]

[24] An exception was a statement by an international law expert, Professor Richard N. Gardner, at a hearing before the Joint Economic Committee of the US Congress in December 1973. He concluded that the oil embargo violated a treaty of 1933 between the United States and Saudi Arabia. According to a key clause in this treaty the two nations will grant each other "most favoured nation" treatment in trade matters, which means that neither nation can apply discriminatory tariffs or other regulations against the other. Gardner also concluded that the oil embargo violated a United Nations declaration of 1970 on "Principles of international law concerning friendly relations and cooperation among states in accordance with the Charter of the United Nations." [54] One of the provisions in the declaration states: "No State may use or encourage the use of economic, political or any other type of measures to coerce another State in order to obtain from it the subordination of the exercise of its sovereign rights and to secure from it advantages of any kind". [55] In a subsequent article in *Foreign Affairs,* Gardner gave the following critical views as to the application of this declaration: "It was the Afro-Asian group in the United Nations, including the Arab countries, that pressed hardest for the principle and for the proposition that it was already part of international law. Of course, their motive was to prevent the United States and other industrialized countries from using economic power as an instrument of political pressure. Not a single voice has been raised in the United Nations to cite the relevance of this authoritative declaration to the Arab oil embargo — which is typical of the 'double standard' that currently prevails in the world organization and accounts for much of the scepticism about the integrity of its decision-making process." [56]

In the same article Gardner also noted that the General Agreement on Tariffs and Trade (GATT) does contain a general prohibition on the use of export and import controls (Article XI) as well as a requirement that both export and import controls should not discriminate between countries (Article I). But for one thing, none of the Arab PE-countries is a party to GATT except for Kuwait. Furthermore, a subsequent GATT article adds exceptions to these rules — and exceptions to the exceptions — which make it extremely difficult to discern any coherent guidelines for national policy. And, more to the point, all of these principles are effectively vitiated by a subsequent GATT article (XXI) which declares that nothing in the GATT shall be construed "to prevent any contracting party from taking any action which it considers necessary for the protection of its essential security interests. . . taken in time of war or other emergency in international relations." [56]

[25] The member countries of the OECD should furnish appropriate information about their refinery projects to the Oil Committee; they should also retain such oil stocks and storage capacity as have been agreed upon; finally, they should apportion their oil supplies in an emergency. This has not applied to Canada and the United States in view of the special position of these two countries in the matter of oil supplies. [57]

On 29 June 1971 the Council of the OECD had recommended that the members of the European OECD area (except Finland) should achieve as soon as possible a stock level of at least 90 days' average inland consumption of the previous calendar year. [58]

As to the arrangement for apportionment, the Council of the OECD in 1972 confirmed its earlier decided principles for such emergency sharing. This implies that oil supplies should be apportioned, according to the following principles and criteria: (*a*) bunker requirements in Europe for ocean-going vessels and air transport should be met in full, after effecting all possible economies; (*b*) the remaining available supplies of each oil product in short supply should be apportioned as follows: (i) 90 per cent of such supplies should be automatically allocated to member countries in the same proportion as each member country's normal consumption of the product to that of all the European member countries; and (ii) 10 per cent of supplies should be subject to special allocation in such amounts and in such proportions as the Oil Committee may from time to time determine in view of the conditions existing when the allocations are made; any portion of such supplies not specially allocated should become subject to allocation under subparagraph (i) above; (*c*) member countries requesting a special allocation would be expected to have taken reasonable measures to optimize substitution by other forms of energy; (*d*) in determining the amount to be allocated to individual member countries under (*b*) (ii) above, the Oil Committee should give special consideration to the existence of any or all of the following factors: (i) serious economic difficulties due to the lack of oil, especially in member countries in the course of economic development; (ii) climatic difficulties and seasonal factors; (iii) unexpected delays or losses of supplies (for example, as a consequence of strikes or the interruption of other sources of energy); and (*e*) imports and exports of oil products between member countries should be maintained at their normal ratio to available supplies; normal trade in the other forms of energy between member countries should also be maintained.

In an emergency the International Industry Advisory Body (IIAB) shall advise the Oil Committee on matters relating to the availablility of oil for OECD Europe and shall assist in the implementation of the Oil Committee's recommendations for the apportionment of available oil supplies. [59]

26 At the Washington Energy Conference on 11–13 February 1974, the United States declared its willingness to share available energy in times of emergency or prolonged shortages and stated that it was prepared to allocate an agreed portion of the total US petroleum supply provided other IC-countries with indigenous production would do likewise. [60]

27 The OECD Oil Committee reached this conclusion at an extraordinary meeting on 25–26 October 1973. It also noted that arrangements for sharing oil supplies among West European countries could be activated within a week if necessary. [61] At a meeting on 20 November, the Oil Committee again agreed not to declare a state of oil shortage, which would have triggered the sharing of supplies among themselves. [62]

28 Originally, the structure of the European Communities acted against any consensus on energy, with three different Communities each being responsible for different forms of energy. The European Coal and Steel Community was responsible for coal and coke; Euratom for the peaceful uses of nuclear energy; and the European Economic Community for other energy sources. This severe impediment to progress was removed in 1967 when the three Communities were merged. The EEC Commission issued its "First Guidelines for a Community Energy Policy" on 18 December 1968, advocating a policy based on cheap and secure supplies of energy. In response to a partly changed situation, the Commission prepared a set of 46 proposals, which were sent to the Council on 4 October 1972 under the heading "Necessary Progress in Community Energy Policy". In this document, the Commission urged, *inter alia*, that action should be taken to establish or develop contacts between the Community and other energy importing countries (particularly the United States and Japan) and also to improve economic and social cooperation with energy-exporting countries. The EEC

ministers responsible for energy met on 22 and 23 May 1973 but failing to reach any practical decision they simply asked the Commission to produce proposals on the more controversial points by the end of the year. [63] In October 1973, the Commission submitted new proposals for a coordinated EEC energy policy, but the Council never had an opportunity to discuss them before the oil cuts were made in the same month. [64]

29 A few renowned and influential US oil experts had also vigorously espoused the idea of such cooperation among IC-countries. One of them, Professor M.A. Adelman, claimed that the world "energy shortage" was a fiction and that the oil supply was threatened by only one danger: a concerted shutdown by the OPEC nations. The success of OPEC largely depended on the policies of the United States and other IC-countries, which should therefore act together to avoid becoming the victims of such restrictions. [67] Another expert, Dr Walter Levy, proposed that a joint or at least coordinated Atlantic-Japanese energy policy be established as soon as possible, and he also presented an outline of its contents, suggesting that the administration of such a policy be given to a new, special, high-level international energy council. [68]

30 When US Secretary of State Rogers visited Japan in July 1973, he suggested that the two countries pool research and development efforts to construct a new multinational uranium enrichment plant in the United States. [69]

31 Magnetohydrodynamic (MHD) power is power produced by MHD generators which convert heat from ionized gases directly into electricity. The technology is still at the experimental stage but researchers are confident that problems can be solved if sufficient resources are made available. The advantage to be gained is a more efficient power generator which uses less fuel and leaves less pollution than the best of present conventional and nuclear systems.

MHD generators, basically expansion engines, are compact, have no moving parts and can accommodate temperatures and corrosive gases that would destroy conventional turbines. Experiments are under way with natural gas which permits a simplified generator design but most experimental facilities at present obtain gases from the burning of coal. In the MHD generator the hot, partially ionized gases, produced in combustion chambers, flow down a duct lined with electrodes and surrounded by coils that produce a magnetic field across the duct. Movement of the gas through the magnetic field generates a current in the gas that is collected at the electrodes. The electricity produced is direct current and must be converted before it can be transmitted over existing networks.

Power plants using MHD generators would use this source to produce only about half of the total electrical output; additional electricity would be produced by a complementary facility, such as conventional steam turbines, using MHD exhaust gases. The overall efficiency of the combined facility is expected to reach 50 per cent and with more sophisticated MHD design 60 per cent. The best conventional and nuclear power plants have an efficiency percentage of 40. [70]

32 In a letter from the French Foreign Minister to the UN Secretary-General, made public on 22 January 1974, France had suggested the urgent need to summon a world energy conference. The French argued that the conference, to be held under the auspices of the United Nations, was needed to devise both general principles of future cooperation between the PE- and IC-countries and to outline practical steps to achieve this. Such planning, the letter suggested, would forestall difficulties between states or groups of states and should be of particular interest to the underdeveloped countries. [77]

One week later, on 30 January, Algerian President Boumediène, in a letter to the UN Secretary-General, suggested that the UN conference proposed by France should be enlarged to cover matters relating not only to energy, but to all raw materials. [78–79] The Algerian proposal became the basis for the UN Sixth Special Session on raw materials which took place between 9 April and 3 May 1974.

33 The difficulties in harmonizing the interests of the United States and Western Europe were officially brought out on several occasions during the first months of 1974. A critical US view of West European policy was particularly spelled out by President Nixon in a speech in Chicago on 15 March when he declared that the United States was indispensable to European security and warned West European nations that they could not have both cooperation with the United States on the security front and confrontation and even hostility on the political and economic fronts. [84] A few days later he toned down his harsh criticism, however, and said that he had no intention of reducing US troop levels in Europe to force greater political and economic cooperation with the United States. [85] Concurrently, Secretary of State Kissinger appealed for "common statesmanship" between the United States and its European allies [86] and asserted that the Atlantic relationship remained the cornerstone of US foreign policy. [87] Foreign Minister Scheel of FR Germany in a major foreign policy speech on 11 April pointed out the following: despite clashes on the economic field and possibly over a number of political questions, the interests of common defence coincided; it was essential not to convey the impression that the Atlantic ties would loosen of themselves; it was important that US troops in Europe should remain at undiminished strength; and that it was equally important that their presence should not be continually called into question. [88]

34 In light of several decisions taken at the Washington meeting, it is interesting to note the following statement made by the Secretary-General of OPEC, Abderrahman Khene, in a speech of 28 January 1974: "Translated into terms of action, we should have to aim at three main targets:

The first target is to decide on a 'drastic revision' of the pattern of energy consumption. That means that, like our ancestors, who respected fire, or certain peoples today, who respect bread because they are hungry or water because they are thirsty, we must learn to respect energy, devoting it strictly to major uses.

The second target is to bring about a dramatic acceleration in research into, and the mobilization of, new sources of energy. To guarantee the maximum chance of success, as we have already said before and as we repeat today, we consider that the consuming nations should pool their scientific and financial resources in order to speed up research. The producing countries should also contribute to the joint effort — and they are prepared to do so.

This is the most fundamental objective. In the short-term view, that is to say, by the end of the century, all the operational results obtained would make possible an appropriate reduction in the share of oil as a source of energy, for the benefit of petrochemicals, chiefly in the manufacture of fertilizers and thus as a source of proteins. In the longer-term view, that is to say, beyond the end of the century, this effort would be devoted to harnessing non-polluting types of energy, which alone can ensure mankind a prospect of survival.

The third target is to plan the use of petroleum with the aim of prolonging the life of this raw material. In fact, our preferred hypothesis would be the wiser one only if the use of oil were planned in close relation with the development of other sources of energy. In other words, it would be necessary to review periodically the level of oil production, on each occasion taking into account known reserves, that is to say, reserves that have already been discovered, and realistically assessing the results achieved by science and technology in harnessing other sources of energy.

On the other hand, these arrangements should take into account the extremely low level of consumption by the majority of mankind. In other terms, a large amount of the savings in consumption achieved elsewhere would have to be redistributed to the poor countries.

In our opinion, these are the broad lines for thought and action by all those who have the power of decision today. They require that everyone must have a clear awareness of the universality of the problem, and to at least the same extent the courage to enunciate and apply universal solutions to that problem." [90]

35 At a news conference in Rome on 14 November 1973, the US Secretary of Agriculture refused to comment on a question as to whether the United States had considered banning US exports of food to Arab countries. [91] A few days later he stated that such a ban "would simply irritate the situation, make negotiations [for an Arab-Israeli settlement] more difficult and would not put any pressure on the Arab countries". He added: "Our grain exports to the Arab nations — even though higher than a year ago — are not high enough to be significant, and in view of the fact that the Russian nation has a much easier grain situation than a year ago they could very easily make up the deficit of anything we cut off." [92] On 25 January 1974 another official spokesman made it clear that the US administration opposed embargoes on agricultural exports and that the United States wanted to continue to be a major exporter of agricultural products. An embargo would undermine the nation's credibility as a reliable supplier. [93]

36 Secretary of State Kissinger stated: "It is clear that if the Arab shutdown of oil to the United States continues unreasonably and indefinitely the United States will have to decide what countermeasures are necessary." Kissinger expressed the hope, however, that it would not come to this. [73]

In another statement, Secretary of Defense Schlesinger is quoted as saying: "It is plain that one should not tempt fate by pushing the concept of national sovereignty too far. The United States is dedicated, and has remained dedicated, to the independence of free states, and that includes the states of the Middle East. But it should be recognized that the independent powers of sovereign states should not be used in such a way as would cripple the large mass of the industrialized world. That is running too high a risk, and it is a source of danger not only from the US standpoint but from the standpoint of the oil-producing nations." Schlesinger expressed his firm belief, however, that the industrialized nations would not come to the contingency of military intervention. [96]

37 It has not been made clear to what extent preparations were actually made for the mining of the oilfields. According to press reports from Kuwait, Foreign Minister Sabah said that such measures had been taken in Kuwait: "Kuwait's oil fields have been surrounded by an explosive belt, explodable the moment actual American military intervention is sensed". [101] There were also reports that Saudi Arabian authorities had wired the Ghawar oil field, which is the largest known single reserve in the world. Prince Abdullah Ben Abdel Azis, commander of the national guard, had been placed in charge of this operation, code-named "Operation Detonation". [102] The consequences of blowing up an extensive oil field are likely to be disastrous because of the immediate effects from fire, heat and pressure on the area of the oil field itself, the risks of the fire spreading to surrounding oil fields and the enormous pollution created by the smog and the fallout of sulphur dioxide.

The difficulties involved in extinguishing oil-well fires are illustrated by the three wells at Abu Rodeis, on the west coast of the Sinai Peninsula, which caught fire on 1 January 1974 when an Israeli Hawk missile was fired at a suspect helicopter and accidentally zoomed in on and hit an offshore oil rig. [103] The fire in one of the wells was brought under control fairly soon, but it took until 18 March 1974 to extinguish the fires in the other two wells by means of an underwater explosion. [104]

38 On 21 May 1973, Senator Fulbright made a much publicized statement in the US Senate concerning the risks of military action being taken in the Middle East

because of its oil reserves: "There is another, more ominous possible scenario for the years just ahead. Recognizing that even a crash program for the development of alternate energy sources is likely to require so great a lead time as to leave us heavily dependent for a decade or more on large oil imports, our present policy-makers and policy-influences may come to the conclusion that military action is required to secure the oil resources of the Middle East, to secure our exposed 'jugular'. One detects something less than advocacy but more than simple apprehension in warnings that the great wealth now accruing to the oil-producing states of the Persian Gulf may somehow pass into the hands of stronger powers.

There is no question of our ability forcibly to take over the oil-producing states of the Middle East. They are militarily insignificant, constituting what the geopoliticans used to call a 'Power Vacuum'. We might not even have to do it ourselves, with militarily potent surrogates available in the region. The Shah of Iran is known to aspire to a 'protecting' role for the gulf region. . . .

I am expressing apprehensions: I am most definitely not making predictions. I would like nothing better than to have them denied and repudiated by all concerned. In the meantime, I take the liberty of advising the Arab states not to underestimate the power and determination of the forces which may coalesce against them. . . .

. . . [T]he Persian Gulf countries would be well-advised not to press too hard and to treat their oil wealth as a kind of global trust, if for no other reason than for their own protection. The meat of the gazelle may be succulent indeed, but the wise gazelle does not boast of it to lions." [105]

Two days later Senator Jackson made strong objections to Fulbright's description of the situation in the Middle East and described his statement about "militarily potent surrogates" acting to secure the oil resources of the Middle East as "utterly irresponsible". [106]

The US State Department was also reported to have issued a firm denial of any such intention. [107]

39 A US scholar, S.M. Schwebel, has particularly underlined the importance of the UN Charter as an inhibition to such military ventures. "Arab oil may become so mixed with Western Security, and Arab oil policy may become so insensate, that Senator Fulbright's warning may enter the sphere of the possible. It might increasingly be maintained that a cut-off of Arab oil would indeed so prejudice vital western security interests that action in "self-defense" however questionable under the Charter, should be undertaken. Such reasoning conceivably could carry the day. But as it is and promises to be, the idea of the United States or less certainly even its "surrogates" seizing oil for oil's sake is implausible. The much-scorned principles of the U.N. Charter, the battered norms of international law, have in fact seeped somewhat into the expectations of many states and into the consciousness of much of mankind. As disputes with Iran yesterday, and with Chile, Peru and Iceland today suggest, the day of gunboat diplomacy has probably passed. Its last hour may well have been the Anglo-French disaster of 1956 at Suez." [107]

40 The following example illustrates the various components making up the posted price a few years before the system changed in the autumn of 1973. [16a]

Posted price	$ 1.80
less cost	0.20
less royalty (12.5 per cent)	0.225
Putative company profit before tax	1.375
Tax (50 per cent)	0.6875
plus royalty	0.225
Government take	0.9125

Since then, the government take has increased substantially, as can be seen from the following survey (dollars per barrel for Arabian light):

Jan	Jan	Oct	Jan
1972	1973	1973	1974
1.45	1.52	3.05	7.00

[41] According to an estimate by a private US bank (Morgan Guaranty Trust) early in 1974, OPEC revenue would amount to about $85 billion in 1974, assuming that production remained at the 1973 level and that there was a 10 per cent price reduction. The Arab share of this revenue could be as much as $50 billion, or more, depending on production levels. This amount could be broken down roughly as follows: Saudi Arabia, $19 billion; Libya, $8 billion; Kuwait, $8 billion; Iraq, $6 billion; Abu Dhabi, up to $4 billion; Algeria, up to $4 billion; and Qatar, up to $1.5 billion. Non-Arab Iran's expected revenue in 1974 would be $17 billion. [109]

One author, R. Krymm, has recently estimated that the additional sums which will have to be transferred from the oil-importing to the oil-exporting countries as a result of the oil crisis will exceed the $60 billion level in 1974. Krymm's estimates for future years are based on the assumption that oil prices will keep pace with general inflation and, on that basis the 1980 figure might exceed $90 billion when expressed in 1973 dollars, or $125 billion in current dollars, if an average 5 per cent annual inflation rate is assumed over the period. [110]

[42] This view was expressed by the Director-General of the Kuwait Fund for Arab Economic Development, Al-Hamad, at a financial symposium in Luxembourg in November 1973: "What we Arab financiers are after is definitely not speculative ventures and at best risky windfalls, but rather sound opportunities for long-term investment capable of both preserving the value of our financial assets as well as enhancing the capacity to transform our lopsided economies into viable modern entities." [112]

At a meeting in Cairo in December 1973, the finance ministers of the Arab League countries agreed to make a gradual transfer of some Arab funds from foreign banks into Arab investment bodies to be used for local development projects. The OAPEC countries are reported to hold such funds on deposit or in short-term securities at a value of $10–11 billion. However, by mid-1974 there were no further reports of any substantial transfers. [113]

[43] Asked about the magnitude of Arab investments in the United States, a representative of the US Department of Commerce gave the following answer at Congressional hearings: "We don't keep any records on any foreign investments in this country in any one single place, but we do have a program oriented toward bringing foreign companies to build plants and create jobs in the United States. Where we can, we pick that information up.

As far as knowing of any Arab direct investments in the United States, we are aware of a few small ventures in trading and banking and of considerable real estate holdings, particularly in Florida, but we do not know the specifics. Most Arab investment in the United States is of the portfolio type, but we have no estimate of the magnitudes." [114]

However, at the beginning of 1974, there were some press reports of Arab capital being invested in real estate in the United States and used for the purchase of US Treasury bills. [115–117]

[44] In July 1973 there were reports of a contract between the National Iranian Oil Co. and the US Ashland Oil, Inc., for a joint venture, which provided NIOC with a 50 per cent interest in Ashland's refining, petro-chemical and service-station operations in the state of New York. This contract was intended to become a pattern for other similar investments by PE-countries. [118–119]

[45] West German Finance Minister Schmidt has emphatically stressed the need for

continued and increased aid to the oil-poor developing IC-countries in view of the fact that their very existence is threatened: "The developing countries are in danger of being left high and dry. Their very existence is threatened by increasing oil prices because they do not have as high a net product as the industrialized countries to draw upon. For those who view the prosperity gap between the rich and poor of this world with concern, every effort must be made to see that the oil producers place that portion of their additional purchasing power which they are unable to absorb at home directly at the disposal of developing countries to make effective the latter's demand for imports from industrialized countries." [120]

46 Among efforts to mitigate the effects of the increased oil prices in the first half of 1974, the following deserves particular mention: When the Committee of 20 of the International Monetary Fund (IMF) met in Rome in mid-January 1974, the Director, J. Witteveen, suggested that a new "oil facility" should be established to assist countries in financing account deficits caused by higher oil bills. The fund would use its existing resources but might need to supplement them by borrowing, mainly from oil-exporting countries. The IMF would thus act as a kind of middleman between the PE- and IC-countries. The IMF is said to be seeking $5−7 billion for this oil facility. [121] It was reported later that the IMF expected to raise about $3 billion during 1974, and that the oil facility could be in operation by the middle of the year. [122]

The response of different countries to the plan varied considerably. In May, for example, Saudi Arabia expressed strong doubts about the plan. [123] However, as early as February, the Shah of Iran pledged to lend some $700 million to the IMF to be recycled as "oil facilities" to the IC-countries. Iran would also buy some $200 million in World Bank bonds. At the same time, the Shah proposed that a new lending institution be established to provide soft-term loans to developing countries that do not produce oil. Under the Iranian proposal, the new institution would have a total capital in the first year of $2−3 billion, contributed in about equal parts by the PE-countries and by industrial nations. Iran has committed itself to put up a total of $1 billion in 1974 to be used in the three ways described. [124−125]

In another effort on 7 April 1974, the OPEC members decided to establish a special fund to aid, through soft-term loans, the developing countries hit by the higher oil prices. The fund will be financed by voluntary contributions and will start operating as soon as its statutes have been ratified by seven of OPEC's member nations. [126]

The Arab PE-countries have also decided to help finance African purchases of oil and economic development in Africa by setting up funds and increasing the working capital in some existing development banks; this would amount to an output of several hundred million dollars. Arab PE-countries have also increased the working capital of the Arab Bank for Industrial and Agricultural Development in Africa from $195 million to $500 million. [127−130] Transfers of capital from Arab PE-countries to Egypt and Syria, to assist these countries in their war efforts or to directly pay the bills for arms deliveries to these countries, have been made for some years. It has been estimated that these transfers from Saudi Arabia, Kuwait, the United Arab Emirates and Iraq amounted to over $1 billion during 1973−74. [109] Such transfers have also been accompanied by large transfers of capital to be used for the reconstruction of installations damaged during the 1973 October War, for the reopening of the Suez Canal, and for the general economic development of these countries. [131−134] Iran concluded an agreement for substantial economic aid to Egypt at the end of May 1974. [135]

In addition, according to information from the Executive Director of the UN World Food Programme (WFP) on 25 March 1974, Saudi Arabia pledged a $50 million cash contribution to the WFP for 1975−76. This would make Saudi Arabia the second largest contributor to the programme, after the United States. [136]

Venezuela's Minister of Finance, Hurtado, disclosed at the yearly meeting of the

Inter-American Development Bank at the beginning of April 1974 that Venezuela would allocate at least $1.2 billion of Venezuela's oil revenue to a fund for the development of Latin America. [137]

47 Estimates have varied widely as to the overall economic effects of the recent "oil crisis". West German Chancellor Schmidt has stressed that "oil has shaken the very foundations of the present world economic system" and may even "shatter the laboriously built structure of the world economy". [120]

In April 1974, spokesmen of the World Bank said that industrialized countries would have much lower economic growth rates in 1974 than previously predicted and that this would retard the growth of developing nations as well. The World Bank estimated that industrial nations would have an average growth of between 1.3 and 2.4 per cent in 1974. The corresponding estimate in December 1973 had been 3.75 per cent, while real growth in 1973 had been 6.6 per cent. The lower estimates of industrial growth, plus shortages of fuel, fertilizers and commodities, will be particularly reflected in the growth rates of less developed countries. The World Bank estimated that about 40 such countries would require some $15 billion in foreign cash aid to balance their payments. Earlier estimates of an average 6 per cent growth rate among these countries have since been revised to rates ranging from 2 to 6 per cent. [138]

As far as Western Europe is concerned, the UN Economic Commission for Europe (ECE) has estimated that prospects were for a marked slow-down in Western Europe's growth in 1974 even before the increase in oil prices: from about 6 per cent in 1967 to some 4–4.5 per cent in 1974. The ECE foresees that the additional impact of the rise in oil prices could hold back the growth rate a good deal more. The increase in the oil import bills will result in a deterioration in the trade balances of most ECE countries, both in Western and Eastern Europe. Nonetheless, because of the differing importance of oil in their respective trade balances, as well as the differing scope for import savings, the extent of these deteriorations is likely to vary significantly in each case. For the countries of the Council for Mutual Economic Assistance (CMEA), the change will not be very large and the "machinery" for pooling resources is already available. [139]

48 The United States is a member of CENTO's military, economic and counter-subversion committees, and signed bilateral agreements of military and economic cooperation with Iran, Pakistan and Turkey in Ankara in March 1959. [12b] The bilateral "Agreement of Cooperation" with Iran, which was signed on 5 March 1959, provided, inter alia: "In case of aggression against Iran, the Government of the United States of America, in accordance with the Constitution of the United States of America, will take such appropriate action, including the use of armed forces, as may be mutually agreed upon and is envisaged in the Joint Resolution to Promote Peace and Stability in the Middle East, in order to assist the Government of Iran at its request."

The reference to the Middle East Resolution acts to limit the U.S. commitment to cases of "armed aggression from any country controlled by international communism" as provided by Section 2 of that Resolution. [140]

49 However, in the military field, regular exercises are planned and conducted, conferences on technical military matters are held and interaction among military personnel is facilitated and encouraged.

In addition to its defence and security aims, CENTO also seeks the peaceful economic development of the region through cooperative effort. In this field, CENTO cooperation has focused on the establishing of railway, road and telecommunication links between the member countries. [12b]

50 At Congressional hearings on 6 June 1973, a representative of the US State

160

Department stated that, in brief, the objectives of US interests and policy in the Arabian/Persian Gulf were the following:

"1. Support for indigenous regional collective security efforts, to provide stability and to foster orderly development without outside interference. We believe Iranian and Saudi Arabian cooperation, *inter alia* is of key importance as a major element of stability in this area. We also welcome the fact that Kuwait, the United Arab Emirates, and North Yemen are each, in their own way, seeking to strengthen their defensive capacities.

2. Peaceful resolution of territorial and other disputes among the regional states and the opening up of better channels of communication among them.

3. Continued access of gulf oil supplies at reasonable prices and in sufficient quantities to meet our growing needs and those of our European and Asian friends and allies.

4. Enhancing of our commercial and financial interests." [114a]

At the same hearings, on 17 July 1973, a representative of the US Defense Department defined US security interests in the Gulf area in terms of three main considerations. [114b]"First, we wish to contain Soviet military power within its present borders. This interest was paramount during the height of the cold war when we were concerned with Soviet expansion and the adverse effect that expansion could have on the global balance and on our specific interests in the Persian Gulf/Arabian Sea area. Great Britain shared this interest, and until 1971 maintained special treaty relations with Kuwait, Bahrain, Qatar, and the seven Trucial states that kept the peace in the Gulf. With the gradual improvement in relations between the U.S.S.R. and Iran and between the U.S.S.R. and ourselves, the threat of Soviet overt military action against the sovereignty and independence of states in the Persian Gulf and the Arabian Peninsula has lessened and is no longer a cause of immediate concern.

We also have a security interest in access to Persian Gulf oil. Prior to 1970, our main interest in the Persian Gulf oil was economic. Less than 3 per cent of our oil came from the Gulf areas. But in that year it became clear to many of us that the United States was going to need to import increasing quantities of Persian Gulf oil in the future. Projections vary, of course, but conservatively we estimate that, if present trends continue, the U.S. will import about half of its oil requirements in 1980 and that half of this will come from the Persian Gulf. Saudi Arabia and Iran will account for much of these Gulf imports.

Another security interest is continued free movement of U.S. ships and aircraft into and out of the area, and continued access to logistic support facilities on Bahrain for our small Middle East force."

51 In an interview in May 1973, the Shah gave the following explanation for Iran's increased defence costs: "As for our own expenditure, you must compare it to what potential adventurers in the region are spending. And bear in mind that our 31 million people will be 37 million in five years time. Not only do we have national and regional responsibilities but also a world role as a guardian and protector of 60 per cent of the world's oil resources." [141]

One obvious expression of Iran's wish to act as the protector of stability in the region is its military presence in Oman — which controls the entrance of the Hormuz Strait together with Iran — to assist the Oman government in its efforts to control the guerilla war in Dhofar. It has been reported that the Iranian forces in Oman number 8 000 soldiers, of whom 3 000 are stationed in Dhofar. [142]

52 The Continental Shelf Convention of 1958 allows coastal states exclusive rights to explore and exploit the mineral resources of the continental margins out to the 200-metre isobath, and beyond, to where the depth of the superjacent waters admits of exploitation. It is now clear that sea-bed resource jurisdiction could extend well beyond the 200-metre depth, although there is still uncertainty as to the outer limit of such jurisdiction.

[53] Israel's oil output from the Sinai oil fields amounts to between 100 000 and 120 000 b/d (5—6 million t/y). Due to the supplies from these fields, Israel was left, by and large, unaffected by the OAPEC oil cuts during the October War. (For further information about Israel's oil situation, see appendix 2. p. 90.) The main oil source in the Sinai desert is the Abu Rodeis fields, about 130 km south of the Suez Canal. [153]

[54] A recent report by a shipping consultants' company (H.P. Drewry) shows that eleven ports in Western Europe, six in the Arabian/Persian Gulf, three in Japan and two on the US Gulf Coast are expected to be able to accept 500 000 dwt tankers when they enter service. [162]

[55] There are numerous advantages to supertankers. First, in the initial investment, it takes less labour, steel and shipyard design to build a tanker to carry 100 000 tons of crude oil than it does to build two of 50 000-ton capacity each. The savings in steel is also a major concern and results from the fact that the "skin" of any container increases only as the square of its dimensions, whereas the volume enclosed rises as the cube. Operating costs per ton-mile are also lower. Supertanker crews are only slightly larger than those required by smaller tankers. Insurance costs per ton-mile falls off as size increases and bunker costs per ton-mile are less for the "giants". One cost that is greater for the supertankers is that of necessary shore facility modification and in-port handling charges. These disadvantages are largely offset when supertankers are used over long hauls on long-term regular service. [163]

[56] At US Senate hearings in January 1973, representatives of the Department of Defense stated that one of the most obvious corollaries of dependence on foreign oil or gas imports is the need to secure the sea lanes in time of crisis or war. Interruption of the sea lanes now carries a far greater threat of the security, economy and well-being of the United States than before, when the country had a sufficient production base of its own as guarantee of a continued energy supply. The volume of oil imports to the United States will soon be so large that imposition of a wartime convoy system would automatically impose sizeable reductions in the amount of oil which could be moved, despite the fact that the capacity of one modern tanker may be equivalent to 10 World War II tankers. Also, under conditions of global war, long and vulnerable sea lanes to Africa, the Middle East and Indonesia, together with shorter routes within the Western hemisphere, would require protection over virtually their entire lengths. The Department of Defense further stated that the United States did not possess nearly enough resources in terms of escorts, sea-control vessels and aircraft to provide the degree of protection that would be required.

Consequently, there are several ongoing programmes aimed at providing the wherewithal to protect oil shipments. At the hearings referred to above, the Department of Defense stated that the most dangerous and constant threat to sea-lane security was the nuclear-powered submarine. Thus, it was argued, special emphasis must be given to antisubmarine warfare (ASW) capability. As an example of such US efforts, it may be noted that the new SSN—688 class submarine, entering service in 1974, was designed specifically to protect high-value commercial targets and naval forces against a submarine threat. [173]

[57] US Chief of Navy Operations Zumwalt said: "In a conflict situation it must be expected that the Soviets would attack our seaborne petroleum supply. The Soviets' capability to interdict our sea lines of communications is growing. But would they choose to use it that way, and if so, how? I believe we cannot afford to

ignore the fact that the Soviets have the capability to attack our seaborne petroleum supply. It is becoming a major fact in our economy. A large investment in itself, and an even larger factor in the performance of our industry. Seaborne oil imports represent a vulnerable pressure point that could be used to coerce us over some issue that is entirely unrelated to oil or the Middle East. This, of course, in the light of the fact that the Soviets have no dependence on oil externally." [173b]

58 Ras Tanura, Saudi Arabia's main oil port, can already accept 500 000-tonners, and may well be expanded to take vessels of 700 000 dwt or more. Ju'aymah is to become Saudi Arabia's second oil port, with a single buoy mooring for 450 000-tonners planned for 1974. Iran has four VLCC ports, of which the most important, Kharg Island, has recently been expanded to take 500 000-tonners drawing 95 feet. Kuwait's Mina al-Ahmadi can accept partly-laden tankers of 500 000 dwt and Mina Abdallah, 210 000 dwt partly-laden. Iraq has no VLCC facilities, but will probably expand Khor al-Amaya to 330 000 dwt by 1976. Qatar, Abu Dhabi, Dubai and Oman each have one terminal able to handle 300 000-tonners, and Qatar's Halul Island can now accept 500 000 dwt vessels. Egypt has a VLCC terminal at Ras Shukhair in the Gulf of Suez. [162]

59 According to the Department of Defense, the United States has a fairly low military preparedness in the Arabian/Persian Gulf area. It was stated that "to bring any of these naval capabilities to bear in the Persian Gulf area could require as much as a month. Our Middle East force, normally comprising just two or three destroyers, would require augmentation to have significant combat capability.

An all-nuclear task group could reach the area in 9 days from Guam, but would take twice as long from the United States. An amphibious task group, operating from the continental United States, would require nearly a month to reach the Persian Gulf." [173a]

60 The 26-kilometre broad Bab-el-Mandeb Strait, which is divided into two seaways on each side of the island of Perim, was blockaded by Egyptian naval forces supported by forces from Yemen and Democratic Yemen during the 1973 October War. It seems evident that Israel made the lifting of this blockade an unconditional prerequisite for its participation in the ceasefire agreement. [175]

61 During World War I, the German raiders "Wolf" and "Emden" did a considerable amount of damage to Allied shipping in a series of daring hit-and-run attacks. During World War II, a more concerted and sustained campaign was responsible for the sinking of nearly 250 Allied vessels in the area between Lourenço Marques and Cape Town alone. [177]

62 In 1955, the UK and South Africa concluded a Simonstown Agreement, under which Britain handed over the Simonstown Naval Base to South Africa. However, Britain maintained base facilities which could be used even in a war in which South Africa remained neutral. The agreement also provided for "joint seaward defence" and for the supply of $50 million worth of naval vessels. These ships now constitute the bulk of South Africa's navy. [143a]

63 The number of large ports currently capable of handling tankers, south of Somalia on the African east coast and south of Nigeria on the west coast, is limited to those shown in the table below.

Country/port	Maximum vessel size dwt
Kenya — Mombassa	50 000
Tanzania — Dar Es Salaam	20 000
Mozambique — Beira	45 000
— Lourenço Marques	45 000
South Africa — Cape Town	80 000
— Durban	210 000
Cabinda	100 000
Congo — Pointe Noire	20 000
Gabon — Gamba	250 000[a]
— Port Gentil	100 000

a Partly loaded.
Source: See reference [178].

[64] The number of good navigation routes leading from the Indian Ocean to the southwest Pacific available to ocean-going ships is small. The five reasonably practical routes go through the straits of Malacca, Sunda, Lombok, Torres and the waters south of Australia.

The northernmost passage, Malacca, is approximately 500 nautical miles in length. The eastern end of Malacca leads into the Singapore Strait which has some narrow and relatively shallow sections; some spots have a mid-channel depth of only 72 feet due to shifting bottom sands. South of the island of Singapore the only safe seaway (more than 60 feet deep) is just one mile wide. Thus, Malacca is considered unsafe for the all-weather passage of ships drawing 65—70 feet or over — in other words, for supertankers of about 250 000 dwt and larger.

To the south the next straits of any significance are Sunda and Lombok, both located in the Indonesian Archipelago. Sunda Strait lies between the islands of Sumatra and Java and is deep enough for all existing ships or those presently in the planning stage. After transitting the Strait from the west, ships must then make the long passage (up to 700 miles) through the Java Sea and Makassar Strait. Lombok Strait, lying between the islands of Lombok and Bali, provides the safest passage for supertankers and is the most frequently used. Its minimum water depth exceeds 100 feet.

Since both of the above routes require a long passage through Indonesian internal waters, it seems important to note several of Indonesia's political viewpoints concerning its territorial waters and their use: (a) Indonesia proclaimed in 1957, and reiterated in 1960, that its territorial sea was determined by measuring from straight baselines drawn from island to island under the Archipelago Doctrine; (b) Indonesia claimed that there was to be no innocent passage on its inland seas but that it would permit ships to transit those waters at its descretion; (c) the entire archipelago, including all the waters lying between the islands, would be considered as an entity and subject to complete Indonesian sovereignty.

Should the Lombok and Sunda Straits be closed due to the possibility of Indonesia "exercising its discretion" and thereby denying the use of its internal waters to outsiders, there remains only one alternative route between the Arabian/Persian Gulf and Japan, the route circumnavigating Australia, south of New Guinea, and then passing by the Solomon Islands on its way to Japan. (Although the Torres Strait between Cape York, Australia and New Guinea is not part of the Indonesian Archipelago, it is much too shallow for supertankers or ships that draw in excess of 37 feet). By taking the alternative Australian route, the trip from the Arabian/Persian Gulf oil fields to Japan would be about 14 000 miles, one way, as compared to 8 000 miles via the Lombok route and 6 800 miles for the Malacca passage. [163]

Another potential option to the route through the Malacca Straits is a possible passage through the narrow portion of the Malay Peninsula. This passage could take the form of either a canal or a pipeline.

In 1966 the Japan Land Research Institute, a private venture, made a feasibility study for what is called the Kra Canal. At that time, the government of Thailand protested about the study to the government of Japan and in 1968 the Overseas Technical Cooperation Co. of Japan sounded out the opinions of the Thai government again. The Thai reaction was still negative probably because of a desire not to offend Singapore by implying a lessening of its strategic importance. [163] Nevertheless, in 1972 the Thai government ordered a preliminary study, which was delivered in September 1973, on the possibility of using nuclear energy to dig the canal. The report was never published and the committee working on the subject was dissolved by the new Thai government, in power from October 1973. It was reported that the Thai government had abandoned the canal project, the costs of which have been estimated to be from $5–20 billion. [185]

Acceptance of a pipeline across southern Thailand is more likely. The Marubeni Iida Co. of Japan completed its basic exploratory study in cooperation with the Thai government in July 1971. This work indicated that a pipeline with a capacity of from 190 to 380 million barrels a year could be constructed for about $250 million. Such a pipeline would handle only about 20 per cent of the present Japanese requirement and hardly guarantee sufficient future supplies.

Both the pipeline and the canal proposals suffer from the same flaw as the presently available Indonesian routes — dependence on the goodwill of a foreign government for the uninterrupted flow of vital oil supplies.

Finally, it might be added that the alternative of deepening the Malacca and Singapore Straits has been proposed and Japan has been actively engaged in continuing efforts with the countries bordering these straits to complete a detailed survey. However, nothing has materialized so far. [163]

65 Indonesia declared its intention to extend its territorial waters to 12 miles in 1960, while Malaysia made a similar decision in 1969. These declarations imply that the narrowest passages of the Straits of Malacca and Singapore would no longer be international water. The narrowest point of Malacca is 8.4 nautical miles; in the outlet where it is a part of Malaysian and Indonesian territory, the width of the sea passage is 11 nautical miles. The narrowest point of the Straits of Singapore is 3.2 miles. [186]

66 It is generally recognized that a state may exercise certain well-defined rights within its territorial waters. It may, for instance, enact sailing regulations applicable to all ships within its territorial waters.

A state's control over foreign merchant vessels is, however, subject to their right of innocent passage. "Innocent passage", as incorporated into the Geneva Convention of 1958, is defined as that passage which "is not prejudicial to the peace, good order or security of the coastal state".

For reasons based on the right of security and self-defence, a state may forbid or limit the access to its territorial waters of foreign warships. Whether such ships enjoy the same right of innocent passage as merchant vessels is a controversial question. The predominant view seems to be that such passage should not be denied in time of peace when the territorial waters are so placed that passage through them is necessary for international traffic. Under a special provision in the Geneva Convention, submarines are required to navigate on the surface, and to show their flag. [188]

67 TAP-line was closed for 100 days after the 1967 Arab-Israeli War. In 1969 it was

closed for 110 days when Palestinian guerillas sabotaged it. On 20 January 1973 it was breached by an explosion between the Rifaa and Shuba pumping stations in Saudi Arabia, which halted operations for four days. Oil tanks at the Medreco refinery and the TAP-line terminal at Zahrani in Lebanon were attacked on 14 April 1973 by raiders of unknown nationality. A second attack on the pipeline itself, close to its terminal at Zahrani, occurred only two days later. [191–193]

[68] On 7 October 1973 Egypt made an agreement with the US Bechtel Co, for the construction of a $400 million oil pipeline – the Sumed project – from the Red Sea (Ain Sokhna) to the Mediterranean (Alexandria). This US-Egyptian cooperation was considered at the time as having far-reaching political and economic implications because it marked the first large-scale US involvement in Egypt since the United States decided to withdraw from the financing of the Aswan Dam in 1956. [194] In the middle of April 1974 it was reported, however, that Bechtel had bowed out of the deal and that a group of Italian firms were under consideration. [195–196] Bechtel's withdrawal will supposedly also lead to the cancellation of an offer of a $100 million loan to Egypt by the US Export-Import Bank. Offers for private US capital still seemed to stand during the spring of 1974, however. The project will probably be substantially financed by capital from other Arab countries – Saudi Arabia, Kuwait, Abu Dhabi and Qatar are expected to take 50 per cent of the $400 million equity in the company which will own the Sumed pipeline. [197]

The length of the oil line is to be 320 km; it will partially substitute for the Suez Canal and, once the Canal is open, will supplement it. Crude oil will be brought to the Gulf of Suez in very large tankers and transported through the Sumed pipeline to refineries in the port of Alexandria, there to be processed and shipped onward to Europe in small- or medium-sized tankers; the scheme to be operational by 1976. The capacity of the pipeline is projected to be 1.6 million b/d. When finished the pipeline is projected to give Egypt at least $100 million a year in income. [170]

[69] The line would be over 1 800 km long and would run through some of the most difficult terrain in the Middle East. Construction costs have been estimated at between $800 and $1 000 million. So far, most of the oil companies operating in Iran have shown little enthusiasm for the scheme.

[70] In a speech on 2 April 1974, the Swedish Under-Secretary of Defence, Anders Thunborg, touched upon some of the effects of the energy crisis on the security policy of Sweden. He said, *inter alia,* that the oil stocks in the country must be increased and have a double purpose in the future; namely, to secure supplies both in times of war or threat of war, and also in the case of "peace crises" such as the recent oil crisis. He also warned that oil and other strategic products might in the future be used as catalysts to create disturbances in the international system; countries which control the international distribution of such products have a very strong position and can be tempted to obtain favours from smaller and weaker nations by the mere threat of cutting off supplies of strategic commodities ("threat of economic sanctions"). [198]

[71] Industry uses more energy than any other consuming sector, accounting for 41.2 per cent of all energy consumed in the United States in 1972. The six industrial groups with the most voracious appetite for fuel account for 77 per cent of all energy used in manufacturing. These are: food processing; paper; chemicals; petroleum refining; stone, clay and glass products; and the primary metals (particularly aluminium and steel). [199]

An interesting study of the amounts of energy used for industrial processes has been made by two researchers at the University of Chicago, R. Stephen Berry and

Margaret F. Fels. They studied the amount of energy used to manufacture the materials in a typical 1967 US automobile. They found that by far the most costly step in an automobile's manufacture is the production of the 1.6 tons of iron and steel which are fabricated into car components. The energy consumed in the coke oven, blast furnace, steel furnace and hot-rolling mill processes represented over 80 per cent of the total energy. The total free energy consumed in the manufacture of a new automobile was estimated to be 37 275 kwh, which roughly equals three tons of oil. [200]

72 The Battelle Columbus Laboratories, Ohio, made a brief overview of the energy requirements of the US Department of Defense (DoD) in 1972, based on data assembled in interviews with various representatives of the DoD and the individual services. Below are some of the observations made in this report. (Original data were collected in natural units and converted to British thermal units, Btu's, using for petroleum products (residuals, jet fuels, distillates, gasoline) a conversion factor where 1 barrel equalled 5.55 x 10^6 Btu's.) [206]

Observations on DoD consumption
1. Total DoD consumption of energy amounted to 2 460 thousand billion Btu's.
2. Roughly 60 per cent of this energy was consumed in the United States, the remainder overseas.
3. Petroleum-derived products accounted for 78 per cent of total DoD energy consumption.
4. Jet fuel accounted for 43 per cent of DoD energy consumption, followed by residuals at about 18 per cent.

Observations on DoD's US consumption compared to total US consumption
1. The total energy consumed by the DoD in the United States was 1 430 thousand billion Btu's or 1.9 per cent of total US energy consumption.
2. Consumption of coal, natural gas and electricity by the DoD in the US accounted for even smaller fractions of US consumption of these items.
3. The DoD's US consumption of products derived from petroleum accounted for 3.9 per cent of total US petroleum consumption.
4. Jet-fuel consumption by the DoD in the US was about 30 per cent of US consumption, followed by residual fuel at 4.4 per cent.

Observations on DoD's total energy consumption compared to total US consumption
1. The DoD's total energy consumption (domestic and foreign) was 3.2 per cent of the US energy consumption.
2. Total consumption of coal, natural gas and electricity by the DoD was a very small fraction of US consumption.
3. The DoD's total consumption of petroleum products was 7.7 per cent of US consumption of these products.
4. Total jet-fuel consumption by the DoD was over 53 per cent of US consumption.

The DoD's consumption of uranium for energy has not been included in the above information because the uranium fuel used is on lease from the USAEC. Essentially, all uranium thus consumed is for powering US Navy ships.

In a breakdown of the energy and petroleum requirements of the armed services, the consumption in 1971 was apportioned as follows:

	Percentage of total DoD energy	Percentage of energy derived from petroleum within each service	Percentage of total DoD petroleum consumption
Air Force	48	86	53
Navy	31	81	33
Army	18	49	14
Other	3	–	

[73] Due to the effect of the changed conditions on its oil supply, the US Department of Defense had to make up a loss of roughly 300 000 b/d from domestic supplies, which constituted 1.8 per cent of the 17.9 million b/d then consumed in the United States. On 1 November 1973, President Nixon invoked the Defense Production Act of 1950, according to which the Department of Defense can impose on petroleum producers a first-priority claim for military over domestic needs. The US government thereby ordered 22 oil companies to supply 825.9 million gallons (19.6 million barrels) to be delivered by January 1974. [210–211]

However, in March it was reported in the press that, from January on, Arab oil had started to flow again to US military forces abroad, although the embargo was not lifted until a couple of months later. This informal easing of restrictions, which involved about 100 000 b/d or about half the fuel and other petroleum products with which US military forces overseas were being supplied before the October War and the subsequent cut-off of all supplies to the United States, helped the US Defence Department to gradually rebuild its reserves and avoid serious reductions in the training and readiness of air and naval combat forces. Iran continued to supply oil to the US military at a level of about 50 000 b/d. At the height of the fuel crisis in December, military petroleum stockpiles were reportedly down to about 70 per cent of their normal amount. In March this proportion had risen to 85–90 per cent. [212–214]

In January it was reported that the Defense Department had been allocated 637 000 b/d in the first three months of 1974. [213] At hearings at the end of January, Secretary of Defense Schlesinger was reported to have stated that the oil companies had been "relatively slow" in making the mandatory government allocations of fuel deliveries to the military. These allocations would have to be increased during the spring to maintain the combat readiness of the armed forces, which had to take various conservation measures, such as cutting back on training and reducing both flying time (by 18 per cent) and ship-steaming time (by 20 per cent). [214]

[74] At Congressional hearings before the Subcommittee on the Near East and South Asia on 23 July 1973, Mr Robert Hunter, a senior fellow of the Overseas Development Council, presented a statement in which he very perceptively outlined some of the problems and threats involved in an arms race in the Arabian/Persian Gulf area:

"a. The concept of 'military balance' may not apply. In very few areas of the world is it possible to argue that the introduction of armaments on both sides of a potential conflict actually reduces the risk of open fighting. There are certain requirements, including a clear line of confrontation; 'deterrent' capabilities on both sides; adequate command and control over forces; and a relationship between 'warning time', intelligence-gathering, and political decision that can prevent the starting of war by accident. In few of the states facing possible conflict in the Persian Gulf do any of these factors exist; in none of them (with the possible exception of Iran in relationship to Iraq) do they all exist. Indeed, with the introduction of high-performance military equipment into an area of short distances and flat terrain, arms themselves can make open conflict more rather than less likely, even where neither party desires a shooting war. Thus it is not clear that high-performance equipment for Kuwait, for example, would markedly increase its 'security', if it would thereby appear 'provocative' to Iraq, yet would still lack adequate protection against a preemptive attack. Kuwait's security may be linked in part to Iran's deterrent capabilities; but that in itself is no argument for overarming Kuwait. Similarly, the further supply of high-performance equipment to both Iran and Saudi Arabia could make open fighting more likely, as an accidental outgrowth of competitions-in-influence between the two countries, especially with regard to naval forces in the Gulf itself. Nor is it sufficient to try distinguishing in the gulf between 'offensive' and 'defensive' equipment (though an emphasis on the latter may help): with the exception of armaments like ground-based anti aircraft defen-

168

ses, most high-performance 'defensive' equipment deployed in such close quarters can be used for 'offensive' purposes, as well. This lesson has been demonstrated repeatedly in confrontation between Israel and its Arab neighbors.

b. No outside power can provide military stability. — This is a useful political lesson, learned following the withdrawal of Britain from the Gulf. Its role there was primarily political; not military. Thus no outside military presence can hope to make up the British presence, without political relations that cannot be duplicated. In the same vein, outside powers need to be chary of believing that the outside supply of military arms can themselves provide stability, whether within or between countries. Rather, any outside involvement (if at all) should be concentrated upon policies — that is, on trying to resolve potential conflicts, where possible, without the use of military instruments in any form. Furthermore, if conflict becomes inevitable (as it may well become in some parts of the Gulf), it is likely to be less intense — and more quickly ended — if there has not been a spurious attempt to build up arms 'balances' in advance. There would also be value for us in not having been the supplier of arms to a belligerent, or to a regime that is overthrown in internal conflict.

c. Arms races usually take on a life of their own. . . It is sometimes believed that the development of political conflict leads to the introduction of weapons, but not the other way around. Nowhere does this latter statement appear to be the case. In the Gulf, as elsewhere, we can expect that a buildup of arms, in any country, will lead to a buildup elsewhere. This will happen for reasons of strategy, rightly or wrongly applied, and also for reasons of prestige. Indeed, it is ironic that a standard of national power, based upon military might, is being introduced in the Persian Gulf at the very moment when this standard is being depreciated among the major states of the world. Furthermore, outside suppliers of arms tend to make matters worse, either by their own example (as in the past), or by sending military support personnel along with the weapons. Almost inevitably, these personnel help stimulate demands for even more arms, and help to foster a cast of thinking that relates national prestige to the size of armies and number of weapons. Perhaps it is too late to stop this trend in the gulf; but that is no reason for promoting it." [114c]

75 The risks involved in a development that is not guided by such a spirit of cooperation have been emphasized by a number of official and non-official authors. Here two statements representing both these categories are cited. Melvin A. Conant of the Exxon Corporation has stated: "If some means for encompassing the interests of all concerned cannot be found, the search for single-government answers will lead to chaos and conflict. There is a limited period of time in which to work towards a multilateral solution. Pressures to arrive at some answers will increase as oil demands soar and the vital interests of states become ever more inextricably involved in its supply. Unless substantial progress is made towards a community solution the temptation to reach a 'national' one may then prove irresistible, and to our common loss." [15]

Helmut Schmidt, Chancellor of FR Germany, gave a similar warning. "On a worldwide scale, it will not be possible to reduce the differences in the levels of wealth unless the more advanced industrialized nations develop their own resources in close coordination with one another and with the primary-producing countries. If they fail to do so, the result might be social storms which could even seriously jeopardize world peace. If it can be assumed that most of the developed countries with a high level of prosperity have a great preference for peace, and that most of the less-developed countries have a high preference for increased wealth, there must be a level on which a convergence of preferences would stabilize the international political situation at a higher level of prosperity for both the wealthier and currently poorer countries. It would, therefore, serve the efforts to maintain peace on a worldwide scale if a comprehensive policy of economic cooperation were to be pursued rather than a policy of economic 'apartheid'." [120]

References

1. Häfele, W., "Energy Systems", *IAEA Bulletin,* Vol. 16, No. 1–2, February/April 1974, pp. 3–48.
2. OECD document C(74) 82 (final).
3. *The Energy Policy Report,* No. 1 (Washington, Ford Foundation, The Energy Policy Project, August 1972).
4. Bergsten, C.F., "The Threat from the Third World", *Foreign Policy*, No. 11, Summer 1973, pp. 102–24.
5. Mikdashi, Z., "Collusion Could Work", *Foreign Policy,* No 14, Spring 1974, pp. 57–68.
6. Krasner, S.D., "Oil Is the Exception", *Foreign Policy*, No. 14, Spring 1974, pp. 68–84.
7. Bergsten, C.F., "The Threat Is Real", *Foreign Policy*, No. 14, Spring 1974, pp. 84–90.
8. Rouhani, F., *A History of OPEC* (New York, Praeger, 1971) pp. 141–45.
9. Mikdashi, Z., "Cooperation Among Oil Exporting Countries with Special Reference to Arab Countries: A Political Economy Analysis", *International Organization*, Vol. 28, No. 1, Winter 1974, p. 1.
10. UN document A/RES/1803 (XVII).
11. UN document A/RES/2158 (XXI).
12. *The Middle East and North Africa 1973–74* (London, Europa Publications, 1973) p. 124.
    (a)_____, pp. 67–68.
    (b)_____ , pp. 108–11.
    (c)_____ , pp. 64–65.
    (d)_____ , p. 374.
13. Odell, P., "Oil and Western European Security", *Brasseys' Annual 1972*, pp. 64–68.
14. Odell, P., *Oil and World Power, A Geographical Interpretation* (Harmondsworth, Penguin, 1972) p. 3.
15. Conant, M.A., "Oil: Cooperation or Conflict", *Survival,* Vol. 15, No. 7, January/February 1973.
16. Schurr, S.H. and Homan, P.T., *Middle Eastern Oil and the Western World* (New York, Elsevier, 1971) p. 120.
    (a)_____, p. 11.
17. "Unnecessary Intermediaries", *Die Presse*, 27 January 1974.
18. "Oilmen Admit Giving Saudis Data", *International Herald Tribune*, 25 April 1974.
19. Hansen, J., "A New Era in International Oil Economy", *Aussenpolitik*, English edition, Vol. 24, February 1973, pp. 200–209.
20. *Host Government Participation in the Oil Trade,* Report prepared by Research Division H.P. Drewry (Shipping Consultants Ltd.) No. 20.
21. "Participation: Kuwait Ratifies 60/40 Agreement", *Petroleum Economist,* June 1974, p. 212.
22. Snyder, B., "Indonesia Is Aiming for a 2 Million bpd Rate by 1976", *World Oil,* September 1973, pp. 39–41.
23. "Venezuela Cutting Oil Output", *Financial Times,* 10 April 1974.
24. Harris, H., "Oil Supplies Must be Cut to Save Resources Says OPEC Leader", *Financial Times,* 19 April 1974.

25. Anderson, R.H., "Egyptian Aide Threatens Reprisal Against US Oil", *New York Times*, 8 January 1972.
26. "Saudis Warn U.S. on Israeli Policy, Oil Production", *International Herald Tribune*, 20 April 1973.
27. "4 Arab Nations Briefly Stop Pumping Oil in Symbolic Act", *International Herald Tribune*, 16 March 1973.
28. Hoagland, J., "Faisal Warns U.S. on Aiding Israel", *International Herald Tribune*, 7 July 1973.
29. "Les Pays Arabes Producteurs de Pétrole Menacent de Réduire leur Production", *Le Monde*, 10 July 1973.
30. Hijazi, I., "Saudi Warning to US on Continued Aid to Israel", *Financial Times*, 12 July 1973.
31. Hijazi, I., "Saudis May Restrict Oil Expansion after UN Veto", *Financial Times*, 30 July 1973.
32. "Faisal Reportedly Resisting Pressure for US Oil Cutoff", *International Herald Tribune*, 31 August 1973.
33. Hijazi, I., "Feisal Warns Arabs on 'Oil Weapon' ", *Financial Times*, 31 August 1973.
34. Ottaway, D.B., "Saudi Arabia Warns U.S. of Oil Cuts", *International Herald Tribune*, 5 September 1973.
35. Beeston, R., "US Faces Saudi Arabia Oil Cutback Over Arms for Israel", *Daily Telegraph*, 6 September 1973.
36. Berger, M., "Kissinger Sees Lifting of Oil Embargo Soon", *International Herald Tribune*, 23 January 1974.
37. Farris, F., "Arabs Get Kissinger Warning", *International Herald Tribune*, 7 February 1974.
38. Hoagland, J., "Riyadh Ups Oil Exports to the U.S.", *International Herald Tribune*, 29 March 1974.
39. Hoagland, J., "Saudis Reportedly Authorize Aramco to Boost Production", *International Herald Tribune*, 1 April 1974.
40. "Production Increases Allowed", *Petroleum Economist*, May 1974, p. 174.
41. "L'O.U.A. Invite les Etats Producteurs à Etendre l'Embargo à la République Sud-Africaine, à la Rhodésie et au Portugal", *Le Monde*, 23 November 1974.
42. Morris, J.A., "Saudi Admits Ineffectiveness of Oil Embargo on US, Dutch", *International Herald Tribune*, 18 January 1974.
43. "Supplies to Rotterdam Are Rising", *Petroleum Economist*, March 1974.
44. "Persian Gulf Oil Cuts Seen as Moderate", *International Herald Tribune*, 7 February 1974.
45. O'Toole, R., "Half of the Arab Oil 'Leaked' to U.S. Is Coming from Libya", *International Herald Tribune*, 1 January 1974.
46. "US Study Details Arab Oil Leaks during Boycott", *International Herald Tribune*, 10 April 1974.
47. "Aramco Denies It Imported Embargoed Saudi Arabia Oil", *International Herald Tribune*, 13 April 1974.
48. Saxon, W., "Shah of Iran Claims Embargo Has Not Cut US Oil Imports", *International Herald Tribune*, 25 February 1974.
49. "Simon Calls Shah's Words 'Irresponsible' ", *International Herald Tribune*, 26 February 1974.
50. "Iran Premier Assails Simon over US Oil Imports", *International Herald Tribune*, 27 February 1974.
51. Wren, C.C., "Moscow Angrily Denying Role in Arab Oil Embargo", *New York Times*, 6 December 1973.
52. "Du 'Brut' d'Origine Soviétique Serait Vendu aux Etats-Unis", *Le Monde*, 17 February 1974.
53. "Russians Fed Oil to America Amid Boycott", *International Herald Tribune*, 2 April 1974.

54. Dale, E.L., Jr., "Saudi Oil Embargo Is Termed Breach of '33 Treaty with US", *New York Times,* 19 December 1973.

55. UN document A/RES/2625 (XXV).

56. Gardner, R.N., "The Hard Road to World Order", *Foreign Affairs,* Vol. 52, No. 3, April 1974, p. 567.

57. OECD Statutes, 14 December 1960, Chapter 8, articles 100–102.

58. OECD document C(71) 113 (final).

59. OECD document C(72) 201 (final), annex.

60. "Major Oil-Consuming Countries Meet at Washington to Discuss the Energy Problem", *Department of State Bulletin,* 4 March 1974, pp. 201–206.

61. Wigg, R., "French Clash with US as OECD Decides not to Activate Oil-Sharing Scheme", *Times,* 27 October 1973.

62. "OECD Decides Not to Activate Plan for Sharing Oil Stocks", *International Herald Tribune,* 21 November 1973.

63. Thomas, J. "Battle for an EEC Energy Policy", *New Scientist,* 1 November 1973, pp. 330–33.

64. EEC document COM(73) 1320.

65. *President Nixon's Message to Congress on Energy, 18 April 1974,* White House press release fact sheet.

66. *Kissinger Address at Associated Press Luncheon, 23 April 1973,* Press release, United States Information Service, Stockholm.

67. Adelman, M.A., "Is the Oil Shortage Real? Oil Companies as OPEC Tax-Collectors", *Foreign Policy,* No. 9, Winter 1972–73, pp. 69–107.

68. Levy, W.J., "An Atlantic-Japanese Energy Policy", *Foreign Policy,* No. 11, Summer 1973, pp. 159–90.

69. Hazelhurst, P., "US Urges Japanese to Persuade Oil-Rich Nations to Invest in Developed Economies", *Times,* 17 July 1974.

70. Hammond, A.L., *et al., Energy and the Future* (Washington, American Association for the Advancement of Science, 1973) pp. 25–28.

  (a)_____, p. 48.
  (b)_____, p. 4.
  (c)_____, pp. 11–16.
  (d)_____, pp. 79–94.
  (e)_____, pp. 55–60.
  (f)_____, pp. 61–66.
  (g)_____, p. 50.

71. "The White House Text of Remarks Made by President Nixon to the Press 8 September after a Meeting with his Energy Advisers", *Congressional Quarterly,* 15 September 1973, p. 2447.

72. "The White House Text of President Nixon's 7 November Address to the Nation on the Energy Emergency", *Congressional Quarterly,* 10 November 1973, p. 2965.

73. "Kissinger Says Arab Oil Ban Will Not Change U.S. Policy", *International Herald Tribune,* 22 November 1973.

74. Berger, M., "Kissinger Urges Joint Energy Unit", *International Herald Tribune,* 13 December 1973.

75. *USA Document* (Stockholm, United States Information Service, 11 January 1974).

76. Lemaitre, P., "Les Neuf Souhaitent que la Conférence de Washington 'Explore les Meilleures Formes de Dialogue' Entre Utilisateurs et Producteurs de Pétrole", *Le Monde,* 7 February 1974.

77. "France Proposes World Conference on Energy", *Times,* 22 January 1974.

78. "La Proposition Francaise de Conférence Doit Etre Elargie au Problème de Matières Premières", *Le Monde,* 1 February 1974.

79. Balta, P., "Le Président Boumediene Demande une Réunion de l'Assemblée-Générale de l'ONU", *Le Monde,* 1 February 1974.

80. "US Proposals Accepted at Brussels Oil Conference", *International Herald Tribune*, 14 March 1974.
81. "Oil Users Meet", *International Herald Tribune*, 5 April 1974; and "U.S. Sets Conditions on Oil Pooling", *International Herald Tribune*, 19 June 1974.
82. Haworth, D., "EEC Seeks Conference with Arab Countries", *International Herald Tribune*, 5 March 1974.
83. "Les Etats Arabes Forment une Commission pour le Dialogue avec l'Europe des Neuf", *Le Monde*, 27 May 1974.
84. Siner, R., "Nixon Warns W. Europeans on Economic Confrontation", *International Herald Tribune*, 16—17 March 1974.
85. "European Officials Welcome Nixon's Softer Line on EEC", *International Herald Tribune*, 21 March 1974.
86. Farris, F., "Kissinger Appeals for Halt to Europe Anti-U.S. Policy", *International Herald Tribune*, 22 March 1974.
87. Goshko, J.M., "Kissinger Asserts European Relations Are 'Cornerstone' of US Policy", *International Herald Tribune*, 25 March 1974.
88. "Scheel Says Common Market Has Not Hit US 'Too Hard' ", *International Herald Tribune*, 12 April 1974.
89. Hofmann, P., "Saudi Sees 'Disaster' If Bloc Forms to Battle Oil Nations", *International Herald Tribune*, 14 January 1974.
90. Khene, A., (Secretary-General of OPEC), "New Developments on the Oil Scene", An address given in Vienna to Österreichische Gesellschaft für Aussenpolitik und Internationale Berziehungen, 28 January 1974.
91. "Official Says US Considered Halting Food Sales to Arabs", *International Herald Tribune*, 15 November 1973.
92. Gwertzman, B., "US Retaliation on Oil Rejected", *New York Times*, 20 November 1973.
93. "U.S. Lifts Curbs for 5 Months on Wheat Imports", *International Herald Tribune*, 26 January 1974.
94. *Report prepared for the Foreign Affairs Committee by the Foreign Affairs Division, Library of Congress (inserted as Appendix 6 in a report of 20 December 1973 to the Committee on Foreign Affairs entitled The United States Oil Shortage and the Arab-Israeli Conflict)* (Washington, US Government Printing Office, 1973).
95. "Suppose the U.S. Decided to Retaliate Against the Arabs. . .", *US News & World Report*, 10 December 1973.
96. Schlesinger, J.R., "Arabs Risking Use of Force", *International Herald Tribune*, 8 January 1974.
97. "Minister Hotar Spränga Oljefält", *Dagens Nyheter*, 23 November 1973.
98. "Le Président Boumediène: Si l'Occident Tente d'Employer la Force, il Subira une Catastrophe", *Le Monde*, 5 December 1973.
99. "Saudis Repeat Oilfield Warning", OPEC press release, in *Arab World*, 8 January 1974.
100. "Minering Redan Klar i Oljefält", *Dagens Nyheter*, 10 January 1974.
101. Coughlin, W.J., "Fears of Invasion by U.S. Rise in Mideast; Oil Fields Mined", *International Herald Tribune*, 12 January 1974.
102. "Armed US Intervention Rumours", *Africa Diary*, 5—11 February 1974.
103. "Oil Fire Forces Israelis to Halt Sinai Production", *International Herald Tribune*, 3 January 1974.
104. Daniel, L., "Dead Sea Oil Search", *Financial Times*, 28 March 1974.
105. *Congressional Record*, 21 May 1973, p. S 9444.
106. "Fulbright Warns of a War over Oil", *New York Times*, 22 May 1974.
107. Schwebel, S.M., "A Takeover of Kuwait", *Washington Post*, 26 June 1973.
108. *Statement by Treasury Secretary George P. Schultz before the Washington Energy Conference, 11 February 1974*, Memorandum for the Press, Washington, 19 February 1974.

109. Johns, R., "Area Begins to Flex Its Money Muscle", *Financial Times,* 16 April 1974.
110. Krymm, R., "The Economic Impact of Oil Prices", *IAEA Bulletin,* February—April 1974, pp. 60—65.
111. McLachlan, K., *Spending Oil Revenues; Development Prospects in the Middle East to 1975,* QER Special No. 10 (The Economist Intelligence Unit Ltd., 1972) p. 1.
112. Ellington, W., "Arab Investments in West Seen Growing", *International Herald Tribune,* 24—25 November 1973.
113. "Arabs to Remove Some of Funds Banked in West", *International Herald Tribune,* 7 December 1973.
114. *New Perspectives on the Persian Gulf,* Hearings before the Subcommittee on the Near East and South Asia of the Committee on Foreign Affairs, House of Representatives, 93rd Congress, 1st Session, June 6, July 17, 23, 24 and November 28, 1973 (Washington, US Government Printing Office, 1973) p. 172.
   (a) _____, p. 7.
   (b) _____, p. 39.
   (c) _____, pp. 78—80.
   (d) _____, p. 57.
115. "Arab Oil Men Invest in US Real Estate", *International Herald Tribune,* 12—13 January 1974.
116. "Arab Said to Buy US Treasury Bills", *International Herald Tribune,* 2 February 1974.
117. Silk, L., "Part of the Huge Arab Oil Revenues Is Beginning to Flow Back to West", *International Herald Tribune,* 26 April 1974.
118. Marder, M., "Iran, U.S. Oil Company Sign 50—50, 'Well-to-Pump' Deal", *International Herald Tribune,* 26 July 1973.
119. Berger, M., "Iran, U.S. Oil Firm Sharing Seen as Pattern in Industry", *International Herald Tribune,* 27 July 1973.
120. Schmidt, H., "Struggle for the World Product", *Foreign Affairs,* Vol. 52, No. 3, April 1974, p. 449.
121. Coleman, F., "IMF Planning Strategy on Oil Price Rise", *International Herald Tribune,* 17 January 1974.
122. Lewis, P., "$3000 Million Expected for IMF Oil Facility", *Financial Times,* 28 April 1974.
123. Nossiter, B.D., "Yamani Rejects Plan for IMF Loan Agency", *International Herald Tribune,* 10 May 1974.
124. "Iranian Loan Plan to Ease Oil Cost Burden", *Times,* 6 February 1974.
125. "Fund Advances Work on New Oil Facility as Iran Pledges to Lend Its Financial Aid", *IMF Survey,* 4 March 1974, pp. 65—66.
126. "OPEC to Aid Poorer Nations", *International Herald Tribune,* 8 April 1974.
127. Field, M., "Investing Money Locally", *Financial Times,* 16 April 1974.
128. "Kuwait Heads the Way in Handling Surplus Funds", *Financial Times,* 16 April 1974.
129. "KFAED Capital Raised, Activities Extended", *Arab Report and Record,* 16—31 March 1974, p. 105.
130. "Arab Shares in African Banks", *Arab Report and Record,* 16—31 March 1974, p. 119.
131. "$50 Million Grant to Syria", *Arab Report and Record,* 15—28 February 1974, p. 66.
132. "Kuwaiti Aid for Reopening Suez Canal", *Arab Report and Record,* 1—15 March 1974, p. 81.
133. "Saudis, Kuwait Boost Arab Aid", *International Herald Tribune,* 18 April 1974.
134. "L'Arabie Saoudite Fait un Don de 100 Million de Dollars à l'Egypte", *Le Monde,* 19 April 1974.

135. Housego, D., "Iran to Help Egypt Widen Suez Canal", *Financial Times,* 31 May 1974.
136. Shannon, D., "Saudis Promise $50 Million to the World Food Program", *International Herald Tribune,* 27 March 1974.
137. "Svensk Bankkredit i Santiago", *Svenska Dagbladet,* 3 April 1974.
138. "World Bank Cuts 1974 Estimates of Growth Rates", *International Herald Tribune,* 18 April 1974.
139. Pre-publication Text of the Economic Survey of Europe in 1973, ECE (XXIX)/1.
140. *Fiscal Year 1974 Authorization for Military Procurement, Research and Development, Construction Authorization for the Safeguard ABM, and Active Duty and Selected Reserve Strengths, Part 1, Authorizations, March 28, 29; April 2, 1973,* Hearings before the Committee on Armed Services, US Senate, 93rd Congress, 1st session, (Washington, US Government Printing Office, 1973) p. 168.
141. "An Interview with the Shah of Iran", *International Herald Tribune,* 14 May 1973.
142. Viennot, J-P., "L'Intervention des Forces Iraniennes en Oman", *Le Monde Diplomatique,* June 1974.
143. *The Arms Trade with the Third World* (Stockholm, Almqvist & Wiksell, 1971, Stockholm International Peace Research Institute).
    (a) _____ , p. 677.
144. *World Armaments and Disarmament, SIPRI Yearbook 1972* (Stockholm, Almqvist & Wiksell, 1972, Stockholm International Peace Research Institute).
145. *World Armaments and Disarmament, SIPRI Yearbook 1973* (Stockholm, Almqvist & Wiksell, 1973, Stockholm International Peace Research Institute).
146. *World Armaments and Disarmament, SIPRI Yearbook 1974* (Stockholm, Almqvist & Wiksell, 1974, Stockholm International Peace Research Institute).
147. *The SIPRI Arms Trade Registers* (in preparation).
148. Burrell, R.M., "The Persian Gulf", *The Washington Papers,* No. 1 (New York, Library Press, 1972).
149. "Mideast States Bitterly Contest Oil Claims", *International Herald Tribune,* 10 April 1973.
150. "Der Grenzkonflikt am Persischen Golf", *Neue Zürcher Zeitung,* 6 April 1973.
151. Housego, D., "Keeping the Pot Boiling", *Financial Times,* 12 July 1973.
152. Scott-Plummer, S., "Ten-Year Battle for Gateway to the Gulf", *Times,* 14 April 1973.
153. "Arab Oil Cuts Leave Israel Unaffected", *International Herald Tribune,* 20 October 1973.
154. de Silva, M., "Big Brother Eyes the Oil", *Financial Times,* 23 January 1974.
155. "Ingen Uppgörelse om Mittlinjen i Östersjön", *Svenska Dagbladet,* 26 April 1974.
156. "Oil in the Baltic", *Petroleum Economist,* May 1974.
157. " 'Differences' with Malta over Seabed", *Arab Report and Record,* 15—28 February 1974, p. 69.
158. "Venezuelan Prospects Now", *Petroleum Press Service,* December 1972, pp. 448—51.
159. Clark, A., "Oil on Falkland Islands", *Japan Times,* 16 December 1973.
160. "Oil's Role in Seaborne Trade", *Petroleum Press Service,* March 1972, p. 93.
161. *World Tanker Fleet Review, 31st December 1973* (London, John J. Jacobs & Company Ltd., 1974).
162. "New Havens for the Giants", *Petroleum Press Service,* December 1973, p. 463.
163. Miller, R.A., "Indonesia's Archipelago Doctrine and Japan's Jugular", *U.S. Naval Institute Proceedings,* October 1972.

164. "Egypt Plans to Start Work on Clearing Canal in March", *International Herald Tribune,* 1 February 1974.
165. "Egypt Sets Plan to Open Suez Canal", *International Herald Tribune,* 7 February 1974.
166. "Egyptian Units Begin Work Removing Suez Canal Mines", *International Herald Tribune,* 8 February 1974.
167. Tanner, H., "Egypt Clearing Mines, Shells at Canal, Sees Oct. Opening", *International Herald Tribune,* 22 February 1974.
168. "U.S. to Help Egypt Clear Mines", *International Herald Tribune,* 19 March 1974.
169. "Soviet Navy Seeks Role in Clearing Suez Canal Mines", *International Herald Tribune,* 28 March 1974.
170. "Egypt at the Crossroad", *Petroleum Economist,* March 1974, pp. 91—93.
171. "US Copters Finish Suez Channel Sweep", *International Herald Tribune,* 23 May 1974.
172. *The Economic Effects of the Closure of the Suez Canal,* Study by the Secretariat of UNCTAD, United Nations TD/B/C, 4/104/Rev. 7 (New York, 1973).
173. *Oil and Gas Imports Issues, January 10, 11 and 22, 1973,* Hearings before the Committee on Interior and Insular Affairs, United States Senate, 93rd Congress (Washington, US Government Printing Office, 1973) Part 3, pp. 740—41.
    (a)_____, pp. 750—52.
    (b)_____, p. 745.
174. *Strategic and Tactical Antisubmarine Warfare,* SIPRI Monograph (in preparation).
175. "Unklarheit über Bab-el-Mandeb", *Neue Zürcher Zeitung,* 28 November 1973.
176. Martin, L., *Arms and Strategy, An International Survey of Modern Defence* (London, Weidenfeld & Nicolson, 1973) p. 229.
177. Burrel, M., "The Cape Route and the Oil Trade", *The Round Table,* 1973: 251, pp 353—61.
178. "Worldwide Tanker Ports — Present and Possible", *International Petroleum Encyclopedia,* 1973, pp. 233—34.
179. Szulc, T., "A 'New Beginning' for Portugal", *Washington Post,* 2 May 1974.
180. Schmidt, D.A., "Military Chiefs of US, South Africa Confer Quietly", *Christian Science Monitor,* 10 May 1974.
181. Wilson, A. and Masterman, S., "NATO Plans to Protect African Cape Route", *Observer,* 19 May 1974.
182. Watson, P., "Secret NATO Plan to Protect South Africa", *Sunday Times,* 19 May 1974.
183. Keatley, P., "NATO Row over Cape Defences", *Guardian,* 20 May 1974.
184. "NATO — New Waters?", *Economist,* 25 May 1974, p. 52.
185. Pomonti, J.-C., "Le Projet de Canal dans l'Isthme de Kra Semble Etre Abandonné", *Le Monde,* 17 January 1974.
186. Oliver, E.F., "Malacca: Dire Straits", *US Naval Institute Proceedings,* June 1973, p. 28.
187. Väyrynen, R., "Conflict of Interest in Territorial Waters: Iceland, Ecuador and the Straits of Malacca", *Instant Research on Peace and Violence,* No. 3, 1973, pp. 123—48.
188. Colombos, C.J., *International Law of the Sea,* 6th ed. (London, Longmans, 1967) pp. 132—35.
189. Cheng Huan, "The Legal Aspects", *Far Eastern Economic Review,* 15 April 1972, p. 19.
190. "Des Pipe-lines qui ont une Importance Stratégique", *Le Monde,* 12 October 1973.

191. "Explosion Breaches Tapline", *Arab Report and Record,* 16–31 January 1973, p. 38.
192. "Oil Tanks Attacked by Unknown Raiders", *Arab Report and Record,* 1–15 April 1973, p. 158.
193. "Second Attack on Tapline", *Arab Report and Record,* 16–30 April 1973, p. 182.
194. Tanner, H., "American Presence in Egypt's Economy", *International Herald Tribune,* 8 October 1973.
195. Tanner, H., "Bechtel Quits Egypt Pipeline Deal", *International Herald Tribune,* 13 April 1974.
196. Robinson, A., "Italy Wins Sumed Contract", *Financial Times,* 16 April 1974.
197. "Arab States to Finance Pipeline Construction", *Africa Diary,* 8–14 January 1974.
198. Thunborg, A., *Energikrisen och Svensk Säkerhetspolitik,* (Stockholm, Försvarsdepartementet, Sekretariatet för Säkerhetspolitik och Långsiktsplanering inom Totalförsvaret, April 1974).
199. *Exploring Energy Choices; A Preliminary Report of the Ford Foundation's Energy Policy Project,* The Ford Foundation, 1974.
200. Barry, R.S. and Fels, M.F., *Production and Consumption of Automobiles: An Energy Analysis of the Manufacture Discard and Reuse of the Automobile and its Component Materials* Report to the Illinois Institute for Environmental Quality, July 1972.
201. "Steel Industry Top User of U.S. Energy", *International Herald Tribune,* 27 December 1973.
202. *Active Duty and Selected Reserve Strengths,* Hearings before the Committee on Armed Services, US Senate, 93rd Congress, 1st session, Part 2, Authorizations, April 10, 12, 13, 17, 26, 30; May 7, 1973 (Washington, US Government Printing Office) p. 609.
203. "American Fuel Oil Found Insufficient for Peak Bombing of N. Vietnam", *Times,* 13 January 1973.
204. "Uncertainties Cloud Predictions For Aviation Fuel This Winter", *Aviation Week & Space Technology,* 24 September 1973, p. 50.
205. *Management of Defense Energy Resources,* Report of the Defense Energy Task Group, 15 November 1973, US Department of Defense, 1973.
206. Sullivan, R.W., *et al., A Brief Overview of the Energy Requirements of the Department of Defense* (Columbus, Ohio, Battelle Columbus Laboratories, August 1972).
207. "Singapore Halts Fuel to U.S. Units", *New York Times,* 15 November 1973.
208. Getler, M., "Oil Boycott Begins to Affect U.S. Pacific Fleet Operations", *International Herald Tribune,* 16 November 1973.
209. "DoD to Boost its Domestic Fuel Store", *Aviation Week & Space Technology,* 26 November 1973.
210. Getler, M., "U.S. Forces Abroad Preempt Fuel From Domestic Supplies", *International Herald Tribune,* 17–18 November 1973.
211. Finney, J.W., "Fuel is Diverted for the Military", *New York Times,* 28 November 1973.
212. Getler, M., "U.S. Forces Got Arab Oil During Embargo", *International Herald Tribune,* 21 March 1974.
213. Finney, J.W., "Military Rations of Oil Raised 2 Per Cent", *New York Times,* 8 January 1974.
214. Finney, J.W., "Schlesinger Testifies Fuel Allocations to Military Must Be Raised This Spring", *New York Times,* 1 February 1974.
215. "Libya Warns Bonn It Risks Having Its Oil Supplies Cut", *International Herald Tribune,* 2 November 1973.
216. "U.S. Navy Tries Liquefied Coal, New Economical, Clean Fuel", *International Herald Tribune,* 17–18 November 1973

217. Vansant, C., *Strategic Energy Supply and National Security* (New York, Praeger, 1971) pp. 64–74.
218. Pretty, R.T. and Archer, D.H.R., eds., *Jane's Weapon Systems 1973–74* (London, Sampson, Low, Marston & Co, Ltd., 1973), p. 54
219. *US Energy Outlook, A Report of the National Petroleum Council's Committee on US Energy Outlook,* December 1973, pp. 3–4.
220. "Energy: The Growing Choices", *Economist,* 20 April 1974, p. 60.
221. "Energy", *International Canada,* October 1973, pp. 251–52.
222. *Oil, the Present Situation and Future Prospects* (Paris, OECD Oil Committee, 1973) p. 192.
     (a) _____, p. 23.
     (b) _____, pp. 220–22.
     (c) _____, pp. 179–82.
223. Luetheus, W.L., "The Key to Canada's Future", *Financial Times Survey on Canadian Energy,* 14 May 1974.
224. "How Much More Oil?", *Petroleum Press Service,* December 1973, p. 466.
225. Farndon, R., "North Sea Oil Production Likely to Equal Two Thirds of UK Requirements by 1980", *Times,* 15 May 1973.
226. Hamilton, A., "Oil Independence by 1980", *Financial Times,* 22 May 1974.
227. "La Norvège Pourrait Produire en 1981 Environ 50 Millions de Tonnes de Pétrole par An", *Le Monde,* 19 April 1974.
228. "Safeguarding Europe's Supplies", *Petroleum Economist,* May 1974, pp. 166–69.
229. Becker, A.S., *Oil and the Persian Gulf in Soviet Policy in the 1970's,* P-4743-1 (Rand Corporation, May 1972) p. 7.
230. *Soviet Oil to 1980,* QER Special No. 14 (London, The Economist Intelligence Unit, June 1973) p. 28.
     (a) _____, p. 18.
     (b) _____, p. 3.
231. "Rethinking Soviet Policies", *Petroleum Economist,* March 1974, pp. 99–101.
232. Tiratsoo, E.N., *Oilfields of the World* (Beaconsfield, Scientific Press Ltd., 1973) p. 115.
     (a) _____, p. 23.
     (b) _____, p. 94.
233. Bakke, D.R., "Soviet Union Indicates Plans for Development of Arctic Oil and Gas", *Offshore,* November 1973, pp. 37–40.
234. "The Soviet Factor", *New Scientist,* 21 February 1974, pp. 472–74
235. Kaiser, R.G. "Russia Shifts on Oil Development", *International Herald Tribune,* 27 May 1974 *and* "Russia Needs and Fears Western Know-how", *Times* 6 June 1974.
236. Shobad, T., "Estonia's Expanding Oil Shale Industry Helps Supply Soviet Union", *New York Times,* 13 January 1974.
237. "East Europe's Fading Surplus", *Petroleum Economist,* June 1974, pp. 204–205.
238. Lascelles, D., "The Strains Within Comecon", *Financial Times,* 22 May 1974.
239. Weeks, L.G., "Offshore Successes Raise for East/Oceania Potential", *World Oil,* May 1973, pp. 87–94.
240. Sakino, H., "Japan and Her Maritime Defence", *US Naval Institute Proceedings, Naval Review 1971,* p. 115.
241. *Oil and Economic Growth,* QER Special No. 15, (London, The Economist Intelligence Unit, 1974) p. 34.
     (a) _____, p. 30.
     (b) _____, p. 24.
242. "Energy Forecast Revised", *Petroleum Economist,* June 1974, pp. 215–16.
243. Hymans, H., "Coal: A Revival in Japan", *Far Eastern Economic Review,* 4 March 1974.

244. "Japan and Siberia: Is This What It was All About?", *Economist*, 6 April 1974, p. 44.
245. "La Population a Dépassé le Cap des Sept Cents Millions d'Habitants", *Le Monde*, 22 September 1973.
246. "La Production Chinoise de Pétrole Attaindrait Déja 50 Millions de Tonnes", *Le Monde*, 1 June 1973.
247. Smith, C., "Japan Heartened by China Oil Figures", *Financial Times*, 8 January 1974.
248. Lelyveld, J., "Chinese Oil-Output Figures are a Puzzle", *New York Times*, 9 January 1974.
249. Lelyveld, J., "China is Increasing Oil-Export Deals; Deliveries for 1974 Expected to Triple", *New York Times*, 5 January 1974.
250. "US Companies and China's Oil Development", *New York Times*, 3 March 1974.
251. "Chou En-Lai's Million B/D", *Petroleum Economist*, February 1974, pp. 49—50.
252. *People's Republic of China, Atlas* (US Central Intelligence Agency, Washington, 1971) pp. 64—67.
253. Burchett, E., "Chinese Tap Taching Potential", *Far Eastern Economic Review*, 14 January 1974, pp. 45—46.
254. "China's Oil Industry", *Current Scene*, Vol. XI, No. 11, 1973, pp. 21—23.
255. "Openings in China", *Petroleum Press Service*, October 1972, p. 363.
256. "Drilling Pushed in China's Pohai Gulf", *Oil and Gas Journal*, 31 December 1973, p. 74.
257. Leslie, J., "China Buys US Oil-Drilling Equipment", *International Herald Tribune*, 10 April 1974.
258. *Sea-bed Mineral Resources*, Progress Report by the Secretary-General, UN document A/AC 138/90, 3 July 1973.
259. *World Energy Supplies 1961—1970*, UN document ST/STAT/SER. J/15, (New York, United Nations, 1972) p. 46.
260. Hsinhua, news release, 31 March 1974.
261. "India: Economic Problems Aggravated", *Petroleum Economist*, December 1973, pp. 466—67.
262. Simons, L.M., "India May Improve Ties to U.S. in New Gandhi Deals with Iran", *International Herald Tribune*, 30 April 1974.
263. Hornsby, M., "No Escape from the Oil Drought", *Times*, 12 January 1974.
264. Sharma, K.K., "India's Energy Problems' Charity Begins Abroad", *Financial Times*, 5 March 1974.
265. Rangan, K., "Oil Strike Lifts Sagging Spirits in India", *New York Times*, 9 March 1974.
266. Sarkar, J., "Indian Crisis", *Far Eastern Economic Review*, 24 September 1973.
267. "Iraqi Crude For India", *Times of India*, 28 April 1974.
268. "Russia to Supply Crude Oil", *Petroleum Economist*, January 1974, p. 13.
269. "Iran Cuts Oil Price in Deal with India", *Financial Times*, 23 February 1974.
270. Mascarenhas, A., "Driven by Dung Power", *Sunday Times*, 17 February 1974.
271. "New Perspectives in Pakistan", *Petroleum Press Service*, February 1972, p. 58.
272. "Oil Prices Threaten Bangladesh Recovery", *Times*, 29 April 1974.
273. *News Review on South Asia* (Institute for Defense Studies and Analyses, June 1973) p. 33.
274. "The Oil Crisis Has Seriously Affected Sri Lanka", *IMF Survey*, 21 January 1974, p. 26.
275. "Indonesia Said to Be Capable of Doubling its Oil Production", *International Herald Tribune*, 8 November 1974.
276. Goldstone, A., "The Oil Bonanza: Pertamina's Risky Strategy", *Far Eastern Economic Review*, 24 December 1974, p. 25.

277. "South China Sea Potential", *Petroleum Press Service*, October 1973, p. 373.
278. "Thailand: High Hopes of Oil", *Petroleum Economist*, March 1974, p. 110.
279. Wong Puan Wam, "Malaysia Oil: The 'Sweet' Smell of Unexpected Riches", *Financial Times*, 23 August 1973.
280. McCashlin, J.C., "Cebu Island Shows Hold Hope for Philippines", *Oil and Gas Journal*, 31 December 1973, p. 163.
281. "Firms Eye Oil in North Vietnam", *International Herald Tribune*, 10 October 1973.
282. "Hanoi Accelère les Recherches de Pétrole et de Gaz Naturel", *Le Monde*, 6 January 1974.
283. "Zukunftssorgen in Singapur: Politische und wirtschaftliche Folgen der Ölknappheit", *Neue Zürcher Zeitung*, 1 January 1974.
284. Randall, K., "L'Australie se Trouve dans une Situation Enérgetique très Favorable", *Le Monde*, 27 February 1974.
285. "Australia: Solar Energy Plans", *Petroleum Economist*, May 1974, p. 190.
286. Hunter, A., *Oil Supply in Australia's Defence Strategy*, Canberra Papers on Strategy and Defence, No. 1 (Canberra, Australian National University Press, 1968).
287. *International Petroleum Encyclopedia*, 1974, p. 342.
288. "Oil Imports a Heavy Burden", *Petroleum Economist*, March 1974, p. 110.
289. "Brazil Searches Abroad", *Petroleum Press Service*, May 1973, pp. 182–83.
290. "Brazil – The Hungry Giant", *Petroleum Press Service*, October 1973 pp. 382–84.
291. Simonnot, P., "Tout en Confirmant ses Intentions, le Président du Venezuela n'Indique pas la Date à Laquelle les Compagnies Pétrolières Seront Nationalisées", *Le Monde*, 14 March 1974.
292. "Venezuela: Commission to Study Takeover", *Petroleum Economist*, June 1974, p. 213.
293. "Venezuela Cannot Fill the Gap", *Petroleum Press Service*, November 1973, pp. 413–15.
294. "Monsieur Jobert à Caracas La France s'Intéressa aux Schistes Bitumineux Vénézueliens", *Le Monde*, 28 March 1974.
295. "Latin American Prospects", *Petroleum Economist*, January 1974, pp. 25–28.
296. "Nigeria Sitting Pretty", *Petroleum Economist*, February 1974, pp. 57–59.
297. "West African Output Up", *Petroleum Press Service*, September 1973, pp. 339–41.
298. "Zaire Gulf to Start in Mid-1975", *Facts and Report*, item 463, 7–30 March 1974.
299. Johnson, T.A., "African Oil Rush Spreads", *International Herald Tribune*, 27 December 1973.
300. King, R.E., "Offshore '73: Interest Focuses on North Sea Gulf of Mexico for East", *World Oil*, July 1973, p. 80.
301. "Angola Could Aid Portugal", *Petroleum Press Service*, December 1973, pp. 454–55.
302. "The Real Truth about Gulf Oil Discoveries", *African Development*, (London) January 1974.
303. "Angola: Oil in Cabinda Gulf", *Africa Diary*, 19–25 February 1974.
304. "Cabinda Oil Exports in February", *Facts and Report*, item 464, 7–30 March 1974.
305. "Southern Africa's Oil Crisis", *Africa Bureau Fact Sheet 36*, May 1974.
306. "Energy in the Future", *BP Shield International*, December 1973, p. 2.
    (a) _____, p. 3.
    (b) _____, pp. 8–11.
    (c) _____, pp. 16–23.
307. Frenkel, D.H., "The Energy Crisis: The October 1973 Petroleum Revolution", Part III, *New Outlook*, June 1974, pp. 34–42.

308. Graham, R., "Bab-al-Mandeb: Israel's Soft Spot", *Financial Times*, 6 December 1973.
309. Eliasson, L., "Fotosyntes – Ett Kärnkraftsalternativ", *Svenska Dagbladet*, 28 March 1974.
310. Wilson, C.L., "A Plan for Energy Independence", *Foreign Affairs*, Vol. 51, July 1973.
311. Alburt, F.O., "Coal and the Present Energy Situation", *Science*, Vol. 183, No. 4124, 8 February 1974.
312. Averitt, P., "Coal", *United States Mineral Resources*, Geological Survey Professional Paper 820 (Washington, US Government Printing Office, 1973) p. 140.
313. Geffen, T.M., "Improved Oil Recovery Could Help Ease Energy Shortage", *World Oil*, October 1973, pp. 84–88.
314. Hubert, M.K., "Energy Resources", in *Resources and Man*, A Study and Recommendations by the Committee on Resources and Man (San Fransisco, W.H. Freeman and Company, 1969) p. 197.
315. *Nuclear Proliferation Problems* (Stockholm, Almqvist & Wiksell, 1974, Stockholm International Peace Research Institute).
316. "$210 Million for First Shale Oil-Lease", *New Scientist*, 17 January 1974.
317. "Oil Shale Development Begins", *Petroleum Economist*, January 1974, p. 10.
318. "South Africa Eyes Plants to Make Oil from Coal", *International Herald Tribune*, 5 December 1973.
319. "Signposts at Sasol", *Economist*, 21 July 1973, p. 85.
320. Finn, G., "German Firm Gets U.S. Contracts for Coal-to-Gas Plant Technology", *International Herald Tribune*, 5 December 1973.
321. "How Near is Nuclear Fusion", *Petroleum Press Service*, August 1973, pp. 295–97.
322. "Tapping the Earth's Heat", *Petroleum Press Service*, December 1973, pp. 461–63.
323. "Energy Shortage Stimulates Geothermal Exploration", *World Oil*, December 1973, pp. 37–41.
324. Hammond, A.L., "Solar Energy: Proposal for a Major Research Program", *Science*, Vol. 179, p. 1116.
325. Shumann, W.A., "Man Turns to Sun as Energy Alternative", *Aviation Week & Space Technology*, 14 January 1974, pp. 56–61.
326. Sullivan, W., "Two Test Projects to Seek Power from Ocean's Heat", *New York Times*, 22 April 1974.
327. Smith, G., "Vital Resource of Garbage Attracts Big Industry in U.S.", *International Herald Tribune*, 28 February 1974.
328. Griffiths, E.J., "Hydrogen Fuel", *Nature*, 29 March 1974.
329. Winsche, W.E., Hoffman, K.C. and Salzano, F.J., "Hydrogen: Its Future Role in the Nation's Energy Economy", *Science*, Vol. 180, No. 4093, pp. 1325–32.
330. Fishlock, D., "Multinational Hydrogen Plan Proposed", *Financial Times*, 24 January 1974.
331. Reed, T.B. and Lerner, R.M., "Methanol: A Versatile Fuel for Immediate Use", *Science*, Vol. 182, No. 4119, 28 December 1973, pp. 1299–304.
332. Valéry, N., "The Best Substitute for Petrol May be Petrol", *New Scientist*, 24 January 1974, pp. 203–205.
333. Tanner, H., "Egypt to Seek Non-Soviet Arms", *International Herald Tribune*, 19 April 1974.
334. "Schlesinger Urges Study: U.S. Indicates Interest in Arms Sale to Egypt", *International Herald Tribune*, 23 April 1974.
335. Gwertzman, B., "U.S. Assures Israel It Plans No Arms Sale to Egypt, Syria", *International Herald Tribune*, 24 June 1974.
336. Sulzberger, C.L., "Syria Will Not Diversify Sources of Arms", *International Herald Tribune*, 2 May 1974.

337. Merritt, G., "Arms-for-Oil Pact with Feisal: France in Long-term Saudi-Arabian Deal", *Finacial Times*, 9 January 1974.

338. Johns, R., "Franco-Saudi Deal Initially for 3 Years", *Financial Times*, 9 January 1974.

339. "Ryad, Un Important Client de l'Armement Français", *Le Monde*, 27 January 1974.

340. "MM Jobert et Sokkof Décident de Créer une Commission Permanente de Coopération Economique", *Le Monde*, 26 January 1974.

341. "Un Important Contrat Pétrolier Franco-Saoudien Serait Signé en Mars", *Le Monde*, 27 January 1974.

342. Gwertzman, B., "US-Saudi Pact a 'Milestone' for Arms Finances", *International Herald Tribune*, 10 June 1974.

343. "USAF to Deliver F-5's to Saudi Arabia", *Aviation Week & Space Technology*, 12 November 1973, pp. 14—15.

344. "Saudis, Raytheon Sign Missile Deal", *International Herald Tribune*, 9 April 1974.

345. "France Makes Arms Agreement with Kuwait", *Times*, 4 February 1974.

346. "Le Ministre de la Défence Annonce la Conclusion d'un Contrat Prévoyant l'Achat d'Helicoptèrs Français", *Le Monde*, 19 February 1974.

347. "Le Kuwait Achète Dix-Sept Intercepteurs 'Mirage F-1' à la France", *Le Monde*, 17 April 1974.

348. "Kuwait May Buy Communist Arms" *International Herald Tribune*, 14 January 1974.

349. Witkin, R., "Iran to Buy 30 US Jets for $900 Million", *International Herald Tribune*, 12 January 1974.

350. "U.S. Will Sell Teheran 50 More F-14 Jets", *International Herald Tribune*, 13 June 1974.

351. "L'Iran Achète pour 800 Millions de Francs d'Armements Britanniques", *Le Monde*, 24 January 1974.

352. Carr, J., "Bonn Opens Arms Sales Talks with Iran", *Financial Times*, 9 January 1974.

353. "Bonn Said to Sell Iran Arms Plants", *International Herald Tribune*, 13 February 1974.

354. "France to Build Six Gunboats for Iran", *Times*, 28 February 1974.

355. "L'Iran est Disposé à Passer d'Importantes Commandes de Centrales Nucléaires à la France", *Le Monde*, 10 February 1974.

356. "Libya Signs Trade Pact with France", *International Herald Tribune*, 20 February 1974.

357. "Un Accord Général de Coopération a été Signé entre la France et la Libye", *Le Monde*, 21 February 1974.

358. "$2,200 m. Bonn Oil Deal Set, World's Largest Refinery to Be Built in South", *Kayhan*, 2 February 1974.

359. "La Libye Fournira 30 Millions de Tonnes de Petrole par An à l'Italie", *Le Monde*, 27 February 1974.

360. "Saudis, Italians Said to Agree on Oil-Industry Deal", *International Herald Tribune*, 5 February 1974.

361. "Japan Seeks to Go Ahead with Iran Refinery Project", *International Herald Tribune*, 14 February 1974.

362. "Le Japon Offre un Prêt de 1 500 Millions de Dollars à l'Iran", *Le Monde*, 11 January 1974.

363. "Persia Cancels Japanese Deal", *Daily Telegraph*, 4 March 1974.

364. "Japan to Lend $1 Billion in Iraq Oil Deal", *International Herald Tribune*, 18 January 1974.

365. Hedlund, O., "Avtal med Libyen Klart: Sverige Får Olja i Tio År mot Cement, Papper, Stål", *Svenska Dagbladet*, 17 March 1974.

366. Shuster, A., "Britain and Iran Sign Oil-for-Goods Accord, *International Herald Tribune*, 26 January 1974.

367. "Joint US-Iranian Deal to Build Refinery", *Financial Times,* 9 November 1973.
368. "U.S. to Cooperate Actively in Saudi Arabia Development", *International Herald Tribune,* 6 April 1974.
369. Advertisement in *Times,* 17 November 1973.
370. *Middle East Economic Survey,* Vol. 17, No. 2, 2 November 1973, pp. 4–5.
371. *Keesing's Contemporary Archives,* 26 November – 2 December 1973, p. 26227.
372. *Saudi Economic Survey,* 12 November 1973.
373. *Middle East Economic Survey,* Vol. 17, No. 10, 28 December 1973, p. 11.
374. *Arab Report and Record,* 16–31 March 1974.
375. USA-document (Stockholm, US Information Service, 1974).
376. Harris, R., "Threat to Oil Supplies off China Coast", *Times,* 13 December 1973.
377. Fox B., "Now for Far East Oil Disputes", *New York Times,* 17 February 1974.
378. "East China Sea", *Petroleum Press Service,* May 1971, p. 195.
379. "East China Sea", *Petroleum Press Service,* August 1972, p. 310.
380. "South Korea – Japan Oil Agreement", *Financial Times,* 31 January 1974.
381. "Japan – South Korea: Offshore Settlement at Last", *Petroleum Press Service,* August 1973, p. 310.
382. "Japan – South Korea: Offshore Agreement Signed", *Petroleum Economist,* March 1974, p. 107.
383. "China and Vietnam: Like Oil and Water", *Economist,* 26 January 1974, p. 44.
384. "Saigon Holds Talks Over Spratly Isles", *International Herald Tribune,* 4 February 1974.
385. "South Vietnam and China Clash Over Spratlys", *International Herald Tribune,* 6 February 1974.
386. Kaiser, R.G., "Russia Hints Support for Saigon in Strife with China Over Isles", *International Herald Tribune,* 29 January 1974.
387. "Le G.R.P. Sud-Vietnamien Déclare sans Valeur les Permis de Recherche de Pétrole Accordés par Saigon", *Le Monde,* 26 February 1974.
388. "South Vietnam", *Petroleum Press Service,* June 1973, p. 233–34.
389. "South China Sea Potential", *Petroleum Press Service,* October 1973, p. 376.
390. "Thailand", *Petroleum Press Service,* August 1973, p. 311.
391. "Indonesia", *Petroleum Press Service,* April 1972, p. 150.
392. "South East Asia: The Littoral States Get Together", *Petroleum Press Service,* February 1972, p. 71.
393. "Indonesia", *Petroleum Press Service,* September 1973, p. 354.
394. "Thailand Deepening Interest in Andaman Sea", *Petroleum Economist,* June 1974, p. 230–31.
395. Saab, E., "Les Nationalistes Kurdes Rejettent le Statut d'Autonomie Octroyé par le Governement Irakien", *Le Monde,* 13 March 1974.
396. Saab, E., "Le Governement de Bagdad Donne au Général Barzani un Délai de Quinze Jours pour Accepter le Nouveau Statut d'Autonomie", *Le Monde,* 14 March 1974.
397. "Kurdish Leader Warns of Total War with Iraq", *International Herald Tribune,* 28 March 1974.
398. "Kurds Reject Autonomy Offer", *Arab Report and Record,* 16–31 March 1974, p. 102.
399. "Kurds Report Raids on Iraqi Oil, Gas Tanks", *International Herald Tribune,* 4 May 1974.
400. "Kurds' Chief Appeals to West for Support", *International Herald Tribune,* 2 April 1974.
401. "Iraqi Claims U.S. Supplies Arms to Rebel Kurds", *International Herald Tribune,* 11 April 1974.

402. "U.S. Denies Report", *International Herald Tribune,* 11 April 1974.
403. "Kurds Circle Iraqi Troops Turks Report", *International Herald Tribune,* 22 March 1974.
404. "Moscow Charges Turkey Provides Arms to Kurds", *International Herald Tribune,* 27 April 1974.
405. Hoagland, J. "Kurds Ready to Resume Fight as Pact With Iraq Crumbles", *International Herald Tribune,* 22 June 1973.
406. "North of the 62nd Parallel", *Northern Offshore,* No. 6, 1963, p. 70.
407. "The Possibilities of Finding Oil and Gas North of Lat. 62° N." *Northern Offshore* No. 1, 1974, p. 14.
408. "On the Exploration for and Exploitation of Submarine Natural Resources on the Norwegian Continental Shelf etc.", Recommendation of 30th April, 1971, by the Ministry of Industry, *Report No. 76 to the Norwegian Storting (1970–71),* Ministry of Industry, p. 32.
409. *Sveriges Överenskommelser med Främmande Makter,* Traktat angående Spetsbergen, Paris den 9 februari 1920, No. 25 (Stockholm, Norstedt, 1924).
410. *The Statesman's Year-Book 1973–1974* (London, Macmillan, 1972) p. 1208.
411. "Virksomheten på den Norske Kontinentalsokkel m.v., (St. meld. nr 30 1973–74)" Industridepartementet, p. 72.
     (a) ____ , p. 67.
412. Bjerkeholt, F. "M. Bratteli Discute à Moscou de la Frontière Soviéto – Norvégienne dans la Mer de Barents", *Le Monde,* 21 March 1974.
413. Holm, P., "Rustningskontroll på Nordkalotten", *Rapport-16* (Norsk Utenrikspolitisk Institutt) October 1973, p. 47.
414. "Russia and Norway Agree on Barents Sea Talks", *Financial Times,* 20 March 1974.
415. Synhorst, G.E., "Soviet Strategic Interest in the Maritime Arctic", *U.S. Naval Institute Proceedings, Naval Review 1973,* pp. 90–111.
416. Sjaastad, A.C., "Petroleumvirksomheten og Norsk Sikkerhetspolitik", *Notat-69* (Norsk Utenrikspolitisk Institutt) April 1974.
417. Mann, A., "Aegean Sea Oil Row", *Daily Telegraph,* 26 March 1974.
418. "Work Begins in Summer", *International Herald Tribune,* 17 April 1974.
419. "Repercussions of the Aegean Find", *Petroleum Economist,* April 1974, p. 108.
420. *Atlantic News,* No. 611, 15 March 1974.
421. "Greece: Oil Production in Sight", *Petroleum Economist,* June 1974, p. 216.
422. Roberts, S.V., "Greece and Turkey in a Dispute on Oil", *New York Times,* 16 April 1974.
423. Modiano, M. "Greek Warning to Turkey on Seabed Oil Dispute", *Times,* 9 May 1974.
424. Manning, M., "Greece, Turkey Step Back from Brink of Oil War in Aegean Sea", *Sunday Times,* 26 May 1974.
425. "Rival's Ship Maneuver Brings Athens' Alert: Greek-Turk Showdown Looms on Aegean Oil", *International Herald Tribune,* 30 May 1974.
426. "Turks' Oil Probe to Test Greek Reactions", *Financial Times,* 30 May 1974.
427. "Turk Navy's Research Vessel Ends Its Aegean Oil Mission", *International Herald Tribune,* 5 June 1974.
428. "Turkey Gets Oil Protest from Greece", *International Herald Tribune,* 16 June 1974.
429. Carlson, B.K., "Grekland – Turkiet Grälar om Oljefynd", *Svenska Dagbladet,* 11 March 1974.
430. "U.S. May Aid in Aegean Dispute", *International Herald Tribune,* 13 June 1974.
431. "Greece Agrees to Meet Turkey on Oil Dispute", *International Herald Tribune,* 25 May 1974.

432. "U.S. Is Urging Restraint in Aegean Feud", *International Herald Tribune,* 31 May 1974.

433. "Greece, Turkey Meet in June on Sea Shelf Rights", *International Herald Tribune,* 29 May 1974.

434. "Talks Said to Produce Easing of Turkish-Greek Oil Crisis", *International Herald Tribune,* 1 June 1974.

435. "The Aegean: Does the Oil Go With the Islands?", *Economist,* 8 June 1974, pp. 30–33.

436. "France Agrees To Sell Greece 40 Mirage F-1s", *International Herald Tribune,* 14 June 1974.

437. *The Effects of Strategic Bombing on the German War Economy,* The United States Strategic Bombing Survey, Overall Economic Effects Division, 31 October 1945, (Washington) pp. 73–83.

438. Leith, C.K., *et al., World Minerals and World Peace* (Washington, Brookings Institution, 1943) p. 47 and 170–73.

439. Allen, H.R., *The Legacy of Lord Trenchard* (London, Cassell,1972) p. 181.

Addendum

This report went to press in June 1974. Some events occurring between June and September of that year have been listed below to further highlight the contents of the study.

OAPEC (p. 22)

At an OAPEC meeting in Cairo on 10—11 July, the member countries agreed to spend more money on world technological development, open an institute for energy resources and encourage other Arab states to join in the search for alternative energy sources. [1]

COMECON (pp. 22, 78)

After a meeting of the Communist Council for Mutual Economic Assistance (COMECON) on 21 June, plans were announced for a unified power-generation system to safeguard Eastern Europe against the risks of a future·energy crisis. The countries were to draw up an integrated programme for coordinating their five-year plans during the 1976—1980 period. The COMECON countries would give priority to the development of electrical power, while saving petroleum fuel for use in chemical and other industries. [2]

Oil embargo (p. 29)

On 1—2 June 1974, after the Israeli-Syrian disengagement agreement, the oil ministers from the nine OAPEC countries, except Iraq, met to review the lifting of the oil embargo against the United States. It was decided then to continue to make deliveries to the United States, while maintaining the partial embargo against Denmark, and the complete embargo against the Netherlands, Portugal, Rhodesia and South Africa. Algeria announced its decision to lift its embargo on supplies to the Netherlands. On 10 July the OAPEC members agreed to lift completely the embargo on the Netherlands "in appreciation of the desired relations between the Arab nations and the European community". Meanwhile, the partial embargo against Denmark had been tacitly withdrawn. [3]

However, in the strongest statement made by a Saudi official since the lifting of the embargo, Sheik Yamani warned in July that the embargo could be reimposed "very soon", unless the Arabs received assurances that Israel would give up territory conquered during in the 1967 June War. [4]

EEC energy cooperation (pp. 31, 76)

Ministers of the European Economic Community agreed on 17 September to develop a common energy policy. Earlier attempts to frame a common energy policy had failed in July when Britain vetoed a set of principles and guidelines prepared by the EEC Executive Commission. The September agreement included guidelines for *inter alia* a slowdown of energy consumption to be achieved by more rational use and conservation, an increase in nuclear energy production, an intensive use of the EEC's own oil and solid-fuel resources, a diversification of outside supply sources, and joint research and development of new technologies. The ministers also agreed to hold a special meeting before the end of the year to calculate production and consumption target figures up to 1985 and to decide measures for the creation of a common energy market. [5]

Cooperation or conflict (p. 34)

US President Ford at the World Energy Conference, Detroit, 23 September 1974: Because vital resources are distributed unevenly, nations are forced to choose between conflict and cooperation.... [I] n the nuclear age, when any local conflict may escalate to global catastrophe... nations must turn to international cooperation as the best means for dealing with the uneven distribution of resources.... Sovereign nations cannot allow their policies to be dictated... by artifical rigging and distortion of world commodity markets. No one can forsee the extent of the damage nor the end of the disastrous consequences if nations refuse to share nature's gifts for the benefit of all mankind. [6]

US Secretary of State Kissinger at UN General Assembly, 23 September 1974: The increasingly open and cooperative global economic system that we have come to take for granted is now under unprecedented attack. The world is poised on the brink of a return to the unrestrained economic nationalism which accompanied the collapse of economic order in the thirties.

... The early warning signs of a major economic crisis are evident. Rates of inflation unprecedented in the past quarter century are sweeping developing and developed nations alike. The world's financial institutions are staggering under the most massive and rapid movements of reserves in history.

... While the present situation threatens every individual and nation, it is the poor who suffer the most.

... It can be in the interest of no country or group of countries to base policies on a test of strength, for a policy of confrontation would end in disaster for all. Meeting man's basic needs for energy and food, and assuring economic growth while mastering inflation require international cooperation to an unprecendented degree.

... We are prepared to accept substantial investments in the United States and we welcome a greater role for the oil producers in the management of international economic institutions.

The investment of surplus oil revenues presents a great challenge. The countries which most need these revenues are generally the least likely to receive them. The world's financial institutions have coped thus far but ways must be found to assure assistance for those countries most in need of it. And the full brunt of the surplus revenues is yet to come.

But despite our best efforts to meet the oil producers' legitimate needs and to channel their resources into constructive uses, the world cannot sustain even the present level of prices, much less continuing increases. The prices of other commodities will inevitably rise in a never-ending inflationary spiral. Nobody will benefit from such a race. The oil producers will be forced to spend more for their own imports. Many nations will not be able to withstand the pace and the poorer could be overwhelmed. The complex, fragile structure of global economic cooperation required to sustain national economic growth stands in danger of being shattered.

The United States will work with other consuming nations on means of consumer conservation and on ways to cushion the impact of massive investments from abroad. The preliminary agreement on a program of solidarity and cooperation signed. . . in Brussels by the major consumer countries is an encouraging first step.

But the long-range solution requires a new understanding between consumers and producers. Unlike food prices, the high cost of oil is not the result of economic factors. . . . [R]ather it is caused by deliberate decisions to restrict production and maintain an artificial price level. . . . [I] t cannot be in the interest of any nation to magnify the despair of the least developed who are uniquely vulnerable to exorbitant prices and who have no recourse but to pay.

What has gone up by political decision can be reduced by political decision. [7]

Energy Coordinating Group (ECG) (p. 36)

At working sessions of the ECG, held on 8–9 July and 29–30 July, agreement was reached on the broad lines of a scheme for sharing oil resources among the IC-countries in the event of a crisis in supplies.

At a new meeting on 20 September, the ECG members agreed on the text of an emergency oil-sharing agreement to be submitted to their governments for final approval. The approval of the Norwegian government was considered to be particularly doubtful, however, since Norway is expected to become the only major exporter of oil among the countries in the group and therefore would be making the greatest sacrifices in the event of an oil-supply emergency. [8–9].

The agreement contains complicated arrangements whereby oil-sharing would be automatically triggered off in any future fuel crisis. The trigger mechanism would come into effect in two cases: (*a*) if the whole group of ECG countries were affected by a 7 per cent shortfall in supply, and (*b*) if only one or two countries were affected by the same degree of shortage.

The agreement also covers such subjects as stockpiling, demand, restraint measures, the need for pooling of energy information and consultation with the oil companies. It also proposes the establishment of a special agency within the OECD, which would have authority over oil sharing. [10]

EEC – Arab League (p. 36)

On 31 July leaders of the Arab League and the European Economic Community (EEC) met in Paris to begin a political and economic dialogue. As a first step, the two sides agreed to set up a joint commission and several working groups to deal with specific problems of cooperation. [11]

Oil and food (p. 37)

US President Ford at UN General Assembly, 18 September 1974:
The food and oil crises demonstrate the extent of our interdependence. Many developing nations need the food surplus of a few developed nations. And many industrialized nations need the oil production of a few developing nations.

. . . The problems of food and energy can be resolved on the basis of cooperation – or can. . . be made unmanageable on the basis of confrontation.

. . . A global strategy for food and energy is urgently required.

The United States believes four principles should guide a global approach:

First, all nations must substantially increase production. . . To meet aspirations for a better life, production will have to expand at a significantly faster rate than population growth.

Second, all nations must seek to achieve a level for prices which not only provides an incentive to producers but which consumers can afford. It should now be clear that the developed nations are not the only countries which demand and receive an adequate return for their goods. But it should also be clear that by confronting consumers with production restrictions, artificial pricing, and the prospect of ultimate bankruptcy, producers will eventually become the victims of their own actions.

Third, all nations must avoid the abuse of man's fundamental needs for the sake of narrow or national or bloc advantage. The attempt by any country to use one commodity for political purposes will inevitably tempt other countries to use their commodities for their own purposes.

Fourth, the nations of the world must assure that the poorest among us are not overwhelmed by rising prices of the imports necessary for their survival. The traditional aid donors and the increasingly wealthy oil producers must join in this effort. ... It has not been our policy to use food as a political weapon despite the oil embargo and recent oil price and production decisions.

... Now is the time for oil producers to define their conception of a global policy on energy to meet the growing need − and to do this without imposing unacceptable burdens on the international monetary and trade system.

A world of economic confrontation cannot be a world of political cooperation. [12]

Military retaliation (p. 38)

At a Department of Defence news conference on 25 September, Defence Secretary Schlesinger was quoted as saying that the United States regarded the problem of oil prices as one that is detrimental to the world's economy, but it expected to have a solution to the problem through negotiations and amicable discussions. The United States, he said, was not anticipating that there is going to be military conflict.

Schlesinger also ruled out the possibility of using military sales as a lever in negotiations with the PE-countries. [13]

Oil prices (p. 39)

At their meeting in Quito on 15−17 June, the OPEC members announced that they would hold their posted prices for crude oil steady for three more months. At the same time, 11 out of the 12 members agreed to raise their governments' share of oil revenues by 2 per cent. Saudi Arabia disassociated itself from this decision. [14]

At the next meeting in Viennà on 12−13 September, the oil ministers of the OPEC countries, except Saudi Arabia again agreed to maintain a freeze on the basic prices of crude oil for another three months, that is, until the end of 1974, but to raise the average cost of crude oil to the multinational oil companies by 3.5 per cent. [15]

The Secretary-General of OPEC predicts a 12 per cent price increase for oil in January 1975. [16]

OPEC income (p. 39)

In a World Bank report, issued in July and entitled *Prospects for the Developing Countries* (not for public use but quoted in the press), the OPEC countries are projected to have a current account surplus with the rest of the world running at the rate of $60−70 billion (in 1974 dollars), including $12−15 billion with the other developing countries. If, in future, oil prices rose at the same rate as levels of inflation, the annual OPEC revenues would rise from $24 billion in 1974 to $108 billion in 1975, $173 billion in 1980 and $256 billion in 1985. The accumulated reserves of all OPEC countries could rise to $650 billion by 1980 and to about $1 200 by 1985. At the present level of exports, a variation of one dollar per barrel (or 10 per cent) in the price of oil is equivalent to a change in the world's deficit with OPEC of over $10 billion per year. [17–18]

The US Treasury Department estimated in the middle of September that the PE-countries would have receipts of about $80 billion in 1974, of which they will have to invest about $55 billion outside their own countries. [19]

Investments in IC-countries (p. 41)

On 17 July the West German company Friedrich Krupp GmbH and the Iranian government announced an agreement under which Iran is to take a 25 per cent share in the capital of Friedrich Krupp Huettenwerke AG, a major steel-producing company currently 95 per cent owned by Friedrich Krupp GmbH. Iran will nominate one representative to each of the two companies' supervisory boards. The agreement also provides for the establishment by Krupp and Iran of an investment company in Zurich that will promote joint ventures and investments by the partners. In comments in the United States to the deal, it was pointed out that it would cost the oil states only about 75 per cent of their excess dollar earnings in a single year to acquire a controlling interest in eleven giant US corporations, including A.T.&T., Boeing, General Motors, IBM, ITT, US Steel and Xerox. [20–22]

Kuwait has offered to pay $246 million for a British commercial real-estate company (St. Martin's Property Corp.). It is so far the largest Arab investment in the West to have been disclosed. [23]

The PE-countries invested about $7 billion in the United States and about $3 billion in the United Kingdom during the first eight months of 1974, according to estimates by the US Treasury Department. It also estimated that the OPEC countries may have earned a surplus of roughly between $25 billion and $28 billion during the same period. Of the estimated $7 billion invested in the United States, the Treasury said that about $4 billion went into various types of marketable US government securities. Most of the remainder was placed with commercial banks and a smaller part was invested in corporate securities and real estate. [24]

Iran and Egypt have agreed on a protocol of cooperation valued at $850 million. Included in the agreement, under which Iran will invest on a large scale in Egypt's economic development, is the study of a second multinational pipeline from Suez to Port Said – which would carry primarily Iranian crude oil to the Mediterranean – and Iranian participation in widening the Suez Canal. [25–26]

It was disclosed on 22 July that the UK had arranged with Iran for a loan of $1.2 billion to help compensate for the British trade deficit. [27]

Assistance to oil-poor countries (pp.43, 159)

Delegates to the meeting of the Council of Ministers of the Organization of African Unity (OAU) agreed on 9 June to accept an offer by Arab PE-countries of a $200 million low-interest loan for poor African states hard hit by the rising costs of oil.

The Arab PE-countries refused, on the other hand, to reduce the price of oil for these states. Some African states, (for instance, Kenya and Ethiopia) complained that the offer was not sufficient. [28—29]

At its special session in April 1974, the UN General Assembly requested the Secretary-General of the United Nations to set up a coordination mechanism for emergency relief to countries particularly hit by the oil situation. The Secretary-General called upon Dr Raul Prebisch to head a fund-raising drive for this facility. The EEC later announced that, over a two-year period, it would be willing to contribute $500 million to the emergency relief effort for the most seriously affected countries — subject to the condition that other countries contribute $2.5 billion (USA $500 million, the rest of the industrialized world $500 million and the OPEC-countries $1 500 million). Some of these countries have indicated commitments but not yet of the magnitude required to meet the EEC condition. [30]

Economic situation of OECD countries (pp. 44, 160)

In its half-yearly economic outlook published in July, the OECD warned that the economic situation facing the OECD countries today is more difficult than it has been for many years. Inflation has recently accelerated further and is now running at an unprecedented and alarming rate. The OECD area's balance of payments on current account has swung from its normal surplus to a position of very substantial deficit, which will amount to as much as $40 billion in 1974. The forecasts suggest a continuation of inflation at very high rates as the price rises for oil and other commodities continue to permeate the OECD economies.

It was also pointed out that cooperation and consultation between governments have never been more necessary than they are today, although the initial fears of a scramble for current balance positions had so far proved unfounded. At the OECD ministerial meeting in May, all governments, conscious of the danger of conflicting attempts to improve national competitive positions, agreed upon a declaration stating their determination to avoid recourse for a period of a year, to new restrictions on trade or other current transactions. [31]

Disputed territories (Arabian/Persian Gulf) (p. 49)

In a report to the United Nations Security Council on 21 May, the Secretary General said that Iraq and Iran had agreed to settle their border dispute as a result of mediation by UN special representative Luis Weckmann Munoz. The agreement was reported to include strict observance of the March 1974 ceasefire, simultaneous withdrawal of troops from both sides of the border and the resumption of talks. The Security Council on 29 May unanimously passed a resolution welcoming the agreement. China refused to take part in the voting on the grounds that the UN should not interfere in border disputes. However, at the end of August, there were once again reports about clashes along the Iranian-Iraqi border. In a letter to the chairman of the UN Security Council, Iraq charged that Iran had massed troops at strategic points along the common border in violation of the 7 March ceasefire agreement. Iraq stated that the strength of the Iranian military build-up alone the border on 21 August reached three armoured divisions, two infantry divisions and an independent infantry brigade. [32—33]

On 29 July Saudi Arabia and Abu Dhabi reached an agreement settling their

25-year dispute over the Buraimi Oasis and their desert frontiers. With the border defined, the governments of the two states and their concessionaire companies can now explore and develop the area's oil potential jointly or separately. No details of the agreement have been announced but there has been mention of Abu Dhabi relinquishing an area on the Arabian/Persian Gulf that will provide Saudi Arabia with a corridor through Abu Dhabi territory to the southern gulf, in return for the Buraimi Oasis. [34]

At the end of July Iran and Oman signed an agreement demarcating the continental shelf in the Persian Gulf between them. The agreement gives 50 miles of territorial waters to each country. Oman thus becomes the sixth Arab state on the southern littoral of the Gulf to have signed continental shelf agreements with Iran. (Earlier Saudi Arabia, Qatar, Abu Dhabi, Dubai and Bahrain had concluded similar treaties). The only areas still undemarcated are the headwaters of the Gulf, where the borders of Iran, Iraq and Kuwait meet and where the continental shelf can be divided only after the three countries agree on their land frontiers. [35]

Disputed territories (English Channel) (p. 50)

Britain and France are reported to be in dispute over the division of the Western Approaches to the English Channel, where geological studies have indicated excellent prospects of finding oil. [36]

Suez Canal (p. 52)

According to an announcement by the Suez Canal Authority at the beginning of September, the Suez Canal will be opened to normal shipping by March 1975. [37]

Military protection of sea lanes and oil installations (p. 61)

In a press report of 25 July, referring to a recent survey commissioned by the US Navy, the conclusion was drawn that the assured supply by sea of oil and other essential minerals in the event of war with the Soviet Union has become the primary problem facing NATO. US fears over the British review of defence expenditure therefore centre not so much on a reduction of ground forces available in Central Europe but on a possible cutback in British convoy escorts and sea-control ships. [38]

Norway will have to double its air force because of the need to protect its extended territorial waters and the oil reserves under them, according to a press report on the negotiations for aircraft acquisitions by four NATO countries (Norway, Denmark, the Netherlands and Belgium) in the summer of 1974. [39]

A Soviet trawler was reported to have sailed very close to British oil and gas installations in the North Sea (the Indefatigable field 60 miles off the coast of Norfolk) on 25 June 1974. Soviet seamen were believed to have taken photographs and measurements of the installations. A Royal Navy destroyer was sent to hail the Soviet vessel but it had vanished by the time the warship arrived. The incident caused the British Foreign Ministry to express concern to the Soviet authorities who were asked for assurances that this would not happen again. In the British press several articles subsequently dealt with the need to increase the capability to protect the oil and gas installations (including pipelines) in the North Sea in future against, for instance, attacks from sabotage groups. No British forces are specifically earmarked for this task; officially, any trouble of this kind (involving a drilling rig or a production platform) is a matter for the nearest police authority. [40–47]

Arms sales (pp. 44–48, Appendix 4)

The United States sold arms valued at some $8.5 billion during fiscal year 1973/74. This was almost double the arms sales for the previous fiscal year. In a list supplied by the US Department of Defense, the major recipient countries included, *inter alia,* Iran ($3.7 billion, or almost half the total), Israel ($2.1 billion) and Saudi Arabia (some $600 million). [48–49]

On 28 August France lifted its embargo on arms sales to belligerent countries in the Middle East, an embargo imposed in 1967. Arms sales to the four countries under the embargo, Egypt, Syria, Jordan and Israel, would in future be decided on a "case-by-case basis". [501] Two weeks later it was reported that France and Israel would hold talks on the renewal of arms sales in October 1974. [51]

Iran is reported to have expressed an interest in purchasing 250 of the F-17 light-weight fighters being developed by the Northrop Corp. for the US Air Force. [52]

Iran has also asked the US government for "basic information" on the A 10 close support planes produced by Fairchild Industries, according to US Department of Defense officials. [53]

Israeli officials stated in the beginning of August that Syria had received more than $2 billion in new and sophisticated arms from the Soviet Union in the past 10 months, causing a significant shift in the military and political balance in the region. The Soviet arms transfers included, *inter alia*, two squadrons of MiG-23s, heavy guns and Scud surface-to-surface missiles. The Syrian air force was therefore considered to be 25 per cent stronger than it was on the eve of the 1973 October War, and its surface-to-air missile system about 20 per cent larger. [54]

Economic and technical agreements (pp. 116–17, Appendix 5)

On 14 June, during President Nixon's visit to Egypt, a declaration of friendship and cooperation was made, under which the USA pledged to strengthen the economic links between the two countries. The declaration also announced the beginning of negotiations for an agreement on cooperation in nuclear energy under which the United States will sell nuclear reactors and fuel to Egypt. A provisional contract was signed on 26 June between Egypt and the US Atomic Energy Commission for the supply of uranium for the proposed atomic power programme. [55–56]

During his visit to Israel on 17 June, President Nixon promised to negotiate with Israel on agreements to supply the same kind of nuclear technology for peaceful purposes that he had promised to Egypt a few days earlier. The same type of provisional contract was signed on 26 June between Israel and the US Atomic Energy Commission for the supply of uranium for the proposed atomic power plants. [57–58]

On 27 June Iran and France signed a 10-year agreement of cooperation on a broad range of industrial projects worth about $4 billion. Iran agreed to pay $1 billion in installments, as advance payment for prospective industrial goods. It was reported by official spokesmen that the agreement included increased oil deliveries by Iran, but the amount was not specified. France has received or will receive orders for the following equipment: five atomic power plants of 1 000 megawatts each; one steel plant; military equipment including high-speed patrol boats; a subway system for Teheran; a large calibre natural gas pipeline and 12 large tankers. France has also been asked to participate in the electrification on the Iranian railway system. [59—60] In an agreement between the United States and Iran, announced on 28 June, the USA agreed to supply two nuclear reactors to Iran. On 1 July another agreement was signed, under which the United States will convert Iranian uranium into nuclear fuel for electricity and other peaceful uses. The value of the agreement is $130 million. [62—62]

Iraq and Italy signed a 10-year agreement on 18 July for about $3 million worth of Italian aid in exchange for Iraqi crude oil. Under the agreement, Iraq will export to Italy 10 million tons of crude oil a year in addition to Italy's normal oil purchases from Iraq. In return, Italy will assist in agricultural and industrial training, help with desalination and irrigation schemes, improve infrastructure networks, and build petrochemical installations, a power station, a foundry, food processing plants and low-cost housing. [63]

On 1 August the Japanese Mitsubishi Industrial group announced an agreement with Saudi Arabia's state-owned company Petroleum and Mineral Corp. (Petromin), to build a $3 billion petrochemical complex in Saudi Arabia by 1980. [64]

On 16 August Japan and Iraq signed a $1 billion agreement providing for Japanese credits to Iraq for economic development projects in exchange for crude oil and oil products. The development projects were expected to include an oil refinery, a petrochemical complex, cement and fertilizer plants and a aluminium smelter. In return, Iraq is to supply Japan a total of 160 million tons of crude oil and products over the next 10 years. [65]

Disputed territories (South East Asia) (p. 135)

At the beginning of September, South Viet-Nam moved a naval task force into the Gulf of Thailand and in a note to the Khmer Republic, threatened to seize a French-US oil rig if it was not moved from disputed waters within 10 days. The US and French owners subsequently decided to dismantle their rig. An offical of the US embassy in Saigon was quoted as saying: "We're pretty interested in seeing that an American oil-drilling rig isn't blown up by military action". [66—68]

Disputed territories (Aegean Sea) (p. 141)

The Prime Ministers of Greece and Turkey (Androutsopoulos and Ecevit) met during the NATO meeting in Brussels at the end of June to exchange views on the Aegean Sea oil dispute. The Turkish Premier reportedly proposed that the pending issue should be referred to a special procedure of committees and subcommittees. Greece rejected the procedure as a pointless innovation, referring instead to diplomatic channels as the best means for the solution of any problem. At a news conference Prime Minister Ecevit said that the Greek rejection could only lead to a deterioration of relations between the two countries. He added that Turkey would go on with its "summer programme" of exploration for oil in the disputed waters. Prime Minister Androutsopoulos in his turn accused Turkey of reverting to threats and of provoking a dispute between the two countries. [69—70]

Participation (p. 150)

An agreement was signed on 11 June between the government of Saudi Arabia and Aramco — which has produced about 95 per cent of the Saudi crude oil — under which Saudi Arabia will obtain a 60 per cent share of oil profits backdated to 1 January 1974. [71]

The Secretary-General of OPEC predicted in September that Saudi Arabia would acquire 100 per cent control of Aramco before the end of 1974. [72] According to some information, the Saudi Oil Minister had indicated that such a total take-over might occur already at the end of October. [73]

Oil embargo (p. 152)

A report prepared for the Senate Foreign Relations subcommittee on multinational corporations showed that the Arab oil embargo was almost 100 per cent effective in cutting back petroleum exports to the United States and that, on balance, Arab slowdowns in production hit the USA twice as hard as the rest of the world. The study challenged the view that the embargo had been violated by imports of more than 500 000 b/d into the United States, and that the oil shortages were manipulated by oil companies seeking higher profits. In fact, the report maintained that oil imports into the USA fell from 1.2 million b/d in September 1973 to 19 000 b/d in January and February 1974. The oil available for US consumption dropped 6.1 per cent during the four worst months of the shortage compared with 3.4 per cent in the rest of the world. [74]

Cooperation (p. 154)

In a second article in *Foreign Affairs,* US oil expert Walter J. Levy repeated the urgency for increased world oil cooperation, particularly between the oil-importing countries. He stressed the need for "a recognition by the producing countries that even in an austerity situation any attempt to hold prices high might result in worldwide dangers to which they could not be immune". "We are all interested", Levy said, "in the maintenance of a peaceful cohesion among Middle East countries. But they must recognize that. . . their own independence could not be safely assured if the United States and its allies were to be fatally weakened *vis-a-vis* the Soviet Union." He declared that it would not be "in their self-interest to refuse to supply the vital oil needs of the world or to insist on an unmanageable level of prices, and risk the economic, political and strategic consequences of such policies". [75]

Addendum references

1. *International Herald Tribune*, 12 July 1974.
2. *International Herald Tribune*, 22 June 1974.
3. *Keesings Contemporary Archives*, 15—21 July 1974, p. 26618.
4. *Financial Times*, 22 July 1974.
5. *International Herald Tribune*, 18 September 1974.
6. Information from US Embassy, Stockholm.
7. Information from US Embassy, Stockholm.
8. *Petroleum Economist*, August 1974, p. 296.
9. *International Herald Tribune*, 1 August 1974.
10. *International Herald Tribune*, 21 September 1974.
11. *International Herald Tribune*, 1 August 1974.
12. Information from US Embassy, Stockholm.
13. *International Herald Tribune*, 26 September 1974.
14. *Petroleum Economist*, July 1974, p. 251.
15. *Economist*, 21 September 1974.
16. *International Herald Tribune*, 21 September 1974.
17. *International Herald Tribune*, 29 July 1974.
18. *International Herald Tribune*, 30 July 1974.
19. *International Herald Tribune*, 20 September 1974.
20. *International Herald Tribune*, 18 July 1974.
21. *International Herald Tribune*, 19 July 1974.
22. *New York Times*, 20 July 1974.
23. *International Herald Tribune*, 7 September 1974.
24. *International Herald Tribune*, 20 September 1974.
25. *Financial Times*, 31 May 1974.
26. *Petroleum Economist*, July 1974.
27. *International Herald Tribune*, 23 July 1974.
28. *New York Times*, 9 June 1974.
29. *Le Monde*, 11 June 1974.
30. *Economist*, 7 September 1974.
31. *OECD Economic Outlook*, 15 July 1974. pp. 7—8.
32. *Arab Report and Record*, 16—31 May 1974.
33. *International Herald Tribune*, 2 September 1974.
34. *Platt's Oilgram*, 31 July 1974.
35. *Platt's Oilgram*, 30 July 1974,
36. *Times*, 20 July 1974.
37. *International Herald Tribune*, 5 September 1974.
38. *International Herald Tribune*, 25 July 1974.
39. *Dagens Nyheter*, 8 August 1974.
40. *Times*, 27 June 1974.
41. *Times*, 28 June 1974.
42. *Times*, 3 July 1974.
43. *Times*, 16 July 1974.
44. *Times*, 24 July 1974.
45. *Times*, 24 July 1974.
46. *Daily Telegraph*, 19 July 1974.
47. *Daily Telegraph*, 23 July 1974
48. *International Herald Tribune*, 11 July 1974.
49. *New York Times*, 25 August 1974.

50. *International Herald Tribune,* 29 August 1974.

51. *International Herald Tribune,* 10 September 1974.

52. *International Herald Tribune,* 12 July 1974.

53. *International Herald Tribune,* 3 August 1974.

54. *International Herald Tribune,* 19 August 1974.

55. *International Herald Tribune,* 15 June 1974.

56. *International Herald Tribune,* 27 June 1974.

57. *International Herald Tribune,* 18 June 1974.

58. *International Herald Tribune,* 27 June 1974.

59. *International Herald Tribune,* 28 June 1974.

60. *International Herald Tribune,* 3 July 1974.

61. *International Herald Tribune,* 29 June 1974.

62. *International Herald Tribune,* 2 July 1974.

63. *Arab Report & Record,* 16−31 July 1974.

64. *International Herald Tribune,* 2 August 1974.

65. *New York Times,* 17 August 1974.

66. *International Herald Tribune,* 4 September 1974.

67. *International Herald Tribune,* 6 September 1974.

68. *International Herald Tribune,* 7 September 1974.

69. *International Herald Tribune,* 28 June 1974.

70. *International Herald Tribune,* 1 July 1974.

71. *Le Monde,* 12 June 1974.

72. *International Herald Tribune,* 21 September 1974.

73. *International Herald Tribune,* 17 September 1974.

74. *New York Times,* 26 July 1974.

75. *Foreign Affairs,* July 1974, pp. 690−713.